PROBLEMS IN UNDERGRADUATE PHYSICS

VOLUME III

OPTICS

BY

V. L. GINZBURG, L. M. LEVIN
D. V. SIVUKHIN, E. S. CHETVERIKOVA

TRANSLATED BY

D. E. BROWN

TRANSLATION EDITED BY

D. TER HAAR

PERGAMON PRESS
OXFORD · LONDON · EDINBURGH · NEW YORK
PARIS · FRANKFURT

Pergamon Press Ltd., Headington Hill Hall, Oxford
4 & 5 Fitzroy Square, London W. 1
Pergamon Press (Scotland) Ltd., 2 & 3 Teviot Place, Edinburgh 1
Pergamon Press Inc., 122 East 55th Street, New York 22, N.Y.
Pergamon Press GmbH, Kaiserstrasse 75, Frankfurt-am-Main

First edition 1965

Library of Congress Catalog Card Number 64-25443

This translation has been made from the Russian book Сборник задач по общему курсу физики, часть II (revised edition) published by Fizmatgiz, Moscow, 1960, and includes amendments and additions supplied by the authors during the course of the translation.

CONTENTS

PROBLEMS

ANSWERS AND SOLUTIONS

PREFACE

THIS set of four books of problems is based on a translation of a Russian collection which has been in use by students in physics at Moscow State University and the Moscow Physico-Technical Institute for a number of years. Where appropriate, answers and solutions to the problems are given in the second part of each volume.

During the course of the translation of these volumes, the authors provided a large list of amendments and additions to their Russian text and these have all been incorporated in this English edition. Many of the additional problems are on topics which have developed during recent years.

The standard of the problems is roughly equivalent to an undergraduate course in physics at a British university, or senior year physics course at an American university: it varies from the simple to the rather sophisticated. They can be used in conjunction with almost any textbook on physics at the appropriate level.

D. TER HAAR

PROBLEMS

§ 1. Geometrical Optics

1. When an opaque disc of radius r is illuminated, an umbra of radius r_1 and penumbra of radius r_2 are obtained on a screen at a distance d from the disc. The light source is also in the form of a disc, the straight line joining the centres of the discs being perpendicular to their planes and to the plane of the screen. Find the size of the light source and its distance from the illuminated disc.

2. The diameter of the photosphere of the sun is about 1,390,000 km, the average distance of the sun from the earth is about 150,000,000 km and the distance varies only slightly. The distance from the centre of the moon to the earth's surface varies from $\approx$ 357,000 km to $\approx$ 399,000 km. When is the eclipse of the sun total and when is it annular, if the moon's diameter is 3480 km?

3. Explain why the light passing through a slit from a source gives an image of the source on a screen placed behind the slit when the slit is small, and gives an image of the slit when it is large.

4. A ray from the sun is incident on a small square mirror and after reflection hits a screen. What is the shape of the illuminated part of the screen and how does it change when the distance between the mirror and screen varies?

5. A long narrow horizontal slit, illuminated by a bright extensive light source, is placed in front of a square wire mesh, the wires of which are horizontal and vertical. After passing through the slit and the mesh, the light falls on a remote screen. Describe the picture obtained on the screen. What happens if the slit is turned through (1) 90° and (2) 45°, about the perpendicular to the plane of the mesh? Consider two cases: (1) when the mesh has the shape shown in Fig. 1 (a) and (2) when it has the shape shown in Fig. 1 (b).

How is the picture on the screen affected if the slit and mesh in the previous problem change places?

6. Two mirrors are inclined to one another to form a wedge of angle α. A ray in the plane perpendicular to the edge of the wedge is incident on the mirrors. Show that the angle δ of deflection of the ray from its initial direction after reflection from the two mirrors is independent of the angle of incidence. Calculate δ.

7. Write in vector form the laws of reflection and refraction of light rays at the plane boundary between two transparent isotropic media. The light passes from medium 1 with index of refraction n_1 to medium 2 with refractive index n_2. The directions of the incident, reflected and refracted rays are characterised by the unit vectors $\boldsymbol{r}_0$, $\boldsymbol{r}_1$, $\boldsymbol{r}_2$. The unit vector $\boldsymbol{N}$ normal to the boundary is directed from medium 2 to medium 1.

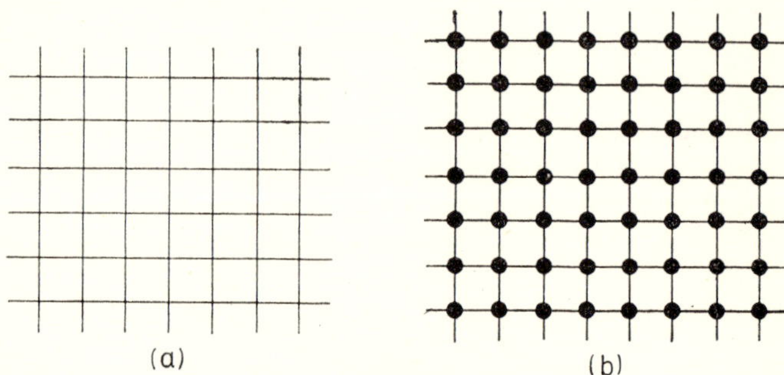

FIG. 1

8. Show that a light ray reverses its direction when reflected successively from three mutually perpendicular mirrors.

9. A trihedral pyramid is obtained by cutting off a corner of a glass cube with silvered faces. A light ray is incident through the base of the pyramid and is successively reflected from the three remaining mutually perpendicular faces. Show that the light reverses its direction on leaving the pyramid.

10. Find all the images of an object situated between two mirrors inclined at 60° to one another. Draw the path of the rays giving the image of the object after two successive reflections from the two mirrors.

11. Determine the number of images of an object located between two plane mirrors forming an angle α to one another, on the assumption that the number $m = 2\pi/\alpha$ is an integer.

12. A light ray is incident on a refracting prism via the face AD and is reflected in turn from faces BC and BD, before leaving via the face AC, as shown in Fig. 2. The ray lies in the plane perpendicular to the edge of the prism. The angles B and A of the prism are equal to α and 2α respectively, whilst angles C and D are equal to one another. Show that the angle δ of deflection of the departing ray from the initial direction is independent of the angle of incidence. Calculate δ. Given the path of the ray indicated, will the prism give spectral resolution?

13. Explain why the track of the moon, but not an image of the moon's disc, is visible in the sea on a moonlit night.

14. Find the size of the sun's image obtained in a reflector with a radius of curvature of 16 m. The diameter of the sun $\approx 1{\cdot}4 \times 10^6$ km, and the distance of the earth from the sun $\approx 150 \times 10^6$ km.

15. The radius of curvature of a concave mirror is 40 cm. Find the position of an object such that its image is real and magnified two times. Find the position such at the image is imaginary and magnified two times.

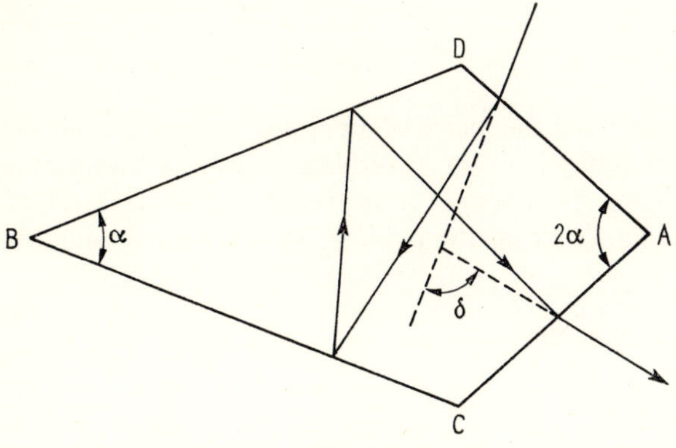

FIG. 2

16. To measure the focal length of a mirror, a lighted candle is placed 10 cm from it. A sharp image of the candle is obtained on a screen 30 cm from the mirror. Find the focal length f of the mirror.

17. Prove geometrically and analytically that, if a spherical mirror MM (Fig. 3), which is silvered on the side 1, reflects an object P at P', it will reflect P' at P when silvered in the side 2.

18. Find the shape of a mirror that reflects parallel rays in such a way that they appear to issue from a single point behind the mirror.

19. A vessel containing mercury rotates uniformly about a vertical axis with angular velocity $\omega = 1\ \text{sec}^{-1}$. The surface of the mercury assumes a concave shape and is used as a mirror. Find the focal length of this mirror.

20. Prove geometrically that, if a light ray issuing from a point *A* strikes a point *B* after reflection from a plane mirror, the length of the path of the ray is less than the length of any other path passing from *A* to the mirror, then to *B*.

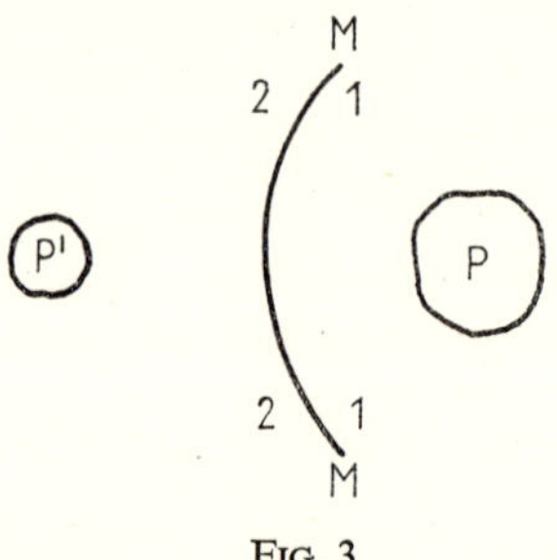

FIG. 3

21. Prove that the image of a point in a spherical mirror can be drawn as follows. From an arbitrary point *A* we draw straight lines *AO* and *AC* joining *A* to the vertex *O* and the centre of curvature *C* (Fig. 3). From the point *P* we draw the straight line *PD*,

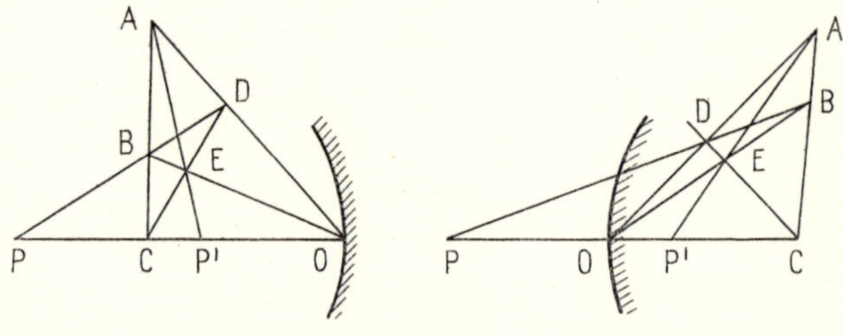

FIG. 4

intersecting *AO* and *AC* at the points *D* and *B*. The straight line *AP'*, joining *A* to the point of intersection of the diagonals *BO* and *CD*, cuts the optical axis at the point *P'*, which is the image of the point *P*.

22. Show that, if a light ray issuing from a point *A* is incident at a point *B* after refraction at the plane boundary dividing two media, the optical length of the ray is less than the optical length of any other ray joining A and B.

23. Deduce from Fermat's principle the formula for a spherical mirror and the formula for a thin lens.*

24. On incidence on the plane boundary between two media a ray is partially reflected and partially refracted. What is the angle of incidence φ if the reflected ray is perpendicular to the refracted ray?

25. Show that, if a light ray passes through several media separated by parallel plane boundaries, the direction of the departing ray depends only on the direction of the entering ray and on the refractive indices of the first and last media.

26. Find the deflection of a light ray incident at an angle $\varphi = 70°$ on a parallel plane glass plate of thickness $d = 10$ cm. The refractive index of the glass is $n = 1{\cdot}5$.

27. A man standing on the edge of a pond looks at a stone at the bottom. The depth of the pond is $h = 1$ m. What is the distance h' of the image of the stone from the water surface, if the line of sight forms an angle $\varphi = 60°$ with the normal to the water surface? The refractive index of water is $n = 1{\cdot}33$.

28. A small speck lies below a glass plate of thickness $d = 15$ cm. What is the distance x of the visual image of the speck from the upper surface of the plate if the line of sight is perpendicular to the surface, and the refractive index of the glass is $n = 1{\cdot}5$?

29. A flat glass plate 3 mm thick is viewed through a microscope. The microscope is first set up for observing the upper surface of the plate, then the tube adjusted downwards until the lower surface of the plate is clearly visible (for convenience of observation marks are

* The following rule of signs is used in this book. Any distance measured from a mirror or lens (or any other point taken as the measurement origin) in the direction of the light propagation is regarded as positive, and in a direction opposite to the propagation as negative. If the incident light is propagated from left to right, this rule of signs coincides with the rule of signs employed in analytical geometry. The radius of curvature of a spherical surface is measured in the direction from the surface to the centre of curvature. On the contrary, focal lengths are measured in the direction from the focus to the lens or mirror (and in the case of a thick lens or system of lenses, in the direction from the focus to the corresponding principal plane).

made on the plate surfaces). The tube displacement is 2 mm. Find the refractive index n of the plate.

30. An object is situated at a distance $l = 15$ cm from a plane-parallel glass plate. An observer views it through the plate, his line of sight being normal to it. Find the distance f of the image of the object from the face nearer to the observer. The plate thickness is $d = 4{\cdot}5$ cm. The refractive index of the glass is $n = 1{\cdot}5$.

31. How is the focus of a camera affected if a plane-parallel glass plate of thickness $d = 6$ mm and refractive index $n = 1{\cdot}5$ is mounted inside the camera on the path of the ray (perpendicularly to the optical axis)? (The lens is strongly stopped.)

32. An object is placed on the axis of a concave mirror well beyond its focus. A plane-parallel glass plate of thickness d and refractive index n is placed between the focus and the mirror so that the mirror axis is perpendicular to the plate. Show that the introduction of the plate displaces the image to the same extent as a displacement of the mirror by $d(n-1)/n$ along the direction to the object.

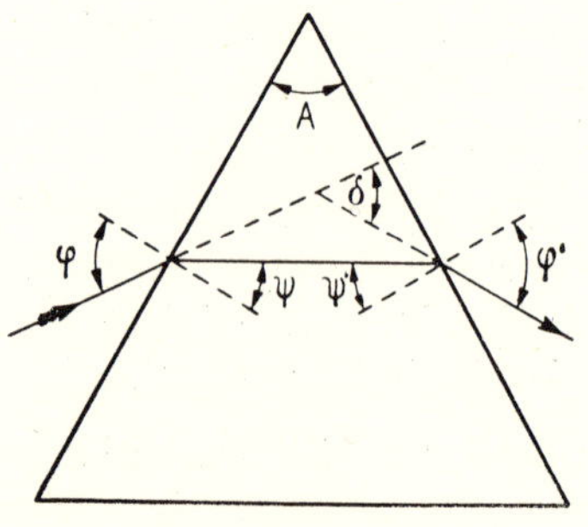

FIG. 5

33. Show that, for a prism of refracting angle A, the angle δ of deviation of a ray is connected with the angles of incidence φ and ψ' and with the angles of refraction ψ and φ' (Fig. 5) by the formula

$$\frac{\sin \frac{1}{2}(A+\delta)}{\sin \frac{1}{2}A} = \frac{n \cos \frac{1}{2}(\psi - \psi')}{\cos \frac{1}{2}(\varphi - \varphi')}.$$

34. Show that the least deviation δ of a parallel pencil in a prism is obtained when the path of the rays in the prism is symmetrical.

Connect the angle of least deviation with the refractive index n of the prism material and with the refracting angle A of the prism.

35. What is the angle δ of least deviation for the sodium D line in a prism with refracting angle 60°? The refractive index for the D line in the prism glass is $n_D = 1{\cdot}62$.

36. After passing through a prism, a light ray is reflected from a plane mirror. Show that, when the path through the prism is symmetrical, the angle of deviation of the reflected ray from the initial direction is independent of the refractive index of the prism.

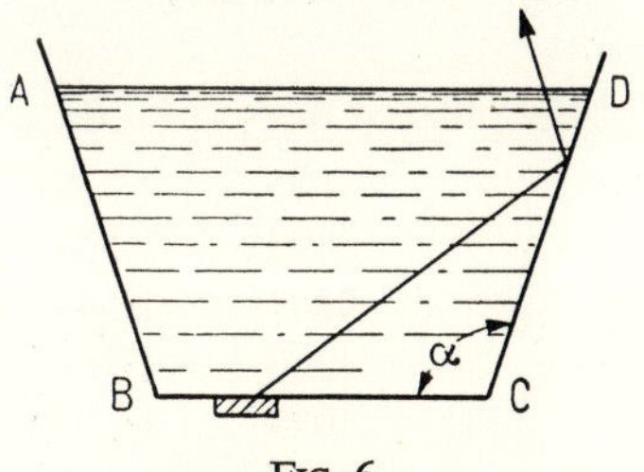

FIG. 6

37. A cylindrical cup containing liquid is placed on a coin which is viewed through the side of the cup. Find the least refractive index n of the liquid for which the coin is not visible.

38. What is the angle α of a trapezoidal vessel $ABCD$ filled with water (Fig. 6) if an object placed under the bottom of the vessel cannot be seen through the sides? The refractive index of water is $n = 1{\cdot}33$. The bottom has a rectangular shape.

39. A light ray is refracted in a prism after moving in a plane perpendicular to the refracting edge of the prism. Show that, if the relative refractive index n of the prism is greater than unity, whilst the angle of incidence remains constant, the ray deviation increases with increasing refracting angle of the prism. Show also that, given the same conditions, the maximum refracting angle of the prism for which the ray can leave it is

$$A = \arcsin\frac{\sin\varphi}{n} + \arcsin\frac{1}{n}.$$

40. Calculate the angle δ of least deviation for a prism with a very small refracting angle A, taking into account second order terms in A.

41. Write an expression for the angular dispersion of a prism in the domain of least deviation. Find the angle at which two rays separate on entering the prism, if they are parallel at incidence. The refractive index for the first ray that undergoes minimum deviation is 1·500, and 1·501 for the second. The refracting angle is 60°.

42. Use the data given below regarding the dispersion of quartz to find the angular dispersion in seconds of arc/Å of a 60° quartz prism in different parts of the spectrum.

Interval	λ in Å	n
	7685	1·5391
1		
	5893	1·5442
2		
	4861	1·5497
3		
	4100	1·5565
4		
	3034	1·5770
5		
	2537	1·5963
6		
	1988	1·6509

43. Calculate the linear dispersion (in mm/Å) in a spectrograph employing a prism as described in the previous problem, in which

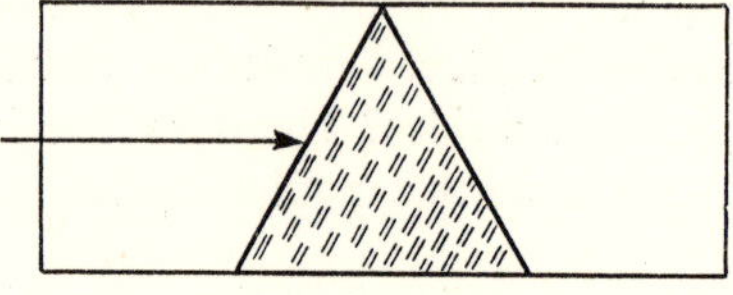

FIG. 7

the chamber has a lens with a focal length $f = 50$ cm (for the intervals indicated in the previous problem).

44. A glass prism is immersed in the liquid filling a long vessel with plane-parallel walls, so that its base rests on the bottom of the vessel as illustrated in Fig. 7. The curves showing the refractive index as a function of the wavelength are shown in Fig. 8 for the glass and the liquid. What happens when a ray of white light enters the vessel and is incident on the prism parallel to its base? Does it resolve into a spectrum, and what are the paths of the yellow, blue and red rays?

45. The optical paths of rays are the same from one position of a wave front to another. Starting from this fact and remembering that the rays are perpendicular to the wave front, show that the magnification given by a telescope is equal to the ratio of the widths of the light pencils before and after passing through the telescope.

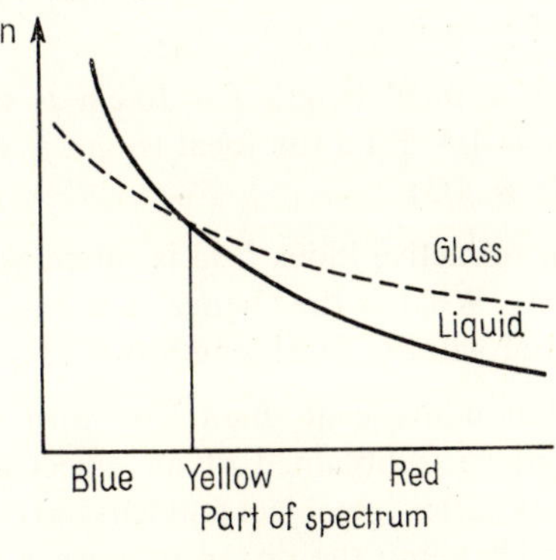

FIG. 8

46. If distant objects are viewed through a prism, in general they appear distorted. One of the distortions amounts to a lengthening or flattening of the image in the direction perpendicular to the edge of the prism. How must the prism be held in order to avoid this particular distortion?

47. How can two glass prisms be arranged to form a "telescope" for viewing distant objects, giving similar images of them whatever the magnification?

48. Use the result of Problem 45 to show that the magnification of a telescope is equal to the ratio of the focal length of the object glass to the focal length of the eyepiece.

49. A thin-walled glass sphere is filled with water ($n = 4/3$). An observer looks along a diameter of the sphere at a grain which is moving along the same diameter. How does the image position of the grain vary if it is displaced from the end of the diameter remote from the observer to the end nearer the observer? The diameter of the sphere is $D = 10$ cm.

50. The frosted glass of a camera is arranged so that the image of an object at a distance of 5 m comes out sharp. Up to what diameter d must the object lens with a focal length of 20 cm be stopped in order for blur not to be noticeable in the reproduction of objects 0·5 m closer to the camera (blur is regarded as unnoticeable if the smearing-out of details does not exceed 0·1 mm)?

51. Find the focal length f of a thin double convex lens bounded by spherical surfaces with radii $r_1 = 25$ mm, $r_2 = 40$ mm; the refractive index of glass is $n = 1{\cdot}5$.

52. A lens with a focal length $f = 10$ cm is made glass with refractive index $n = 1{\cdot}5$. Find the focal length f' of the lens when placed in water ($n = 4/3$).

53. A lens with refractive index 1·53 is submerged in carbon disulphide ($n = 1{\cdot}63$). What is the change in the focal length of the lens now, compared with its focal length in air?

54. Using a thin convergent glass lens with refractive index $n = 3/2$, a real image is obtained of an object at a distance of 10 cm from the lens. After the object and lens have been submerged in water, without changing the distance between them, an image is obtained at a distance of 60 cm from the lens. Find the focal length f of the lens if the refractive index of water is $n' = 4/3$.

55. The focal length of the object glass of a telescope is $f_1 = 60$ cm, and of the eyepiece $f_2 = 4$ cm. The refractive index of the glass of both is $n = 3/2$. The telescope is submerged in water which fills its interior. What new object glass of the same kind of glass must be fitted in place of the old one in order for it to be possible to view distant objects in water? In this case, what will be the magnification of the telescope, if the refractive index of water is $n' = 4/3$?

56. A Galileo telescope with 9 times magnification is 40 cm long. After replacing the object glass and eyepiece by convergent lenses, the telescope still gives the same magnification. Find the local lengths f_1' and f_2' of these lenses, and also the focal lengths f_1 and f_2 of the original object glass and eyepiece of the telescope.

57. A telescope with an object glass of focal length $f = 50$ cm is adjusted for infinity. By what distance Δl is it necessary to adjust the eyepiece in order for objects at a distance of 50 m to be seen clearly?

58. How must an animal's eye be arranged for it to be able to see remote objects in air and in water equally well without a change of accommodation?

59. The image of an object at a distance of 10 cm from a thin lens is erect and magnified 2 times. Find the focal length f of the lens.

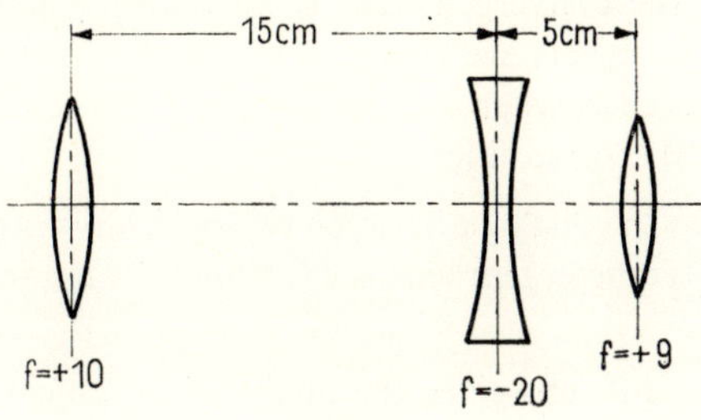

FIG. 9

60. A parallel pencil of light is incident from the left on the lens system illustrated in Fig. 9. Find the position of the point of convergence of the pencil after passing through the system.

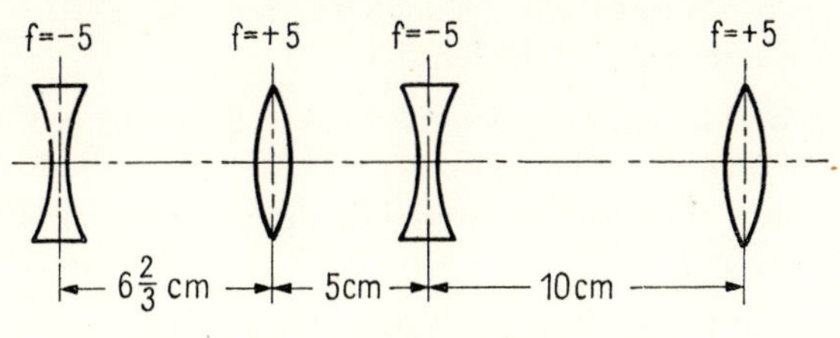

FIG. 10

61. Find the image of a point which is at a distance of 10 cm to the left of the extreme left-hand lens of the system illustrated in Fig. 10.

62. A microscope has an objective with a focal length of 1 cm and an eyepiece with a focal length of 3 cm, the distance between them being 20 cm. At what distance d must an object be situated in order for the final image to be at 20 cm from the eye (which is the least distance for clear vision)? What is the linear magnification now obtained?

63. Show that, if a lens is placed in front of the eye, then moved to one side, it will appear to the observer that an object viewed through the lens moves to the same side, if the lens is divergent, and to the opposite side if the lens is convergent.

Note. The convergent lens is here used as a magnifying glass: the object is placed between the focus and the lens, and an erect image is obtained. If the convergent lens is moved far enough from the eye and distant objects are viewed through it, inverted images are obtained. In this case, when the lens is moved to one side, the image is displaced to the same side.

64. Show that the distance between two optically conjugate points with respect to a convergent lens is $4f$, where f is the focal length of the lens.

65. A convergent lens gives the image of an object on a screen. The height of the image is a. The object is then moved towards the screen whilst keeping the screen and the object fixed, and the image height for a second clear image of the object is b. Find the actual height h of the object.

66. The distance from a small lamp to a screen is $L = 50$ cm. A lens placed between them gives a sharp image of the lamp on the screen at two positions, the distance between which is $l = 10$ cm. Find the focal length f of the lens.

67. The focal length f of a lens is equal to the distance from it to the image of a very remote lamp. What is the distance l of the lamp from the lens if the error in determining the focal length does not exceed p per cent?

68. A concave reflecting galvanometer has a focal length of 1 m. To observe the deflection, it is desirable to use a telescope (subjective reading), for which purpose a lens has to be mounted against the front of the mirror, making the system as a whole equivalent to a plane mirror. Find the focal length of the lens.

69. The system illustrated in Fig. 11 (called objective reading) is used for observing the deflection of a mirror galvanometer. A lens L is mounted in front of the plane mirror M of the galvanometer. Light from the light source S, after passing through the lens L, being reflected from the mirror M and again passing through the lens L, gives a real image on the scale N. Find the focal length f needed for the lens L in order for the source S and the scale N, which are mounted close together, to be at a distance of 1·5 m from the galvanometer. The lens can be assumed very close to the mirror M.

70. A small amount of water is poured into a concave mirror, resting horizontally. The mirror gives a real image of an object on a screen at a distance of 54 cm from the mirror. When the screen is brought towards the mirror, the image reappears at a distance of 36 cm from the mirror. Find the radius of curvature R of the mirror and the distance a of the object from it, if the refractive index of water is $n = 4/3$.

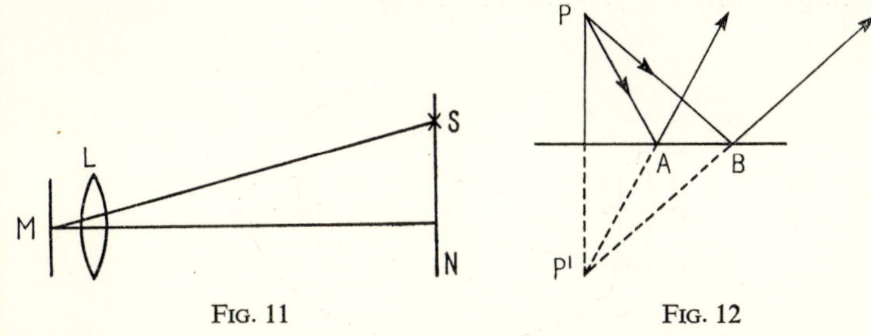

FIG. 11 FIG. 12

71. A camera with a possible extension of 20 cm and a lens with a focal length of 12 cm is required to photograph an object at 15 cm from the lens. What lens has to be added to the camera lens in order for the image to come out sharp with the maximum extension of the camera?

72. If the point P' is the optical image of the point P, we know that the optical path lengths of all the rays joining the points are the same. Let the image P' be obtained by reflection from a plane mirror. As shown in Fig. 12, the path of the step line PBP' is now longer than the path of the step line PAP'. How can these two statements be reconciled?

73. Find the equation of the aplanatic surface of revolution separating two homogeneous media with refractive indices n and n', for pairs of conjugate points P and P', lying on the axis of revolution, of which the point P is at infinity. Investigate the cases: (a) $n'^2 > n^2$; (b) $n'^2 < n^2$; (c) $n'^2 = n^2$.

74. Starting directly from Snell's law of refraction and using the geometrical properties of the ellipse and hyperbola, show that (a) a pencil of light rays incident on an ellipsoid of revolution and parallel to its axis converges at the rear focus of the ellipsoid, if the refractive index of the ellipsoid relative to the surrounding medium is $n = 1/e$, where e is the eccentricity of the ellipsoid; (b) a pencil of light rays incident on one of the sheets of a hyperboloid of two sheets and parallel to its axis transforms after refraction into a divergent pencil of rays, the continuations of which cut one another precisely at the forward focus of the hyperboloid, if the refractive index of the hyperboloid relative to the surrounding medium is $n = 1/e$, where e is the eccentricity of the hyperboloid. (Compare with the previous problem.)

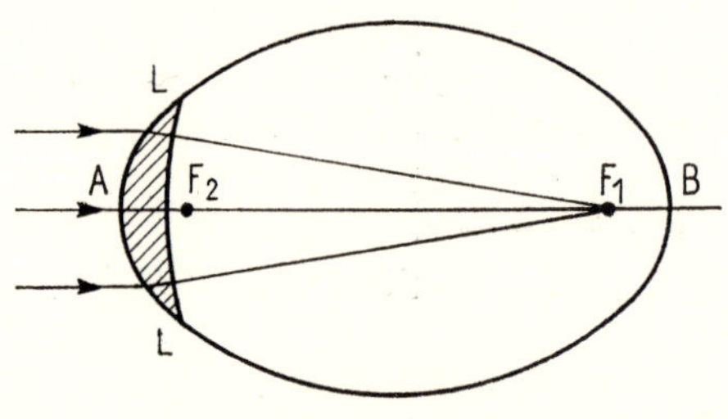

FIG. 13

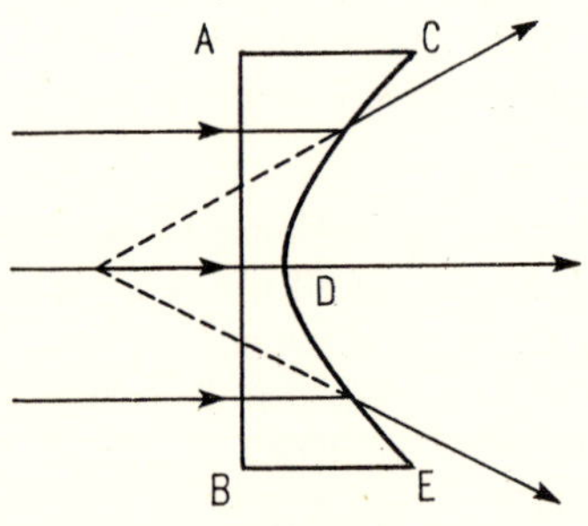

FIG. 14

75. Show that, for the lens of Fig. 13, bounded by the ellipsoid of revolution *BLAL* with foci F_1 and F_2, and by the sphere with centre at F_1, a parallel pencil incident on it is convergent at the focus F_1 if its refractive index is $n = AB/F_1F_2$. The incident rays are parallel to the ellipsoid axis.

Hint. See the previous problem or Problem 73.

76. Show that, for the lens bounded by the plane AB and the hyperboloid of revolution CDE (Fig. 14), incident rays parallel to the hyperboloid axis become divergent, in such a way that the backward continuations of the departing rays intersect at the forward focus of the hyperboloid, provided the refractive index of the lens is equal to the eccentricity of the hyperboloid.

Hint. See Problems 73 and 74.

77. A surface of revolution separating two homogeneous media of refractive indices n and n', and having the property that light rays issuing from a definite point P on the axis of revolution precisely

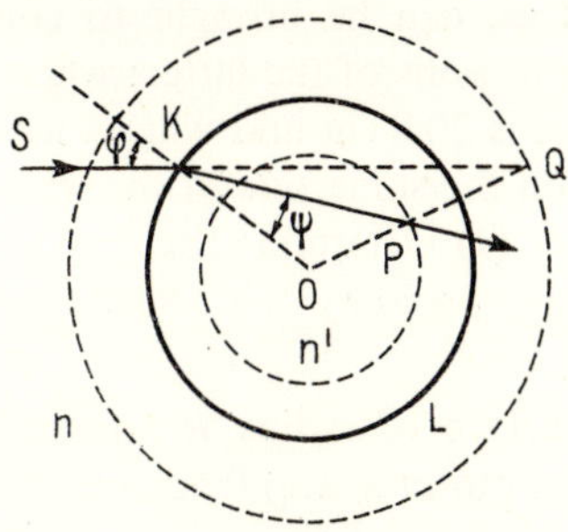

FIG. 15

converge at another point P', also on the axis of revolution, is called a Cartesian oval. Find the equation of the section of this surface by a plane through the axis of revolution PP'. Consider in what cases the curve transforms to a second order curve.

78. Weierstrass invented the following geometrical method of constructing the refracted ray at the surface of a medium. Let the sphere KL of radius R (Fig. 15) with refractive index n' be situated in a homogeneous medium with refractive index n. We draw two concentric spheres of radii $OP = Rn/n'$ and $OQ = Rn'/n$. We continue the incident ray SK to its intersection with the second sphere at the point Q. We join Q to the centre O of the spheres by a straight line. The latter cuts the first sphere at the point P. The line KP is now the refracted ray. Prove this construction. Show also that the points P and Q form a pair of aplanatic points. (See the previous problem.)

79. Using the fact that there is a pair of aplanatic points for a spherical surface, construct an aplanatic lens and find its aplanatic points.

80. One surface of a thin double convex lens is silvered. Find the focal length f of the mirror thus obtained. The radius of curvature of the clean surface is r_1, and of the silvered surface r_2.

81. Two identical thin plano-convex lenses of refractive index n are silvered, one on the plane side, the other on the convex side. Find the ratio of the focal lengths f_1 and f_2 of the compound mirrors obtained, if the light is incident from the unsilvered side in both cases.

82. The image of a luminous object, obtained by reflection from a thin convergent lens, can be brought to coincidence with the object itself at two positions of the latter: when the distance from the object to the lens is 20·0 cm and when the distance is 7·91 cm (both positions are on the same side of the lens). The focal length of the lens is 37·7 cm. (1) Determine the type of the lens. (2) Find the radii of curvature r_1 and r_2 of its surfaces and the refractive index n of the glass.

83. A spherical surface of radius R separates a medium with refractive index n (the object space) from a medium with refractive index n' (the image space). Confining the discussion to paraxial rays, find in the approximation of paraxial optics the connection between the coordinates x, y, z of a point object and the coordinates x', y', z' of the point image. Take as the x axis the principal optical axis, and as the origin the intersection of this axis with the dividing boundary.

Note. See the note to Problem 23 regarding the rule of signs.

84. Use the results of the previous problem to show that, for a centralised optical system, in the approximation of paraxial optics, the coordinates x, y, z of a point object are connected with the coordinates x', y', z' of the point image by the collinear correspondence formulae:

$$x' = \frac{Ax + B}{ax + b};$$

$$y' = \frac{Cy}{ax + b};$$

$$z' = \frac{Cz}{ax + b},$$

where A, B, C, a, b are constants of the given optical system, depending on the choice of origin. An arbitrary point lying on the principal optical axis of the system is taken as the origin in the object space, and another (or the same) point of the same axis as the origin in the image space.

85. Express the coordinates of the focal, principal and nodal points of a centralised optical system and its focal lengths in terms of the constants A, B, C, a, b. (See the previous problem.)

86. What form do the colinear correspondence formulae (Problem 84) take, if the origin is (1) a principal point (coordinates with respect to this system are denoted by the Greek letters ξ, η, ζ); (2) a focal point (coordinates with respect to this system are denoted by X, Y, Z)?

87. Find the positions of the principal planes and the focal lengths for a centralised system consisting of a spherical refracting surface. (See Problem 83.)

88. Show that, in any centralised system, the focal lengths f and f' are connected by

$$\frac{f'}{f} = -\frac{n'}{n},$$

where n is the refractive index of the object space, and n' that of the image space.

Hint. Use the formula $\eta'/\eta = -f\xi'/f'\xi$, the Lagrange–Helmholtz theorem and the definition of principal surfaces.

89. Show that the longitudinal magnification in a centralised optical system is equal to the square of the transverse magnification, if the refractive index of the object space is the same as that of the image space.

Hint. Use Newton's formula $XX' = ff'$.

90. Two centralised optical systems are combined into a single centralised system. The focal lengths of the first system are f_1 and f_1', and of the second system f_2, f_2'. The distance $F_1'F_2$ of the forward focus F_2 of the second system from the rear focus F_1' of the first system is equal to δ (it is called the optical interval of the two systems and is regarded as positive if $F_1'F_2$ has the same direction as the incident light, and as negative in the opposite case). Find the positions of the principal and focal points of the compound system and its focal lengths.

91. Two thin lenses with focal lengths f_1 and f_2 are at a distance l apart, and form a centralised system. Find the focal length f of the system, and the positions of its principal planes.

92. The system of two thin lenses described in the previous problem has to be replaced by a single "equivalent" thin lens, which, whatever the position of the object, will give the same size image as the two-lens system. Find the focal length and the position of the "equivalent" lens.

93. Find the focal length f of a centralised system consisting of two thin lenses with focal lengths f_1 and f_2, spaced a distance l apart, if the space between the lenses is filled with water.

94. Use the results of Problems 87 and 90 to find the positions of the principal planes and the focal lengths of a centralised system consisting of two spherical surfaces with radii of curvature R_1 and R_2, separating homogeneous media with refractive indices n_1, n_2, n_3.

95. Find the position of the principal planes of a thick lens in the form of a sphere. Find the focal lengths f and f' and the positions of the focal points of such a spherical lens, when it is made of (1) water ($n_w = 4/3$) and (2) glass ($n_g = 1{\cdot}5$). What is the refractive index if the focal points do not go outside the sphere?

96. A glass sphere ($n = 1{\cdot}5$) has a radius $R = 4$ cm. (1) Find the distance x' from the centre of the sphere to the image of an object situated 6 cm from the surface of the sphere. (2) Find the magnification of the image.

97. In what cases is the focal length of a thick lens independent of its thickness and precisely the same as the focal length of a thin lens having an equal surface curvature? In these circumstances, is the position of the focus relative to the lens dependent on its thickness?

98. A double convex lens is made of glass of refractive index $n = 1{\cdot}5$ and is surrounded by air. When is it divergent?

99. When does a double convex lens, made of a material whose refractive index is greater than the refractive index of the surrounding medium, operate like a plane-parallel plate?

100. Two identical plano-convex lenses are mounted a short distance apart with their plane surfaces facing one another. Show that the focal length is greater in this case than when the lenses are in contact.

101. There is water ($n = 1{\cdot}33$) on one side and air on the other side of a thin double convex lens made of glass ($n = 1{\cdot}52$). The radii curvature of both surfaces are 20 cm. Find the positions of the principal and focal planes and the nodal points of the system.

102. The radius of curvature r of the spherical surface of a glass ($n = 1{\cdot}52$) plano-convex lens is 26 cm; the lens thickness is 3·04 cm. Calculate the focal length f of the lens and find the position of the image of an object 75 cm from the nearer surface of the lens, when the object is situated (1) on the side of the convex surface, (2) on the side of the plane surface.

103. Find the focal length f and the positions of the principal planes of a double convex thick lens, for which $n = 1{\cdot}5$, $r_1 = 10$ cm, $r_2 = 4$ cm, $d = 2$ cm.

104. Find the positions of the principal planes, the focal points and the focal length of a system of two thin lenses as illustrated in Fig. 16.

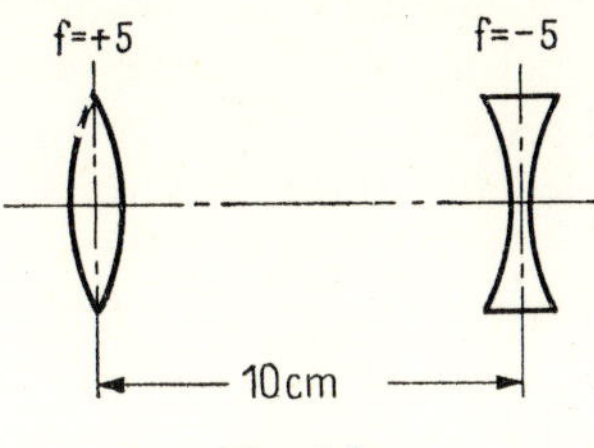

FIG. 16

105. Are an object and its image always visible from the optical centre at the same angles?

Note. The optical centre of a thick lens is the image of the front (rear) principal point when refracted in the front (rear) surface of the lens.

106. If both surfaces of a concavo-convex lens have the same radii of curvature, is the lens convergent or divergent? Find the positions of the principal planes and the focal length of the lens, if its thickness is d, the radius of curvature of each surface is R, and the refractive index $n > 1$.

107. The refracting surfaces of a lens are concentric spherical surfaces. The greater radius of curvature is R, the lens thickness is d, the refractive index $n > 1$. Is the lens convergent or divergent? Find the positions of the principal planes and the focal length of the lens.

108. For what position of an indefinitely small three-dimensional object is its image, given by a centralised optical system, similar to the object itself?

Hint. The necessary and sufficient condition for the image of a small spatial object to be similar to the object itself is that the absolute value of the transverse magnification be equal to the axial magnification. Starting from the equation of a centralised system in Newton's form: $XX' = ff'$, find the axial magnification. On equating this to the transverse magnification, the problem is easily solved.

109. B. B. Golitsyn proposed the following method of finding the refractive index of a liquid. The liquid in question is poured into a cylindrical glass tube, the outer surface of which is marked with two lines parallel to the tube axis, and the apparent distance y_1 between them is measured from the opposite side of the tube. Let y be the true distance between the lines, R_1 the outer, and R_2 the inner radius of the tube. Let n_1, n_2, n be the refractive indices of air, glass and the liquid respectively. Show that the refractive index of the liquid can be calculated from the formula

$$\frac{1}{n} = \frac{1}{n_2}\left(1 - \frac{R_2}{R_1}\right) + \frac{1}{2n_1}\frac{R_2}{R_1}\left(1 + \frac{y}{y_1}\right).$$

110. Ramsden proposed the following method for finding the magnification of a telescope, the eyepiece of which is a convergent lens. The telescope is adjusted to infinity and clamped to an optical bench. The object-glass is unscrewed and replaced by a diaphragm, having, say, the form of a rhombus. The eyepiece gives a real image of this diaphragm, which can be viewed on a screen. Let L be the length of diagonal of the rhombus-diaphragm, and l of its image. Show that the magnification of the telescope is L/l.

111. Ramsden's method (see the previous problem) cannot be used directly for finding the magnification of a Galileo telescope, since its eyepiece is a divergent lens. The following procedure can be adopted for finding the magnification of a Galileo telescope. The telescope is adjusted to infinity and clamped on an optical bench. Another telescope, of known magnification and also adjusted to infinity, is mounted behind the Galileo telescope with its eyepiece towards the latter. A screen is mounted behind the second telescope. The object-glass of the Galileo telescope is next unscrewed and replaced by a diaphragm. The screen is then moved until a real image of the diaphragm is obtained on it. Show that the magnification of the Galileo telescope is

$$N_1 = \frac{D_1}{D_2} N_2,$$

where D_1 is the size of the diaphragm, D_2 the size of the image, and N_2 the magnification of the second telescope.

112. Bessel proposed the following method for determining the focal length of a convergent lens. An object and screen are mounted on either side of the lens with a fixed distance A between them. Generally speaking, there are two positions of the object at which sharp images of it are obtained on the screen (indicate when this is possible). Let a be the distance between these positions, and e the distance between the principal planes of the lens. Find an expression for the focal length of the lens, neglecting squares of the ratio e/A. How can e be determined?

113. Find a formula connecting the distance u from a source to a concave mirror of radius r with the distance v from the mirror to the point A of intersection of the mirror axis with a ray issuing from the source and reflected from the mirror at a distance h from the axis. Neglect terms containing h to powers greater than the second.

114. A point source is at a distance u from a concave spherical mirror with radius of curvature r. Find the longitudinal spherical aberration of rays issuing from the source and reflected from the mirror at a distance h from its axis. Neglect terms containing h to powers higher than the second.

Hint. See the previous problem.

115. The radius of a concave spherical mirror is 50 cm. A point source is situated 100 cm from the mirror on its axis. Find the longitudinal aberration of rays reflected from the mirror at distances of 3, 6, 9 and 12 cm from the axis.

116. Find the longitudinal spherical aberration for a parallel pencil incident on a spherical mirror of 1 m diameter and focal length 10 m.

117. What will be the diameter of the image of a star obtained with the mirror described in the previous problem?

118. In the case of paraxial rays, the formula connecting the distance u from the source to the refracting spherical surface with the distance v from the image to the surface is

$$\frac{n}{v} - \frac{1}{u} = \frac{n-1}{r}$$

(see Problem 83). Show that, for rays intersecting the surface at a distance h from the axis, the distance v' of the image from the spherical surface is connected with u by the formula (neglecting quartic and higher terms in h):

$$\frac{n}{v'} - \frac{1}{u} = \frac{n-1}{r} + \frac{n-1}{n^2}\left(\frac{1}{r} - \frac{1}{u}\right)^2\left(\frac{1}{r} - \frac{n+1}{u}\right)\frac{h^2}{2}.$$

119. Find the longitudinal spherical aberration in a thin lens for rays meeting the lens at a distance h from the axis.

Hint. See the previous problem.

120. Find the longitudinal spherical aberration for a parallel pencil incident on a plano-convex glass lens ($n = 1{\cdot}5$) in the cases: (1) when the lens has its convex face to the beam and (2) when the lens has its plane face to the pencil. The focal length of the lens is 1 m. The diameter of the lens is 10 cm. Find also the transverse aberration in both cases.

121. Find the local lengths for red, yellow and blue rays, and also the longitudinal chromatic aberration (the difference between the focal lengths for the extreme visible rays) of a double convex lens with radii of curvature $R_1 = R_2 = R = 981{\cdot}4$ mm, made of glass with the following refractive indices:

	λ in Å	n
Red rays	6682	1·4835
Yellow rays	5270	1·4907
Blue rays	4046	1·4997

122. In visual observations we usually fix the image formed by the rays of the middle part of the visible spectrum, i.e., the yellow rays. Assuming that the aperture diameter of the lens described in the previous problem is 5 cm, find the diameters d of the circles of dispersion formed by the red and blue rays on focusing on the yellow image.

123. Find the magnification N of a magnifying glass or eyepiece (regarding them as thick centralised systems) as a function of the position of the object and the observer's eye. The coordinates of the object and its image relative to the focal points are X and X'; the coordinate defining the position of the eye relative to the rear focus of the eyepiece is equal to a. For what position of the object is the magnification independent of the position of the observer's eye? What is the position of the eye if the magnification is independent of the position of the object? What is the magnification when the eye is accommodated at the least distance of clear vision $L = 25$ cm?

Note. The magnification of a magnifying glass or eyepiece is the ratio of the angle subtended by the object viewed through the eyepiece to the angle subtended by it at the naked eye when its distance from the eye is the least distance for clear vision.

124. What is the meaning of achromatisation of an eyepiece in relation to focal lengths only, without simultaneous achromatisation in the sense of a combination of the principal planes?

Hint. See the previous problem.

125. Show that two thin lenses, made of the same material, form a system which is achromatised with respect to focal length (for all wavelengths), if the distance between them is $l = \frac{1}{2}(f_1 + f_2)$.

126. One type of Kellner eyepiece is a system, achromatised with respect to focal length, of two thin convergent lenses, the distance l between which is equal to the focal length f_1 of the first lens. Find the focal length f_2 of the second lens, the focal length f of the entire eyepiece and the positions of its principal planes.

127. A Huygens eyepiece consists of a system of two thin plano-convex lenses, with their convex surfaces facing the incident light, achromatised with respect to focal length. To decrease the spherical aberration, Huygens chose the distance between the lenses so that light rays incident on the eyepiece parallel to its principal optical axis suffer the same angular deviations when refracted in the first and second lenses.* Find the relationship between the focal lengths f_1 and f_2 of the two lenses, the distance l between them, the positions of the principal planes of the eyepiece and its focal length f.

128. Why is it that specks are visible on the surface of the first lens in the Kellner eyepiece described in Problem 126, whereas they are not visible in the Huygens eyepiece?

129. The Ramsden eyepiece consists of two plano-convex lenses with the same focal lengths and their convex sides facing one another. The distance between the lenses is equal to two-thirds their focal length. Find the focal length and the positions of the principal planes of a Ramsden eyepiece. Where must the cross-hair lines be situated in order for their image to coincide with the plane of the object image?

130. Write down the condition for achromatisation of two lenses placed in close juxtaposition. What conclusion can be drawn from this condition regarding the focal lengths of the two components of the achromatic lens?

131. Which lens is made of crown glass, and which of flint, in the achromatic object glass of a telescope, binocular, etc., consisting of a double convex and a plano-concave lens?

132. Find the dimensions of an achromatic plano-convex cemented object glass with focal length $f = 1$ m, made of crown ($n_1 = 1{\cdot}5179$, dispersive power $\nu_1 = 60{\cdot}2$) and flint glass ($n_2 = 1{\cdot}6202$, dispersive power $\nu_2 = 36{\cdot}2$). One of the lenses is double convex.

Note. The dispersive power is

$$\nu = \frac{n_D - 1}{n_F - n_C},$$

where the letters D, F, C refer to the corresponding Fraunhofer lines.

133. Write down the condition under which a lens is achromatised with respect to focal lengths for two arbitrary parts of the spectrum.

134. Show that the thick single achromatic lens described in the previous problem is convergent if it is double convex, and divergent if it is convexo-concave.

* This condition is usually not fulfilled in modern types of Huygens eyepieces.

Note. A lens is said to be convergent if its focal length in the object space $f = -f'$ is positive. Otherwise the lens is said to be divergent. See the note on Problem 23.

135. Find the thickness d and focal length f of a thick achromatic double convex lens, both surfaces of which have the same radius of curvature $R = 10$ cm. The lens is made of glass with the following refractive indices:

$$n_{\text{red}} = 1{\cdot}636; \quad n_{\text{blue}} = 1{\cdot}682.$$

136. A light source is projected by a condenser on to the slit of a spectrograph; the image of the source is thereby magnified k times. Show that, given total filling of the object glass of the collimator, the condenser candle-power α_1 and the collimator object-glass candle-power α_2 are connected by the relationship

$$\alpha_1 = (1 + k)\alpha_2.$$

137. When photographing spectra, the photographic plate is not mounted perpendicular to the optical axis of the spectrograph object glass. Find the magnitude β and the direction of the bias angle required by the plate in order for the entire spectrum to be received clearly, given that the refractive index of the optical glass of which the object-glass is made is 1·502 for the C line and 1·510 for the F line, and that the angular dispersion of the spectrograph prism between these lines is $\alpha = 3°$.

Hint. It can be assumed that, if both the C and F lines are focused, the entire spectrum will be sharp. It must also be borne in mind that monochromatic pencils depart from the prism in parallel rays.

138. A light ray is incident on a homogeneous sphere with refractive index n. Is it possible for the refracted ray to suffer total internal reflection inside the sphere?

139. According to Descartes, a rainbow is formed as a result of the reflection of the sun's rays inside drops of water. Rays undergoing a single reflection inside the drops yield the so-called primary bow, whilst the secondary bow is formed by rays that undergo double reflection. The angular dimensions of the bow can be found from the requirement that the angle of deviation of the light ray on reflection and refraction inside the drops be minimal, since in this case a small change in the angle of deviation corresponds to a large variation in the angle of incidence, and hence maximum intensity of the light reflected inside the drop is obtained. What is the angle of incidence φ of the light ray at the drop surface, if it undergoes least deviation on single and double reflection inside the drop? Find the angular radius α of the primary and secondary rainbows for red and violet light. The refractive index of water is $n_{\text{red}} = 1{\cdot}329$, $n_{\text{violet}} = 1{\cdot}343$.

Note. The Cartesian theory of the rainbow is based on geometrical optics and only explains some basic features of the phenomenon. A more detailed explanation requires a consideration of the diffraction of light at the raindrops.

140. The Cartesian theory admits of the existence of higher order rainbows, when the number of reflections of the light inside the raindrops is three, four, etc. Assuming that a ray of sunlight undergoes N reflections inside a drop, find the angle of incidence φ (Fig. 17) which corresponds to an extremal deviation of the ray leaving the

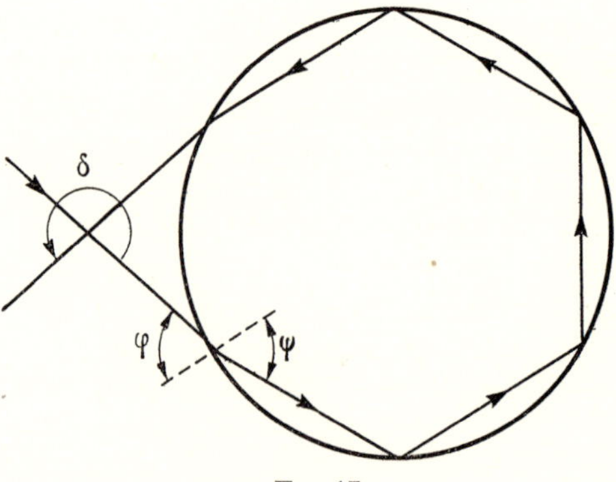

FIG. 17

drop from its original direction. Show that extremal deviation always corresponds to a minimum of the angle of deviation. Find the angle δ of least deviation and the angular radius α for rainbows of the third, fourth fifth and sixth orders, taking the refractive index of water as $n = 1{\cdot}33$. Explain why these bows and bows of higher orders are never observed.

141. A halo, i.e. white, slightly tinged rings round the sun (or moon), is observed when the sky is thinly shrouded by cirro-stratus or high stratus clouds. The halo occurs as a result of the refraction of light rays in randomly orientated ice crystals of regular hexagonal prism form (hexagonal system). Find the visible angular radius of the halo and describe the distribution of the colour in it. The refractive index of ice is $n = 1{\cdot}31$.

142. Show by starting from the law of refraction of light that the radius of curvature ϱ of a light ray when propagated in a transparent isotropic medium with slowly varying refractive index is given by

$$\frac{1}{\varrho} = \frac{d}{dN}(\ln n),$$

where the derivative is with respect to the direction of the principal normal to the ray.

143. Assuming that the refractive index n of air depends only on the distance from the centre of the earth, deduce a formula for calculating astronomical refraction, taking account of the curvature of the earth's surface.

144. Show that, if the curvature of the earth's surface is neglected (which is permissible if the star is not too close to the horizon), the astronomical refraction is independent of the law of variation of the refractive index of air with the altitude, and depends only on n_0 and α_0. Show that, for a heavenly body which is not too close to the horizon, the refraction can be calculated from the approximate formula

$$\alpha_\infty - \alpha_0 = (n_0 - 1)\tan\alpha_0 .$$

145. Find the refraction $\alpha_\infty - \alpha_0$, if the visible zenithal distance α_0 of a heavenly body is 70°, and the refractive index of air at the earth's surface is $n_0 = 1{\cdot}000293$.

146. Assuming that the difference $n - 1$ is proportional to the air density and that the air density varies with the height in accordance with the barometric formula (isothermal atmosphere), deduce an expression for the refraction $\alpha_\infty - \alpha_0$ that takes account of the curvature of the earth's surface.

147. Find the refraction $\alpha_\infty - \alpha_0$ for an isothermal atmosphere, on the assumption that the visible zenithal distance $\alpha_0 = 90°$; the molecular weight of air is $M = 28{\cdot}8$; the acceleration due to gravity is $g = 981\ \text{cm}\,\text{sec}^{-2}$; the temperature $T = 273\,°\text{K}$; the gas constant $R = 8{\cdot}314 \times 10^7\ \text{erg}\,\text{deg}^{-1}\,\text{mol}^{-1}$; the earth's radius is

$r_0 = 6367$ km; the refractive index of air at the earth's surface is $n_0 = 1{\cdot}000293$.

148. The gradient of the refractive index of air close to the earth's surface is approx. 3×10^{-10} cm^{-1}. Find the radius of curvature of a light ray when it is propagated in the atmosphere in a horizontal direction. What gradient is necessary in order for a light ray departing in a horizontal direction to describe a circle about the terrestrial sphere?

149. An absolute optical instrument is one which uses wide pencils and gives a strictly stigmatic image of every point of the object space. Maxwell gave an example of such an instrument, which he called a "fish eye". Maxwell's fish eye consists of an unbounded medium with continuously varying refractive index and possessing spherical symmetry. In such a medium a light ray has a circular shape independently of the point and the direction of its departure.

Find the law of variation of the refractive index of the "fish eye" as a function of the distance r from the centre of symmetry. Show that all light rays departing from an arbitrary point P, after describing circles, again converge at some point P'. Show also that the magnification given by the "fish eye" is equal to the ratio of the refractive index at the place where the object is situated to the refractive index at the point where the image is obtained.

150. Find the minimum radius of curvature of the circle which can be described by a light ray in a "fish eye".

Hint. See the previous problem.

151. Is Maxwell's "fish eye" realisable in electron optics, assuming that the electrons must move in an electrostatic field *in vacuo*?

Hint. Use the analogy between geometrical optics and the classical mechanics of the motion of a particle in a conservative field of force.

152. Using the analogy between classical mechanics and geometrical optics, obtain an expression for the curvature of a ray in a non-uniform isotropic medium.

153. Starting from the formula for the curvature of a ray in a non-uniform medium and using the analogy between classical mechanics and geometrical optics, show that the radius of curvature ϱ

of an electron in an electric field is given by

$$\frac{1}{\varrho} = -\frac{E_N}{2V},$$

where E_N is the component of the electric field along the principal normal to the trajectory, and V is the electrostatic potential, normalised so that the electron velocity is zero at zero potential.

154. The objective of a microscope, satisfying the sine condition, is mounted on an optical bench. A net of curves drawn on a sheet of paper is mounted in front of the front aplanatic point P. The net is viewed by an eye at the second (rear) aplanatic point P'. Find the shape of the curves viewed, if the eye sees their image as a rectangular net of straight lines. The distance a of the net from the point P is large compared with the diameter of the input aperture of the system.

155. Figure 18 illustrates to correct size the drawing that can be used when testing objectives of microscopes by Abbe's method. After removing the eyepiece, the drawing is placed in front of the front aplanatic point of the objective at an exact distance a from it. The observer's eye is placed at the second aplanatic point. If the

FIG. 18

image of the drawing appears as a square net, the objective satisfies the sine condition. After measuring the necessary dimensions on Fig. 18, find the distance a from the front aplanatic point of the objective, at which the drawing has to be placed when testing an objective by Abbe's method. (See the previous problem.)

156. Prove the theorem: Let the point P' be the stigmatic image of the point P, given by an optical system using arbitrarily wide pencils of rays. The necessary and sufficient condition for an infinitesimal element of a plane passing through P to produce a stigmatic image with the aid of wide pencils of rays is that the cosine condition be satisfied for two infinitesimal non-parallel segments lying in this plane and passing through the point P.

Note. The theorem or cosine condition amounts to the following: Let the point P' be the stigmatic image of the point P. We join these points by an arbitrary ray, the directions of which are defined at P, P' by the unit vectors $\boldsymbol{s}$, $\boldsymbol{s}'$. Let Q, Q' be two points indefinitely close to P, P' respectively. The necessary and sufficient condition for the point Q to produce a stigmatic image at the point Q is that the difference $n(\boldsymbol{s} \cdot \boldsymbol{l}) - n'(\boldsymbol{s}' \cdot \boldsymbol{l}')$, where $\boldsymbol{l} = \overrightarrow{PQ}, \boldsymbol{l}' = \overrightarrow{P'Q'}$, be independent of $\boldsymbol{s}$, i.e., of the direction of the ray joining P, P'. Here n is the refractive index in the object space, and n' in the image space. The medium in which the light rays are propagated is assumed isotropic, but it may be non-homogeneous.

157. Prove the theorem: Let an optical system give a stigmatic image of an infinitesimal area. Further, let $\boldsymbol{l}_1$ and $\boldsymbol{l}_2$ be infinitesimal non-parallel segments, intersecting at the edge of the area and lying in its plane. If the segments are tangential to the field of the instrument, the area has an image in the system in which similitude is preserved. The optical length of any segment lying in the area is now equal to the optical length of the segment conjugate to it.

Note. A light ray is said to lie in the field of an instrument if it actually passes through the diaphragm of the object space in the image space. Also, a segment is said to be tangential in the instrument field if all rays tangential to this segment lie in the instrument field.

158. Prove the theorem: Let an optical system produce a stigmatic image of a finite surface and let AB be a line lying on this surface. If at least two rays can be drawn through every point of the line, touching the imaged surface and lying in the instrument field, the optical length of the line AB is equal to the optical length of its image $A'B'$.

159. Prove the theorem: Let the point P' be the stigmatic image of the point P. The necessary and sufficient condition for an infinitesimal element of volume to have a stigmatic image is that the cosine condition be satisfied for three non-coplanar infinitesimal segments through P.

160. Prove the theorem: Similitude is always preserved when stigmatic images of volume elements are formed. The linear magnification is equal to n/n', so that the optical length of an object is always equal to the optical length of its image. In particular, this theorem holds for the images produced by an absolute optical instrument. (See Problem 149.)

161. Prove the theorem: In an absolute optical instrument the optical length of the ray joining conjugate points is the same for all pairs of such points.

162. Prove the theorem: If the refractive indices n, n' of the object and image spaces are constant, an absolute optical instrument is a telescopic system in which the image of any straight line is again a straight line. In the particular case when $n = n'$, the magnification given by the instrument is unity.

163. Prove the theorem: Let the object and image spaces have constant refractive indices n and n' and border one another on a refractive surface. Such an optical system cannot be an absolute instrument. It is also impossible to have an absolute instrument with constant n and n', in which the image is obtained by means of a finite number of refractions at refracting surfaces or by means of a combination of a finite number of refractions and reflections.

164. Prove the theorem: If n and n' are constant, the only absolute optical instrument with a finite number of reflecting or refracting surfaces is a plane mirror or a system of plane mirrors.

§ 2. Photometry

165. A book lies on a table which is 1 m from the base of the perpendicular dropped from the lamp to the plane of the table. The lamp can only be raised or lowered. What is its height h above the table for maximum illumination of the book?

166. It is assumed in photometric practice that the inverse square law can be used if the distance of the photometer from the light source is not less than five times the over-all dimension of the latter.

Show that, for the case of a circular uniformly illuminating disc (i.e. a disc whose surface brightness is the same in all directions) of radius R, a 1 per cent error is obtained by using the inverse square law to calculate the illumination on a perpendicular area at a distance $10R$ from the disc centre.

167. What should be the light distribution curve of a lamp if it is to give uniform illumination on a flat table above which it is hung?

168. A hollow frosted glass sphere is illuminated at one place by a parallel pencil of light, whose cross section is small by comparison with the diameter of the sphere. The walls of the sphere disperse the light in accordance with Lambert's law. What is the brightness distribution over the surface of the sphere?

169. The real image formed by a concave mirror is viewed on a white screen. Find the image brightness as a function of the aperture and focal length of the mirror.

170. Explain why two identical headlamps situated at different short distances from the observer often appear equally bright. Is this always true, and when do the exceptions occur?

171. What illumination E is obtained on a horizontal area illuminated by the hemispherical sky, if the brightness of the sky is assumed to be uniform everywhere and equal to B?

172. A right-angled wedge (Fig. 19) lies in a parallel pencil so that the brightness of the faces is the same. Find the angles α_1, α_2 of the wedge with the pencil. The faces diffuse the light in accordance with Lambert's law.

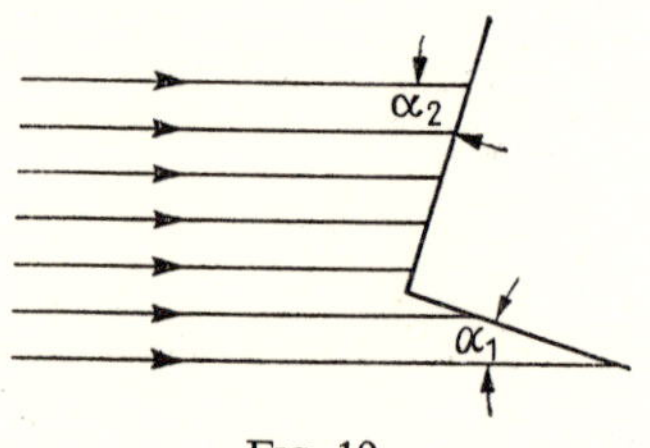

FIG. 19

173. The illumination at normal incidence of the sun's rays on the earth's surface is about 10^5 lux. Assuming that the sun's radiation obeys Lambert's law, and neglecting the absorption of light in the atmosphere, find the brightness of the sun, given that the radius of the earth's orbit is $R = 1{\cdot}5 \times 10^8$ km, and the sun's diameter $D = 1{\cdot}4 \times 10^6$ km.

174. What illumination E must be produced on a white sheet of paper with reflection coefficient $k = 0{\cdot}85$ in order for its brightness B to be 3 candle-power? The paper can be assumed to scatter the light in accordance with Lambert's law.

175. The illumination at normal incidence of the sun's rays on the earth's surface is approximately $E_0 = 100{,}000$ lux. What is the illumination E of the image of the sun given by a lens of diameter $D = 5$ cm and focal length $f = 10$ cm, and free from aberration. The angular diameter of the sun is $\alpha = 30'$.

176. An object is photographed with a two-times reduction by an object lens of small candle-power. What is the change in the illumination of the photographic plate if the picture is taken with 1:1 magnification in the same conditions?

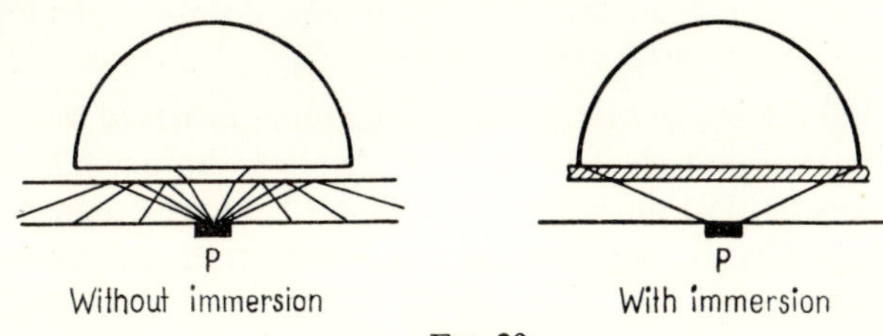

FIG. 20

Hint. The reference to the small candle-power of the lens means that the lens diameter is small compared with the distance to the object, so that the lens area can be regarded as equal to the area of the corresponding spherical segment when calculating the solid angle.

177. An object P lies below the objective of a microscope (Fig. 20). The objective diameter is $D = 3$ mm, its distance from the glass covering the object is extremely small, the refractive index of the covering glass is $n = 1{\cdot}5$, and its thickness is $h = 0{\cdot}2$ mm. How many times is the image brightness increased if an immersion is introduced between the objective and the cover glass, of the same refractive index as that of the cover glass? It is assumed that in both cases the object is placed in liquid of the same refractive index as the cover glass.

Note. In the absence of immersion, the only rays incident from the object on to the objective are those that are incident on the surface of the cover glass at an angle less than the angle of total internal reflection. Thus the solid angle subtended by the objective at the point P is diminished if an immersion is absent. In an accurate calculation it would be necessary to take into account the reflection at the air–glass boundaries, where the dependence of the reflection coefficient on the angle of incidence is given by Fresnel's formula. If this reflection is neglected, as in the present problem, the calculated increase in the image brightness is rather less than the true increase.

178. Find the ratio of the image brightness B' obtained in an aplanatic system to the object brightness B, the radiation of the object being subject to Lambert's law. The refractive indices in the object and image spaces are the same.

179. The real image formed by a convergent lens is first viewed directly, then on a white screen. In each case, how does the image brightness depend on the lens diameter?

180. Find the image brightness of the moon, observed in a telescope with an object glass of diameter 75 mm, with magnification of (1) 20 times, (2) 25 times and (3) 50 times. Take the brightness of the moon seen by the naked eye as unity. Take the diameter of the pupil of the eye as 3 mm.

181. What is the diameter required for the objective of a magnifying glass with 50 times magnification for the image illumination at the retina to be not less than the illumination obtained when viewing the object with the naked eye? The diameter of the pupil of the eye is 2 mm. Neglect light losses in the magnifying glass.

182. The diameter of the object-glass of an astronomical telescope is 18 cm. Assuming that the transmission coefficient of the entire optical system of the telescope is 0·5 and that the naked eye distinguishes stars of the sixth magnitude, find (1) the size of the weakest stars that can be seen with the aid of the telescope, (2) the most advantageous size for a star to be viewed and (3) the size of a star which is visible with a magnification of 10 times. The diameter of the pupil of the eye is 3 mm.

Note. An increase in the size of a star by unity corresponds to a $\sqrt[5]{100} \approx 2{\cdot}5$ times diminution in its visual brightness.

183. What size of star can be viewed through a telescope with an object-glass of 2 m diameter? The naked eye distinguishes stars of the sixth magnitude. The diameter of the pupil of the eye is 3 mm. Neglect the light losses.

184. The image brightness in an optical system is known to be independent of its magnification. Yet when looking through a microscope the image appears less bright when greater magnification is used. Why? Find (1) the image illumination in a microscope with a numerical aperture 1 (dry system) and magnification 625; (2) the image illumination in a microscope with a numerical aperture 1·5 (immersion with $n = 1{\cdot}5$) and magnification 1500. The object illumination is taken as unity. The distance of distinct vision is 25 cm, the diameter of the pupil of the eye is 2 mm. Neglect light losses in the microscope.

185. Find the illumination E produced by an infinitely large illuminating plane at an area which is parallel to this plane, if the brightness of the plane at normal incidence is B and the radiation is subject to Lambert's law.

186. The objectives of the collimator and camera of a spectrograph have the same diameters; the focal lengths of the two may be different. A condenser is used to achieve illumination of the slit, in which the objective of the collimator is completely filled with light. Show that in these conditions the candle-power of the apparatus depends only on the camera objective.

187. The energy flux of the visible radiation of a candle at 1 m distance from it is 6 erg/cm^2 sec. Assuming that the loss in weight of the candle is 8·5 g/hr and that the calorific value of spermaceti is 5800 cal/g, find the efficiency of the candle as a light source.

188. Knowing that the mechanical equivalent of light in the narrow spectral region corresponding to maximum sensitivity of the eye ($\lambda = 5550$ Å) is 0·00160 watt/lumen, estimate the efficiency of a powerful gas-filled incandescent lamp consuming 0·5 watts per candle. It can be assumed as a guide that the average sensitivity of the eye in the spectral region occupied by the lamp radiation is half the maximum.*

189. Find the mean electric field-strength of the sun's light radiation on the earth, taking the solar constant as 2 cal cm^{-2} min^{-1} and neglecting the absorption in the atmosphere.

Note. The solar constant is the mean flux of solar radiation arriving per min at the earth's surface, per cm^2 perpendicular to the direction of the radiation (in the absence of absorption in the atmosphere).

* The problem can be solved more accurately if the energy distribution in the spectrum is known and use is made of the visibility curve for the human eye.

190. Using the data of the previous problem, find the magnetic field-strength H of a light wave arriving at the earth from the sun.

191. What is the magnetic field-strength amplitude H of the light wave at the position of the sun's image, received in a camera with a lens candle-power of 1/4? The angular diameter of the sun $\approx 0{\cdot}01$ radians. Neglect the light losses in the atmosphere and lens.

§ 3. Interference and Diffraction of Light

192. Write the equation of a plane wave, the normal to which is parallel to the unit vector $\boldsymbol{n} = (\alpha, \beta, \gamma)$.

What form does the equation take for a monochromatic wave?

193. Obtain the equation of a wave radiated by (1) a point source (spherical wave) and (2) an infinite thread (cylindrical wave).

194. Show that, if the phase difference of two component vibrations varies randomly with time, the time average of the energy of the resultant vibration is equal to the sum of the energies of the components.

Hint. Assume that all values of the phase difference are equiprobable during the time of observation.

195. In what circumstances do two electromagnetic waves of the same frequency always add up (i.e., whatever the phase relations) in such a way that the intensity I of the resultant oscillation is equal to the sum of the intensities I_1, I_2 of the component oscillations?

196. The directions of propagation of two plane waves of the same wavelength λ form a small angle φ to one another. The waves are incident on a screen, the plane of which is roughly perpendicular to their direction of propagation. Write down the equations of the two waves and add their fields, and thus show that the distance Δx between two adjacent interference bands on the screen is given by

$$\Delta x = \frac{\lambda}{\varphi}.$$

197. What is the change in the expression for Δx in the previous problem if the interfering beams are incident obliquely on the screen?

198. Find the wavelength λ of the monochromatic radiation if, in Young's experiment, the distance of the first interference maximum from the central band is $p = 0{\cdot}05$ cm. The apparatus has the data (Fig. 21): $a = 5$ m, $d = 0{\cdot}5$ cm.

199. A tube of length $l = 2$ cm with plane-parallel glass bases is mounted in the path of one of the rays in Young's interference equipment, and the interference pattern is observed when the tube is filled with air. The tube is then filled with chlorine and the resulting displacement of the interference pattern observed over $N = 20$ bands. The entire equipment is placed in a thermostat and maintained at constant temperature. The observations are carried out using sodium D light ($\lambda = 5890$ Å). Taking the refractive index

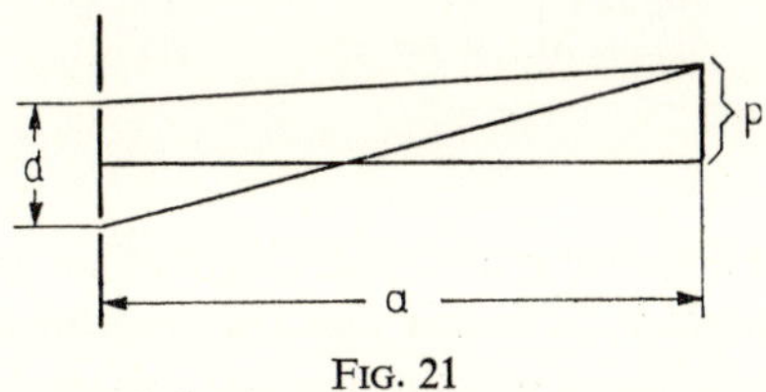

FIG. 21

of air as $n = 1{\cdot}000276$, calculate the refractive index of chlorine. In which direction are the interference bands displaced when the vessel is filled with chlorine?

200. Find the angle α between the Fresnel mirrors (Fig. 22) if the distance Δp between the interference bands on the screen is 1 mm, $a = 1$ m, $r = 10$ cm, $\lambda = 4861$ Å. The interfering rays are incident roughly at right angles on the screen.

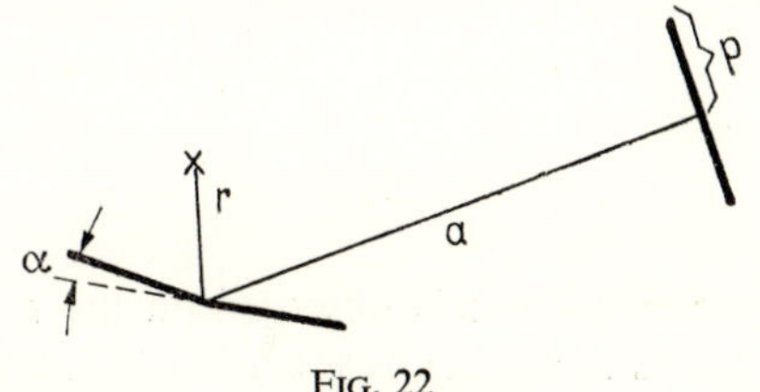

FIG. 22

201. Find the distance p between the centre of the pattern and the fifth light band in an equipment containing Fresnel mirrors (Fig. 22) ($\alpha = 20'$, $r = 10$ cm, $a = 1$ m) for $\lambda = 5890$ Å. The interfering rays are incident roughly at right angles to the screen.

202. Find the distribution of the intensity I on the screen in the Fresnel mirror apparatus (Fig. 22).

203. Find the shape of the surface of equal intensity in the Fresnel mirror experiment, if the source is (1) a point and (2) a slit parallel to the interference lines of the mirrors.

Note. It is assumed that the different parts of the slit are coherent and oscillate in phase. This can be achieved say by illuminating the slit by a plane wave.

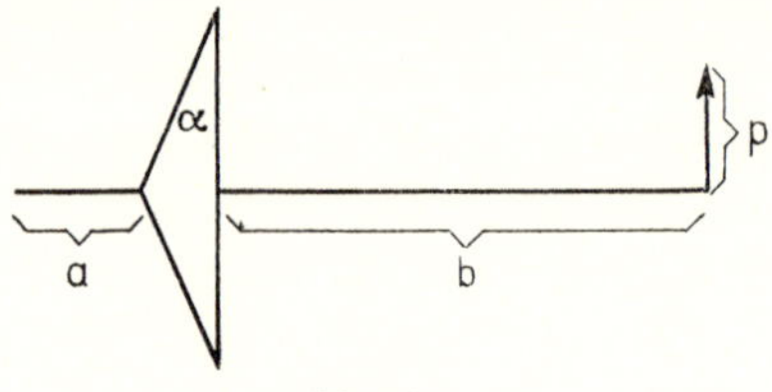

FIG. 23

204. Find the distance p from the centre of the interference pattern to the mth light band in the biprism experiment (Fig. 23). The refractive index of the prism is n, the wavelength λ, the refracting angle α. The interfering rays are incident roughly at right angles to the screen.

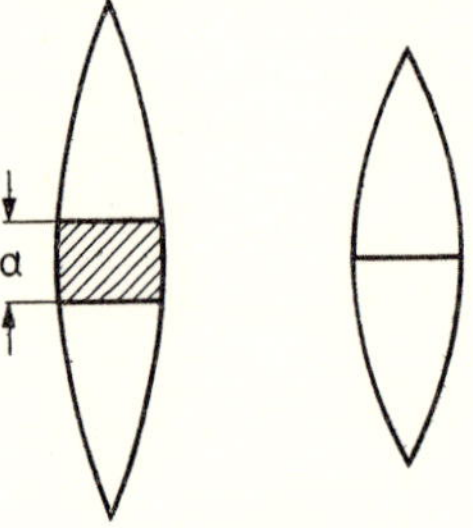

FIG. 24

205. Are interference bands observed on the screen if the light source in the bilens apparatus is moved between the lens and the principal focus (a bilens is obtained by cutting a complete lens and separating the two halves)?

206. A central piece of width a is cut out from a lens of focal length $f = 50$ cm, as shown in Fig. 24. The two remaining halves of the lens are brought into contact with one another. A point source of monochromatic light ($\lambda = 6000$ Å) is located on one side of the lens, whilst there is a screen on the other side, on which interference bands are observed. The distance between adjacent light bands is $\Delta x = 0{\cdot}5$ mm, and remains unchanged when the screen is moved along the optical axis. Find a.

207. For what position of the screen in the system described in the previous problem do the interference bands vanish, if the lens diameter $D = 6$ cm? For what position of the screen is the number of bands a maximum, and what is this maximum?

208. The refracting angle α of a biprism $= 3'26''$. A lens is mounted between a point source of monochromatic light ($\lambda = 5000$ Å) and the biprism so that the width of the interference bands is independent of the distance of the screen from the biprism. Find the distance between adjacent dark bands, if the refractive index of the biprism glass is $n = 1{\cdot}5$. Find the maximum number of bands N which can be observed in this system, if this number can be observed when the screen is $D = 5$ m from the biprism.

209. In the system described in the previous problem, for what position of the screen is the maximum number of interference bands observed, if the distance between the vertices of the refracting angles of the biprism is $l = 4$ cm, and what is this maximum number N? For what position of the screen do the interference bands vanish?

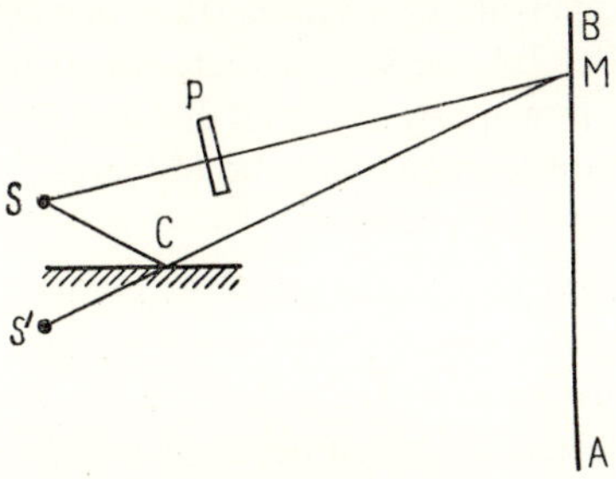

FIG. 25

210. Find the number N of interference bands obtained with the aid of a biprism, if its refractive index is n, its refracting angle α, the source wavelength is λ. The distance of the source from the biprism is a, and the distance from the biprism to the screen is b.

211. The phase reversal when light is reflected from a mirror can be proved experimentally by observing the interference bands in white light with the aid of a Lloyd mirror. A thin plate P (Fig. 25) is mounted in the path SM of the ray, and displaces the interference bands upwards on the screen AB. Let the point M on the screen be so chosen that the optical lengths (SM and SCM) are equal. If there were no phase reversal on reflection or phase change on entering or leaving the plate P, the waves arriving at M via the paths SM and SCM would be in phase. If white light is used, an achromatic light band would be obtained at M. Experiment shows that an achromatic dark band is actually obtained. How does one prove experimentally that the phase reversal occurs on reflection from the mirror, and not when the light enters or leaves the plate P?

212. What condition must the dimensions of a light source satisfy in order to be able to observe interference bands in a system containing (1) Fresnel mirrors and (2) a Lloyd mirror?

213. Light is incident directly from the sun on a screen containing two narrow parallel slits. For what distance D between the slits can interference bands be observed behind the screen? The sun's angular diameter $\alpha \approx 0{\cdot}01$ radian.

Note. Simplify the calculation by replacing the sun's disc by a square of constant surface brightness.

214. A lens of focal length $f = 50$ mm is used to obtain an image of the sun on the aperture of a screen (the aperture size is equal to the image size). Behind the screen there are two narrow parallel slits spaced $D = 1$ mm apart. For what distance l between the screen and the slits can interference bands be observed?

Note. See the previous problem.

215. A light beam of wavelength $\lambda = 5 \times 10^{-5}$ cm is normally incident on a metallic mirror, and standing waves are obtained. What are the distances from the mirror of the first node and first antinode of the electric vector of the light field?

216. Linearly polarised light is incident at 45° on a metallic mirror, covered with a very thin photo-layer (the layer thickness $\ll \lambda$). In one case the vector $\boldsymbol{E}$ lies in the plane of incidence, whilst in another case it is perpendicular to the plane of incidence. In which case is the photo-layer blackened?

217. A thin film is illuminated by a light source. The light reflected from the film is projected by a lens on to a screen. How must the lens be arranged in order for interference bands to be observed on the screen?

218. A transparent plane-parallel glass plate is illuminated by a parallel pencil of monochromatic light, and the angle of incidence, plate thickness, n and λ are so chosen that the reflected light suffers maximum attenuation due to interference between the rays reflected from the two faces of the plate. When the plate thickness is varied within the limits of a wavelength, its reflection coefficient should therefore change. But when the initial thickness is increased by an integral number of wavelengths the coefficient should be unchanged. Hence, whatever the initial thickness, different coefficients should be obtained with different thicknesses. At the same time, for an infinitely thick plate the reflection coefficient is independent of the thickness and is determined by Fresnel's formulae. What is the answer to this apparent paradox?

219. Will a soap film of thickness $d = \lambda/10$ be dark or light in reflected light? The film is in air.

220. For what film thicknesses d do the interference bands vanish when a film is illuminated by light of wavelength $\lambda = 6 \times 10^{-5}$ cm? The film refractive index is $n = 1{\cdot}5$.

221. In winter thin films of ice form on the windows of buses and trams, and give everything seen through them a greenish tinge. Estimate the least thickness of these ice films (take the refractive index of ice as 1·33).

222. Why is the centre of the Newton's rings observed in reflected light usually dark?

223. If the space between lenses of crown and flint glass is filled with an oil whose refractive index is intermediate between the indices of crown and flint, the point of contact of the lenses is surrounded by a light spot in reflected light and by a black spot in transmitted light. Explain this phenomenon.

224. Find the distance Δl between the twentieth and twenty-first light Newton's rings, if the distance between the second and third is 1 mm, and the rings are observed in reflected light.

225. Find the local length f of a plano-convex lens used for obtaining Newton's rings, if the radius of the third light ring is 1·1 mm; $n_{\text{glass}} = 1{\cdot}6$; $\lambda = 5890$ Å. The rings are observed in reflected light.

226. When Newton's rings are observed in reflected blue light ($\lambda = 4500$ Å) with the aid of a plano-convex lens placed on a plane sheet, the radius of the third light ring is 1·06 mm. When the blue filter is replaced by a red, a measurement of the radius of the fifth ring gives 1·77 mm. Find the radius of curvature R of the lens and the wavelength λ_r of the red light.

227. A plane-parallel glass plate lies on one of the surfaces of a biconvex lens. When Newton's rings are observed in the reflected light from a sodium lamp ($\lambda = 5890$ Å), it is found that the radius of the dark ring of order $m = 20$ (the central dark ring corresponds to $m = 0$) is equal to $x_1 = 2$ mm. When the plate is placed on the other surface of the lens, the radius of the dark ring of the same order is $x_2 = 4$ mm. Find the focal length of the lens, if the refracting index of the lens glass is $n = 1{\cdot}5$.

228. Find the radius r of the first Newton's dark ring if benzene ($n = 1{\cdot}5$) is poured between the lens and plate. The radius of curvature of the lens is 1 m. The refractive indices of the lens and plate are the same. The observation is carried out in reflected sodium light ($\lambda = 5890$ Å).

229. A crown glass lens ($n_{cr} = 1{\cdot}50$) lies on a plate, one half of which is also made of crown glass, and the other half of flint glass ($n_{fl} = 1{\cdot}70$). The space between the lens and plate is filled with carbon disulphide ($n = 1{\cdot}63$). Describe the nature of the Newton's rings in reflected and transmitted light.

230. Newton's rings are obtained between two plano-convex lenses whose convex surfaces touch. Find the radius r_m of the mth dark ring, if the wavelength is λ and the radii of curvature of the convex faces are R_1, R_2. The observation is carried out in reflected light.

231. Newton's rings are obtained with the aid of a plano-convex lens with radius of curvature R_1 placed on a concave spherical surface with radius of curvature $R_2 > R_1$. The rings are observed in reflected light. Find the radius r_m of the mth dark ring if the wavelength is λ.

232. In an arrangement for observing Newton's rings, a plano-convex lens is made to be movable in a direction perpendicular to the plate. Describe what happens to the rings when the lens approaches and moves away from the plate. The rings are obtained by using monochromatic light.

233. Describe the change in the sharpness of the Newton's rings on moving the lens in the arrangement described in the previous problem, if the observation is in reflected Na D-line light, and it is remembered that the D-line, instead of being monochromatic, consists of two close spectral lines for which $\lambda_1 = 5890$ Å and $\lambda_2 = 5896$ Å.

234. Find the difference between the wavelengths of the Na D-lines, knowing that the sharpness of the interference pattern observed in a two-beam interferometer is a minimum at the four hundred and ninetieth, one thousand four hundred and seventieth, ..., and maximum at the first, nine hundred and eightieth, ..., band. The mean wavelength of the D-lines $\approx$ 5893 Å.

235. Interference bands are observed for normal incidence of reflected light on a very thin wedge-shaped plate. The distance between adjacent dark bands is $\Delta x = 5$ mm. Knowing that the wavelength $\lambda = 5800$ Å, and the plate refractive index is $n = 1{\cdot}5$, find the angle α between the plate faces.

236. Bands of equal thickness are observed in the air-filled wedge between two plane-parallel glass plates with a very small angle between them. The wedge is illuminated by scattered light. The observation is made by the naked eye (distance for distinct vision $L = 25$ cm) in a direction perpendicular to the wedge faces; the eye can move perpendicularly to the rib of the wedge. Estimate the maximum number N of interference bands which the eye can see in monochromatic light with this method of observation, if the pupil diameter $d = 5$ mm. Estimate the degree of monochromaticity of the light needed for this maximum number of bands to be observed.

237. Bands of equal thickness, obtained in a thin glass wedge with refractive index $n = 1{\cdot}5$ when illuminated by scattered monochromatic light of wavelength $\lambda = 5000$ Å, are projected on to a screen, in front of which a square diaphragm of side $d = 1$ cm is mounted, the distance from the diaphragm to the wedge being $L = 50$ cm. What is the maximum order N of interference that can be observed on the screen? The principal optical axis of the projecting system is roughly perpendicular to the faces of the wedge.

238. A horizontal electrical oscillator is mounted at a height h above an ideally conducting horizontal plane. Draw the polar diagrams of the doublet in the vertical plane perpendicular to its axis, for $h = \lambda/4$; $h = \lambda/2$; $h = 3\lambda/4$; $h = \lambda$. Find the directions at the maxima and minima of the radiation for these cases.

239. The Cherenkov effect amounts to the fact that an electron moving uniformly in a medium of refractive index n can radiate light in certain conditions. Find what these conditions are, and the direction of the radiation, by considering the interference of the waves produced by the electron at different instants.

240. (1) Evaluate the radius of the mth Fresnel zone, if the distance from the source to the zonal plate is equal to a, and the distance from the plate to the observation point is b. The wavelength is λ. (2) Find the radius of the first zone, if $a = b = 10$ m; $\lambda = 4500$ Å.

241. (1) Calculate the radius of the mth Fresnel zone when a plane wave is incident on the zonal plate. (2) Find the radius r_1 for this case, assuming that, as in the previous problem, $b = 10$ m, $\lambda = 4500$ Å.

242. A source distant 2 m from a zone plate gives an image distant 3 m from the plate surface. Where will the image be located if the source moves away to infinity?

243. Find the focal length f of a zone plate for light of wavelength 5000 Å, if the radius of the fifth ring of the plate is 1·5 mm; find the radius r_1 of the first ring of this plate. What happens if the space between the zone plate and the screen is filled with a medium of refractive index n (when $n > 1$)?

244. What is the light intensity I at the focus of a zone plate if all the zones except the first are covered? The light intensity without the plate is I_0.

245. What is the light intensity I at the focus of a zone plate if the entire plate is covered except for the upper half of the first zone? The intensity without the plate is I_0.

246. What is the light intensity I at the centre of the diffraction pattern from a circular screen if it covers all the first zone? The intensity in the absence of the screen is I_0.

247. A bright source can be photographed by interposing between the source and the sensitive plate a smooth opaque sphere. Explain this. The sphere diameter is $D = 40$ mm, the distance from the source to the sphere is $a = 12$ m, the distance from the sphere to the image is $b = 18$ m, the source diameter is $y = 7$ mm. Find the image diameter y'. Will the image be spoiled if the surface of the sphere is mutilated by a series of irregular scratches of a depth h of the order of 0·1 mm? Can the sphere be replaced by a disc?

248. A glass disc, refractive index n (for the wavelength λ) covers one and a half Fresnel zones for the observation point P. For what thickness h of the disc is the illumination at P a maximum?

249. If a circular aperture (e.g. iris diaphragm) is widened so that its radius increases from the radius of one zone to the radius of two zones, the illumination at the point P (P is the image of the source provided by the diaphragm) drops almost to zero. How does this fact accord with the doubling of the total light flux through the diaphragm?

250. A point source of monochromatic light is at a distance a from a circular diaphragm, whilst a screen is on the other side at a distance b from the diaphragm. For what diaphragm radii r is the centre of the diffraction rings observed on the screen dark, and for what light, if the perpendicular from the source to the plane of the diaphragm passes through its centre?

251. A parallel pencil of monochromatic light is incident on a long-focus convergent lens with an iris diaphragm. A screen, on which diffraction rings are observed, is mounted at a distance a from the lens. For what diaphragm radii is the centre of the rings dark, and for what light, if the focal length of the lens is f?

252. In order to obtain photographs of diffraction patterns in cases when the light source and screen are a great distance apart, V.K.Arkad'ev employed a similitude method, in which the real obstacles standing in the path of the beam were replaced by similar models of reduced size. It is required to photograph the diffraction, pattern from a disc of diameter $D = 50$ cm, when a point source is $A = 25$ km from it on its axis, and the screen is $B = 50$ km from it (the plane of the screen is perpendicular to the disc axis). To do this, the disc is replaced by a reduced model of diameter $d = 1$ cm.

Find the distances a and b of the source and screen from the disc, in order to obtain a similar, 50-times-reduced diffraction pattern.

253. One method of measuring the angular diameters of stars is as follows. At the time of the new moon light from the star goes past the edge of the moon and undergoes diffraction at it. Diffraction bands are obtained on the earth's surface, moving with a speed of about 500 m sec^{-1}. In order to observe them, a photoelectric cell is mounted at the focus of the telescope. The current produced is amplified and recorded on moving film with the aid of an oscilloscope. The sharpness of the maxima and minima on the oscillogram depend on the angular diameter of the star. By comparing the oscillogram with the theoretical curve, calculated on the assumption that the star radiates like a uniformly illuminated disc, its angular diameter φ can be determined. Assuming the edge of the moon to be absolutely smooth, estimate what angular diameters of stars are capable of being measured by this method. Estimate the depth of the unevenness of the moon's surface h for it to be possible to obtain diffraction bands. The distance to the moon is $b = 380{,}000$ km.

254. Figure 26 illustrates an arrangement for observing interference bands. A lens is cut into two halves L_1 and L_2 along a diameter and the two halves displaced a considerable distance from one

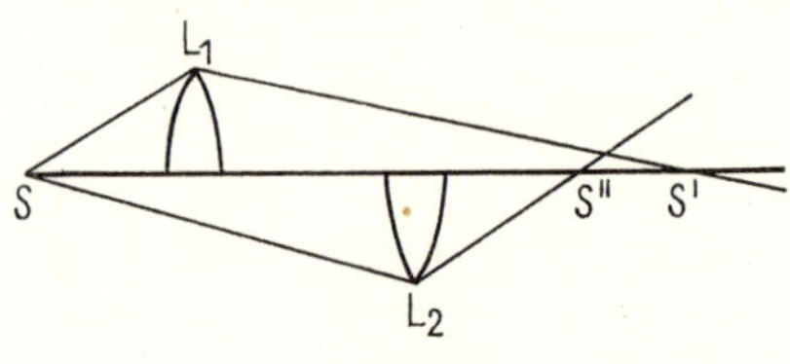

FIG. 26

another along the optical axis. The light source S is on the optical axis. The beam passing through L_1 overlaps the beam through L_2 over the segment $S''S'$, where interference of the two beams occurs. If a screen is placed there, or better, an observation is made through a microscope, interference rings will be seen. Will the centre of the rings be dark or light?

255. The condition for the Fresnel diffraction at an aperture to coincide in practice with the Fraunhofer diffraction is evidently that the maximum phase difference between two rays travelling from different points of the aperture to the screen on which the diffraction pattern is observed be small compared with π. Express this condition in terms of the aperture diameter d, the wavelength λ and the distance r from the screen to the observation point.

256. Find the angular positions of the minima in the case of Fraunhofer diffraction at a slit, using the Huygens–Fresnel principle and dividing the plane of the slit into zones. The grazing angle of the incident light relative to the plane of the slit is α_0. The plane of incidence is perpendicular to the length of the slit.

257. A square aperture is illuminated by a parallel pencil of sunlight, normally incident on the plane of the aperture. Find the dimensions $L \times L$ of the image of the aperture on a screen 50 m away. The side of the aperture is $L_0 = 0{\cdot}2$ cm. Take as the limit of illumination on the screen the position of the first diffraction minimum of the most strongly deviated rays (the visible spectrum is 7000–4000 Å). The plane of the screen is parallel to the plane of the aperture.

258. Will the light intensities be the same in the case of Fraunhofer diffraction at a screen and at an additional aperture, in the centre and outside the centre of the diffraction pattern?

259. A plane light wave is normally incident on an ideally black screen, the dimensions of which are large compared with the wavelength. Part of the energy is absorbed by the screen and part scattered as a result of diffraction. Show that the amount of energy absorbed is equal to the amount scattered.

260. Find the angular distribution of the light intensity in the case of Fraunhofer diffraction at a grating with N slits and period d; the light is normally incident on the grating and the slit width is b.

261. Find the angular distribution of the diffraction minima in the case of a lattice of period d and slit width b.

262. Find the condition for the appearance of a principal diffraction maximum in the case of oblique incidence on a grating (angle of incidence ϑ_0). What form does the condition take if $d \gg \lambda$?

263. An X-ray beam is incident at 89° 30′ on a grating of period 1 μ. The diffraction angle for a second-order spectrum is 89°. Find λ.

264. In what circumstance can mirror reflection be observed from a rough surface at small and large angles of incidence?

265. Can the first and second-order spectra of a diffraction grating overlap when it is illuminated by visible light (7000–4000 Å)?

266. Find the condition for zero intensity of the mth maximum in the case of a diffraction grating of period d and slit width b.

267. Describe the nature of the spectra of a diffraction grating if its constant is equal to (1) twice, (2) three times, (3) four times the slit width.

268. What is the maximum order of the spectrum that can be observed when light of wavelength λ is diffracted at a grating of period d?

269. Determine the wavelength of the spectral line, the image of which, given by a diffraction grating in the third-order spectrum, coincides with the image of the line $\lambda = 4861$ Å in the fourth-order spectrum.

270. What determines the maximum wavelength which can be obtained in the spectrum of a diffraction grating? Find the constant of a grating if it can give an infrared spectrum with wavelengths up to 100 μ.

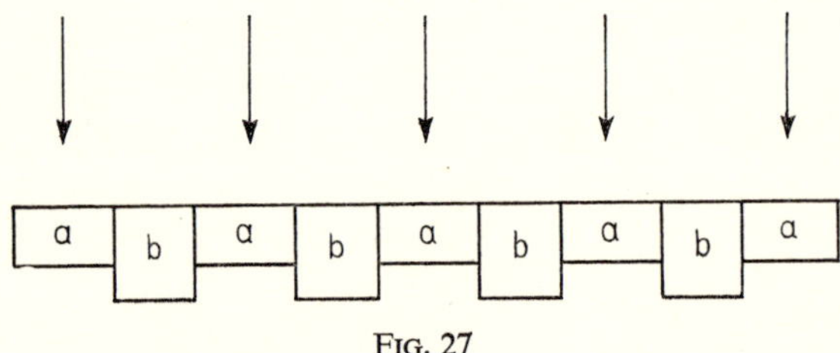

FIG. 27

271. A plane monochromatic wave is normally incident on a one-dimensional phase diffraction grating (Fig. 27). Over the pieces a and b the optical paths are equal to $l_1 = n_1 z_1$ and $l_2 = n_2 z_2$ respectively (n_1 and n_2 are the refractive indices, z_1, z_2 are the corresponding thicknesses). Describe the variation in the intensities of the diffraction maxima and the corresponding diffraction angles when $l_1 \to l_2$.

272. A plane monochromatic wave is normally incident on a one-dimensional diffraction grating of the slit type (Fig. 28). The slits b are completely transparent, whilst the parts a have transmission coefficient α. The grating thickness is infinitesimal compared to the wavelength. Describe the variation in the intensities of the diffraction maxima and the corresponding diffraction angles when $\alpha \to 1$.

273. A transparent periodic structure, the profile of which is illustrated in Fig. 29, is illuminated from above by a plane monochromatic wave, normally incident on the upper face. Given the

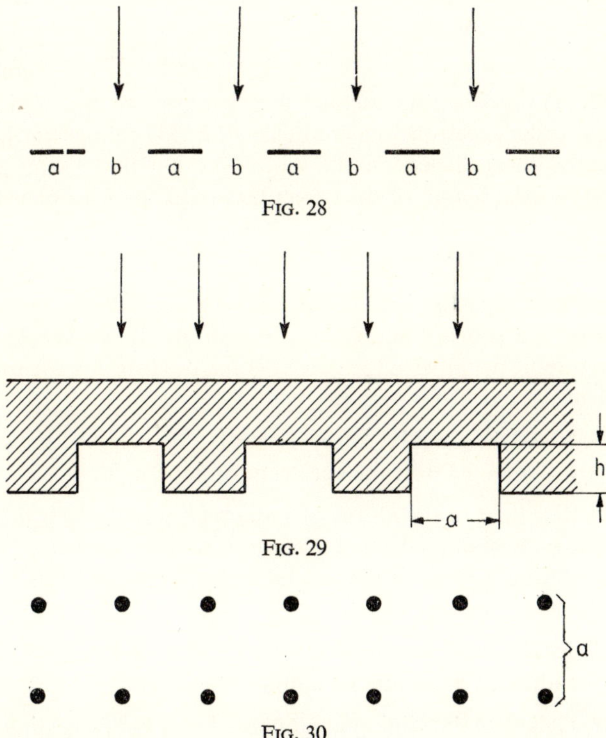

FIG. 28

FIG. 29

FIG. 30

refractive index n, select the depth h in such a way that the principal Fraunhofer diffraction maxima of the first order have the maximum intensity. What is the intensity of the zero-order principal maximum in this case?

274. Two gratings of N co-phased dipoles are mounted a distance a apart (Fig. 30). How does the polar diagram of the system change if the distance a changes? Consider the cases: $a = \lambda/2$, $a = \lambda$, $a = 3\lambda/2$ and $a = 2\lambda$.

275. What change occurs in the polar diagram of a grating consisting of $3N$ equidistant co-phased dipoles if every third dipole is removed?

276. A complex radiating system consists of a finite series of close-spaced dipoles with a uniform distribution of phase along them. How must the phase shift between two adjacent dipoles vary in order for the main lobe of the polar diagram of the entire system to make a circular scanning round a place with constant angular velocity Ω (in the absence of rotation of the system itself)?

277. (1) Calculate the angular dispersion in seconds of arc/Å in the first-order spectrum of a grating having 3937 rulings/cm. (2) Calculate the linear dispersion of a spectrograph with the same grating when the focal length of the object lens is 50 cm. (3) Calculate the reciprocal of the linear dispersion (the number of Å/mm). Assume in the working that the diffraction angles are small ($\cos \vartheta \approx 1$).

278. What spacing is obtained between the yellow line components of the sodium doublet ($\lambda_1 = 5890$ Å, $\lambda_2 = 5896$ Å), on a photographic negative in the spectrograph described in the previous problem?

279. Find the angular dispersion of a grating with constant $d = 5\,\mu$, if $\lambda = 5000$ Å, the spectrum order $n = 3$.

280. The light of the D-line of sodium ($\lambda = 5890$ Å) is normally incident on a plane reflecting grating. Find the number of rulings of the grating per mm if the second-order spectrum is observed at 45° to the normal.

281. Find the angular distance between the principal maximum and the adjacent minimum of a diffraction grating.

282. Calculate the minimum number of rulings of a grating which can resolve the sodium doublet in the first-order spectrum.

283. Calculate the resolving power of a grating of period $2{\cdot}5 \times 10^{-4}$ cm and width 3 cm in the first and fourth-order spectra.

284. Does the resolving power of a grating change with variation of the slope of the primary beam incident on it?

285. Do the resolving power and dispersion domain of a diffraction grating change if the eyepiece in which the diffraction spectra are observed is held fixed and one slit of the grating is closed?

286. A collimator slit S, illuminated by a light source, is at the principal focus of a lens L of focal length $f = 20$ cm. After passing through the lens the light is incident on a diffraction grating, the plane of which is perpendicular to the principal optical axis of the lens. The number of rulings on the grating is $N = 1000$, its period is $d = 0{\cdot}001$ cm. What must be the width x of the collimator slit in order for full use to be made of the resolution of the grating in the neighbourhood of the wavelength $\lambda = 5000$ Å?

287. Find the connection between the exit angle (corresponding to the maximum) from a Lummer–Gehrke plate of thickness h and the refractive index n.

288. Find the angular dispersion and dispersion domain of a Lummer–Gehrke plate, taking into account the dispersion of the refractive index. Regard ε as small (see the answer to the previous problem).

289. What is the number z of interference rays in a Lummer–Gehrke plate of length $L = 30$ cm, thickness $h = 1$ cm and refractive index $n = 1{\cdot}52$?

290. Find the minimum and maximum orders of the spectra that can be observed with the plate described in the previous problem, for the hydrogen line H_β ($\lambda = 4861$ Å).

291. Find the dispersion region and resolving power of the Lummer–Gehrke plate described in Problem 289; $dn/d\lambda$ for the hydrogen line H_β is $-9{\cdot}6 \times 10^{-6}$ Å^{-1}.

292. Determine the angular distance between adjacent maxima for the plate described in Problem 289, for H_β on condition that $\varepsilon = 1°$.

293. What are the changes in the resolution and dispersion region of a Lummer–Gehrke plate if its thickness is doubled and its length remains constant?

294. What are the changes in the resolution and dispersion region of a Lummer–Gehrke plate if its length is doubled and its thickness remains constant?

295. Two Lummer–Gehrke plates have the same geometrical dimensions, but are made of different types of glass. Which plate has the greater resolution, and which the greater dispersion region?

296. What minimum length is required if a Lummer–Gehrke plate ($n = 1{\cdot}5$) is to resolve the doublet structure of the H_α line ($\lambda = 6563$ Å)? The difference in wavelength between the lines of the doublet is $1{\cdot}4 \times 10^{-9}$ cm. Neglect $dn/d\lambda$.

297. What interference pattern is observed when monochromatic light illuminates two crossed Lummer–Gehrke plates, i.e. two plates arranged on a straight line one behind the other but rotated 90° relative to one another.

298. Find the maximum condition, the angular distance between maxima, the angular dispersion and the dispersion region of a Fabry–Perot etalon (introduce the angle of incidence φ and the distance h between the plates).

299. Find the dispersion region of a Fabry–Perot etalon when $h = 1$ cm, $\lambda = 5000$ Å. The angle of incidence is regarded as small.

300. What is the order of the spectrum when working with a Fabry–Perot etalon in the green part of the spectrum ($\lambda = 5500$ Å), if the distance between the plates is 1 cm? The angle of incidence is very small.

301. (1) What is the order m of the spectrum when working in the region $\lambda = 5000$ Å with a Michelson echelon, the height of the steps of which is $b = 1$ cm, whilst the refractive index of the glass is $n = 1{\cdot}5$? (2) Find the angular distance ϑ between the principal maxima for the same part of the spectrum when the step width is $a = 0{\cdot}2$ cm.

302. What is the resolving power required of a spectral apparatus for resolving the doublet of the sodium D-line ($\lambda_1 = 5890$ Å, $\lambda_2 = 5896$ Å)?

303. Find the size of the least base of a prism, made of glass whose dispersion close to the D-line of sodium is $dn/d\lambda = 956 \text{cm}^{-1}$ and which can resolve the yellow sodium doublet ($\lambda_1 = 5890$ Å, $\lambda_2 = 5896$ Å).

304. A spectrograph has a glass prism with base $a = 10$ cm and refracting angle $A = 60°$, set up for working at an angle of minimum deflection close to the wavelength $\lambda = 5000$ Å. The refractive index of the glass of the prism is $n = 1{\cdot}73$, the focal length of the collimator object lens is $f = 25$ cm. What should the collimator slit width b be in order for it to be possible to use fully in practice the theoretical resolution of the prism?

305. Newton's rings, obtained in reflected white light, are projected on to the slit of a spectrograph (with a diffraction grating). The slit is along a diameter of the Newton's rings. Describe the form of the spectrum, if its order and the period of the diffraction grating are such that the diffraction angles ϑ are small, and $\sin\vartheta$ can be put equal to $\tan\vartheta$ in the calculations. How is the spectrum pattern affected if the slit does not pass through the centre of the Newton's rings and is displaced a distance a to one side? Describe qualitatively the change in pattern when the grating is replaced by a prism.

306. A lens diaphragm has a square shape, of side D. A point monochromatic source is located on the principal optical axis of the lens. Find the intensity distribution resulting from diffraction at the edges of the diaphragm, in the plane perpendicular to the principal optical axis and through the focus of geometrical convergence of the rays.

307. An optical system—telescope or microscope—gives a system of diffraction rings as the image of a light source. According to Rayleigh, the minimum distance between two adjacent points which produce separate images is determined by the condition that the central light spot of the rings from the first luminous point be located on the first dark ring of the diffraction pattern produced by the second luminous point. It can be taken as a guide that the eye can distinguish two nearby points if the luminosity maxima at points of their geometrical images exceed the intensity half way between them by not less than 15 per cent. Use this assumption to find whether distinct images of two equally luminous points are in fact obtained when Rayleigh's criterion is fulfilled.

Hint. Assume for simplicity that the diaphragm is square. The results for a circular diaphragm only differ slightly from those for a square one. (See the solution of the previous problem.)

308. Solve the previous problem on the assumption that, instead of being equally luminous, the points are illuminated by the same light source. For instance, we can take two circular apertures in a screen, the diameters of which are small compared with the distance between them. Discuss qualitatively three cases: (1) the apertures are illuminated by a light beam parallel to the principal optical axis; (2) the apertures are illuminated by parallel rays, inclined to the principal axis; (3) the apertures are illuminated by diffuse light.

309. (1) Assuming that, with natural lighting, most of the light is at around $\lambda = 5500$ Å, calculate the minimum resolvable angular distance for an eye adapted to a low brightness level (pupil diameter 4 mm); (2) find the least distance resolvable by the eye between lines ruled on a sheet of paper, situated at the distance for distinct vision (25 cm).

310. What must be the magnification of a telescope in order for it to make full use of the resolution of its object lens?

311. (1) Calculate the resolution of a telescope with an object lines diameter 5 cm. (2) At what magnification is full use made of the resolving power of the telescope? The diameter of the pupil of the eye is $d = 5$ cm.

312. What is the advantage in using a telescope to look at the stars, if no advantage is gained in magnification over the naked eye?

313. Why can the brightest stars, remote from the sun, be observed through a telescope even by day?

314. When observed through a telescope with normal magnification, the luminosity of the image of a star on the retina of the eye is $\alpha = 10$ times less than the luminosity of the sky in day-time, observed through the same telescope. How many times must the diameter of the object lens be increased in order for the luminosity of the image of the star at the retina to become $\beta = 10$ times greater than the luminosity of the image of the sky, if the eyepiece is replaced at the same time as the object lens, in such a way that the magnification of the telescope remains normal?

315. A photographic plate is mounted in the focal plane of the object lens of a telescope. The luminosity of the image of a star on the plate is $\alpha = 10$ times less than the luminosity of the sky in daytime. What must be the percentage increase in the object lens diameter in order for the luminosity of the image of the star on the plate to become $\beta = 10$ times greater than the luminosity of the image of the sky?

316. The sharp-sightedness of birds of prey is legendary. Use diffraction considerations to estimate whether an eagle flying at 1 km above the earth can see a mouse measuring 2 cm, or whether it can only be aware of its presence.

317. Find the minimum length of a line on the moon and the sun, needed for the image of the line in a reflector with a mirror diameter of six metres to be distinguishable from the image of a point.

318. What minimum distance is required between two points on the surface of Mars in order for their images in a telescope (refractor) with an object lens diameter of 60 cm to be distinguishable from the image of a single point? Assume that Mars is observed at the instant of large opposition, when its distance from the earth is a minimum and amounts to 56×10^6 km.

319. A point source is at a distance a from a slit of width D. A screen is mounted behind the slit at a distance b from it, the plane of the screen being parallel to the plane of the slit. The straight line joining the source to the mid-point of the slit is perpendicular to the plane of the screen. Find an approximate expression for the distance x between the central maximum and the first diffraction minimum on the screen, the diffraction angles being assumed small. Find the condition for the expression obtained to be applicable.

320. When an image is obtained by using a small aperture, as in a camera obscura, account has to be taken of the fact that, when the aperture is too small, the image distorts due to diffraction; whereas an increase in the size of the aperture leads to broadening of the light rays proceeding from each point and consequent smearing of the image. Assuming that the distances a and b from the object to the aperture and from the aperture to the image remain fixed, the best aperture size can be found approximately from the requirement that the image of a point, obtained according to the rule of geometrical optics, should coincide in magnitude with the central spot in the diffraction pattern at the aperture from the same luminous point. Find the most suitable aperture size.

Hint. Simplify the calculations by replacing the circular aperture by a slit or square aperture. (See the previous problem.)

321. A camera with a small aperture of length $L = 10$ cm is designed for photographing remote objects. Estimate the camera aperture diameter D at which the resolution is a maximum. The wavelength $\lambda = 5000$ Å.

322. In principle, it is possible to construct a telescope of as high a resolution as desired without an object lens, by replacing the latter by a circular aperture. What must be the length L of the telescope if it is to have the same resolution as an ordinary telescope with an object lens diameter $D = 1$ m? What will be the light intensity S of such a telescope?

323. What change takes place in the resolution of the object lens of a telescope if the central part of it is covered with a circular screen, the diameter of which is small compared with the diameter of the lens?

Hint. Replace the circular lens and screen by square ones.

324. The mirror of a galvanometer has a diameter $D = 5$ mm. Taking account of diffraction effects, estimate the maximum distance of the scale from the galvanometer if readings are to be made with the eyepiece to an accuracy of $l = 0{\cdot}5$ mm.

325. Find the minimum resolvable spacing δ for a microscope in the best illumination conditions, for (1) a non-immersion lens with a numerical aperture $a = 0{\cdot}9$, and (2) the same objective, but with an oil immersion ($n = 1{\cdot}6$). The wavelength in the visual observations is $\lambda = 5500$ Å.

326. (1) What increase in the resolution of a microscope is possible if photography in ultraviolet ($\lambda = 2700$ Å) is used, instead of in green light? (2) Calculate the minimum line spacing that can be resolved by an ultraviolet microscope with an immersion (use the data of the previous problem). (3) What magnification is required by the microscope objective if details on the photographic plate in the plane of the image given by the objective have dimensions of the order 0·5 mm when minimally resolvable?

327. What magnification must a microscope have if full use is to be made of the resolution of its objective?

328. A square wire mesh is projected by a convergent lens on to a screen. A narrow slit is placed in the rear focal plane of the lens. How will the pattern on the screen change when the slit is rotated about the principal optical axis of the lens? How will the pattern vary when the width of the slit is increased?

329. A dish, the shape of a rectangular parallelepiped, contains toluol, in which ultrasonic waves are excited by the vibrations of a piezo-quartz plate. The plate is mounted parallel to one of the side walls of the dish. The ultrasonic waves excited by the plate are reflected from the side walls of the dish. As a result a standing ultrasonic wave is set up in the liquid. What is the spatial period of variation of the refractive index of the liquid in the presence of the standing wave?

330. Figure 31 illustrates a device for observing the diffraction of light in ultrasonics. Standing waves are formed in the dish K. The quartz plate P is mounted parallel to the wall AC, so that the waves radiated by it are propagated in a direction parallel to AB. The diffraction maxima and minima are observed in the telescope T, set at infinity. Show that the diffraction angle ϑ for the mth order maximum is given by

$$\Lambda \sin \vartheta = m\lambda .$$

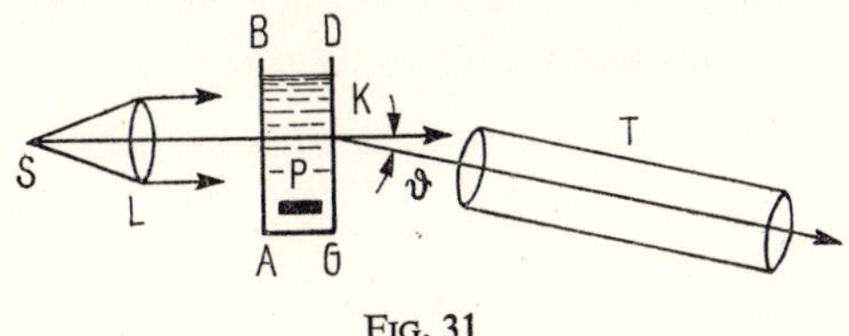

FIG. 31

Hint. Remember that the frequency of the ultrasonic oscillations is very small compared with the frequency of the light vibrations.

331. The device described in the previous problem is used to observe the diffraction of light in an ultrasonic wave in toluol. The source is the green line of mercury ($\lambda = 5461$ Å). Instead of the telescope T a convergent lens of focal length $f = 30$ cm is mounted behind the dish. Diffraction bands are obtained in the focal plane of the lens and are observed through a microscope furnished with a scale. Find the sound velocity v in toluol, if the distance between two adjacent maxima is $\Delta x = 0{\cdot}546$ mm, and the ultrasonic frequency is $\nu = 4000$ kc/s.

332. Is it possible to decide from the nature of the Fraunhofer diffraction pattern in a plane ultrasonic wave whether the diffraction occurs in the travelling or the standing wave? Neglect the ultrasonic absorption.

333. If a liquid in which a standing ultrasonic wave is established is viewed through a microscope, light and dark bands will be visible as a result of the unevenness of the liquid. What is the distance between two neighbouring light or dark bands?

334. How is the solution of Problem 330 affected if we do not neglect the frequency of the ultrasonic vibrations compared with the frequency of the light vibrations?

335. Diffraction bands from two identical parallel slits are observed in the focal plane of a lens L (Fig. 32). S_1 and S_2 are infinitely remote linear sources of monochromatic light, parallel to the slits. For what angular distance between S_1 and S_2 do the diffraction bands disappear, if the distance D between the centres of the slits is large compared with the slit width and the wavelength λ?

336. In the arrangement described in the previous problem the sources S_1 and S_2 are mounted in the focal plane of a collimator lens with focal length f. For what distance x between S_1 and S_2 do the diffraction bands disappear?

337. In the arrangement described in Problem 335, instead of the linear sources S_1 and S_2 a single infinitely remote source is used, its

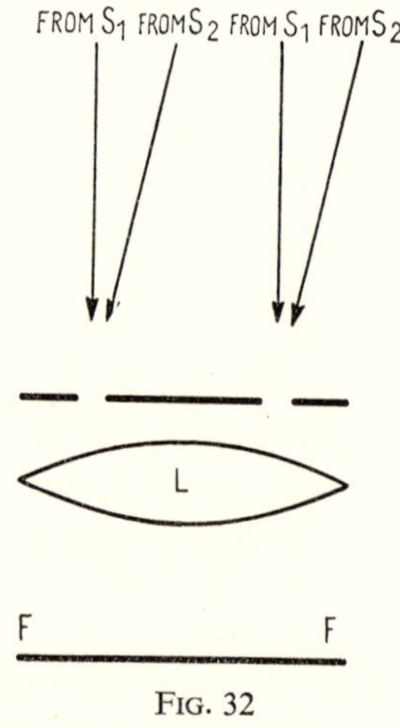

FIG. 32

shape being a rectangle, the long sides of which are parallel to the slits. Assuming that the surface brightness of this source is constant, find the angular width ϑ of the source for which the diffraction bands disappear.

Hint. Split the rectangular source into narrow strips. Assume that each strip is a linear source and use the solution of Problem 335.

338. Figure 33 illustrates a Michelson arrangement for measuring the angular diameters of stars. The mirrors M_1, M_2, M_3, M_4, which are furnished with circular diaphragms, direct into the object lens of a telescope two beams of light which interfere with one another in the focal plane of the lens. What is the shape of the diffraction pattern observed in the focal plane?

339. In the arrangement described in the previous problem, what is the condition for vanishing of the interference bands if the light source is (1) a double star and (2) a single star of finite angular

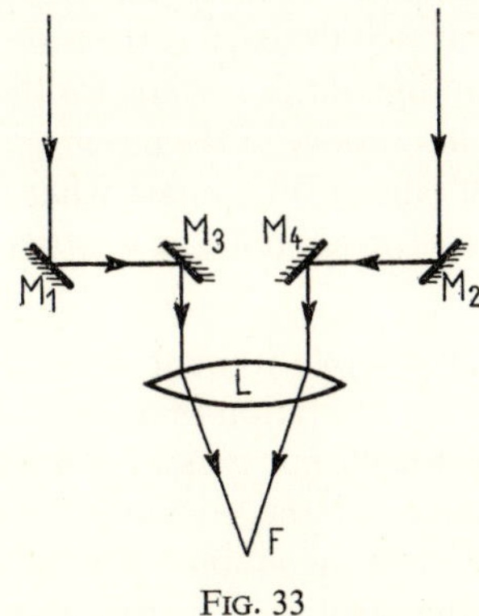

FIG. 33

dimensions? (It can be assumed for simplicity that the star is square-shaped and has constant surface brightness.) How will the interference pattern change when the distance between mirrors M_3 and M_4 changes (Fig. 33)?

340. When measuring the angular diameter of the giant red star Betelgeuse with the device described schematically in Problem 338, Michelson found that the interference bands disappear when the distance between the outer mirrors M_1 and M_2 (Fig. 33) was 306·5 cm. Assuming that the effective wavelength of the light from Betelgeuse is 5750 Å, calculate the angular diameter of the star.

341. A method of photographing objects with the aid of a smooth opaque sphere was described in Problem 247. Estimate the minimum resolvable angular distance $\delta\varphi$ when photographing remote objects by this method.

Hint. The size of the bright spot at the centre of the geometrical shadow from a point source can be estimated from the condition that the first diffraction minimum is obtained when the path difference of the rays from opposite points of the sphere is of the order of a wavelength.

342. Present radio telescopes and equipments for studying the radio emission of the sun and galactic have small resolution on account of the large wavelengths of radio emission. (1) Find the minimum resolvable angular distance $\delta\varphi$ of a radio telescope with mirror diameter $d = 50$ m for the wavelengths $\lambda = 1$ m and $\lambda = 10$ cm.

It has been proposed to increase the resolution by using the diffraction of radio waves at the edge of the moon (see Problem 253). (2) Estimate the resolution of this method for the same wavelengths, on the assumption that the edge of the moon acts like a thin opaque screen with a straight edge. (3) Estimate what the heights h of unevenness on the moon's surface must be in order for it to be possible to use this method.

343. A theoretically possible (though in practice not realisable) method of increasing the resolution of a radio telescope, for studying the emission from the cosmic masses, consists in making use of the diffraction maximum of the emission intensity at the centre of the geometric shadow of the moon from a point source (see Problem 341). Estimate the resolution of this method, find the minimum resolvable angular distance for the same wavelengths as in the previous problem. Discuss the possibility of using this method. The moon's diameter $D = 3470$ km.

344. A passive reflector, e.g., the surface of the sea, can be used as one of the two mirrors (aerials) of a radio interferometer. Find the angular resolution of the interferometer for the wavelength $\lambda = 1$ m, when its aerial is mounted on a cliff $h = 500$ m above the sea.

Hint. The aerial polar diagram is the same for reception as for transmission (this follows from the reciprocity theorem). See Problem 575.

345. What is the maximum angular resolution of a radio interferometer mounted on the earth, when operating at $\lambda = 10$ m?

346. What is the angular resolution of a radio interferometer, one of the aerials of which is mounted on an artificial lunar satellite (it uses reflection from the surface of the moon, which is regarded as plane, since we are concerned with a low-flying satellite). The time of rotation of the satellite round the moon is 10^4 sec (the orbit is circular), the wavelength is 100 m. Why is it desirable to use a lunar, and not an earth satellite in this case?

347. What is the shape of the main lobe of the polar diagram of a receiving aerial which consists of a strip of width d cut out from a parabolic reflector of diameter D?

348. A receiving aerial system of the "cross" type consists of two perpendicular strips (pieces of paraboloid, series of dipoles, etc.) of length D and effective width d. The high frequency signal from each strip is taken to its own receiver, the phase of the signal from one of the strips being switched continuously (reversed) with the aid of a special device (a cable of length $\frac{1}{2}\lambda$ is introduced periodically). The low frequency signals from the two receivers are added, the variable component being filtered out and its amplitude measured. What angular resolution is given by this system and what is its effective reception area (for a parabolic mirror the effective area is equal to the area of the mirror)?

§ 4. Polarisation of Light. Fresnel's Formulae

349. A zone plate is made of polaroid. The polaroid is orientated vertically in all the even zones, and horizontally in all the odd zones. How does the plate operate?

350. An infinite screen consists of two polaroid half-planes, touching each other along a straight line. The principal direction of one half-plane is parallel to this straight line, and of the other perpendicular to it. A parallel beam of natural light of wavelength λ is incident perpendicularly to the surface of the screen. Describe qualitatively the diffraction pattern obtained behind the screen.

351. What change occurs in the resolution of a diffraction grating when half of it is covered by polaroid orientated parallel to the rulings and the other half by polaroid orientated perpendicular to the rulings? Does the resolution of the grating depend on the polarisation of the incident light?

352. Two additional pieces of polaroid are placed in front of and behind the grating of the previous problem; their principal directions are parallel to one another and form an angle of 45° with the rulings on the grating. What is the difference between the resolution of this grating and that of a grating which is completely uncovered?

353. Starting directly from the boundary conditions for the electric and magnetic fields at a vacuum-dielectric boundary, find the reflection coefficient of light when it is normally incident on the boundary. Express the coefficient in terms of the refractive index of the dielectric.

354. What percentage of the light flux is lost by reflection in a prismatic binocular? The refractive index of the prism and glass is 1·5. The arrangement of the binocular is shown in Fig. 34.

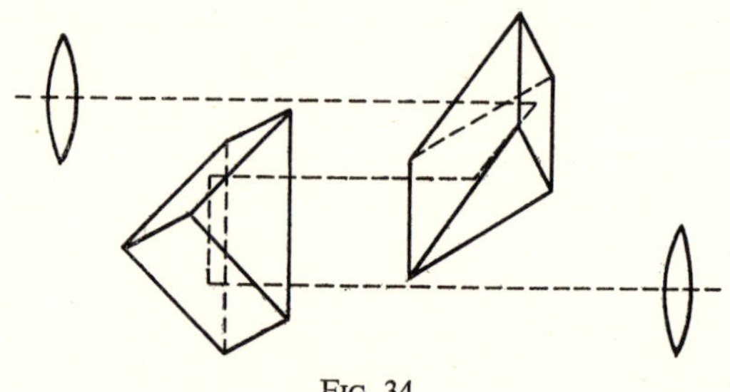

FIG. 34

355. Use Fresnel's formulae to show that the energy of the incident wave is equal to the sum of the energies of the refracted and reflected waves (the light is monochromatic).

356. Use Fresnel's formulae to show that linearly polarised light remains linearly polarised after reflection at the boundary between two transparent isotropic media in all circumstances, except in the case of total internal reflection.

357. The angle between the plane of vibration of polarised light and the plane of incidence is called the azimuth angle. Find the azimuth angle δ of the refracted wave and the azimuth angle ϱ of the reflected wave, if the azimuth angle of the incident wave is α, and the angle of incidence is φ.

358. (1) Find the polarising angle for light reflected from glass with refractive index $n = 1{\cdot}5$. (2) Find the degree of polarisation of the refracted light: $\Delta = (I_s - I_p)/(I_s + I_p)$, when the light is incident at this angle. The light in question is natural.

359. At what angle must a ray be reflected from a rock salt crystal ($n = 1{\cdot}544$) in order to obtain maximum polarisation of the reflected ray? The incident light is natural.

360. A plano-convex glass lens in which the curvature of the spherical surface is small lies on a flat metal surface. Will Newton's rings be observed if light is incident on the lens at the Brewster angle, polarised: (1) in the plane of incidence and (2) perpendicularly to the plane of incidence?

361. In a system for obtaining Newton's rings, a plano-convex lens is made of glass with refractive index n_1 and is placed on a flat glass surface, the refractive index n_2 of which differs substantially from n_1. The system is illuminated by a parallel beam of light which has passed through a polarising prism, whilst the rings are observed in reflected light. Describe qualitatively the effect on the visibility of the rings of a change in the angle of incidence, if the incident light is polarised perpendicular to the plane of incidence. What change occurs if the incident light is polarised in the plane of incidence?

362. Light is incident at an angle φ from a medium *I* on to a medium *II* and is refracted at an angle ψ. Show that the reflection coefficient is unchanged if the light is incident at the angle ψ from medium *II* on to medium *I*.

363. Given two semi-transparent parallel planes, the reflection and transmission coefficients of the first are ϱ_1 and σ_1, and of the second ϱ_2 and σ_2. The incident light is not markedly monochromatic, so that addition of the intensities occurs instead of regular interference. Find the reflection and transmission coefficients ϱ, σ for the system of the two planes.

364. We are given m parallel semi-transparent planes, the reflection and transmission coefficients of each of which are ϱ and σ. Find the reflection and transmission coefficients ϱ_m and σ_m for the complete system of planes. (See the previous problems as regards the incident light.)

365. A Stoletov stop consists of plane-parallel glass plates of refractive index $n = 1{\cdot}5$. Light polarised in the plane of incidence is incident on it at Brewster's angle. Sketch the graphs of the reflection and transmission coefficients of the stop as functions of the number N of plates.

366. Natural light is incident at an angle φ on a Stoletov stop, consisting of N glass plates of refractive index n. Find the degrees of polarisation Δ and Δ' of the transmitted and reflected light, and the ratio I_s/I_p of the intensities of the principal components of the transmitted light.

367. Find the degree of polarisation of the light reflected from a glass surface at angles 0°, 45°, 56° 51′ and 90° (the refractive index $n = 1{\cdot}53$). The incident light is natural.

368. Find the degrees of polarisation of the refracted ray when it leaves a glass plate of refractive index $n = 1{\cdot}5$ and the angles of incidence are 20°, 45°, 60° and 80°. The incident light is natural.

369. A Stoletov stop consists of ten thin plane-parallel glass plates on which a ray is incident at the polarising angle. Calculate the degree of polarisation of the refracted ray as a function of the number N of plates through which it has passed ($n = 1{\cdot}5$). The incident light is natural.

370. Deviations from Fresnel's formulae for the reflection of light from transparent isotropic media are observed experimentally. Fundamentally, there are two types of deviation: (1) there exists no polarising angle, at which light with the electric vector lying in the plane of incidence is not reflected at all; (2) on reflection of linearly polarised light, the plane of vibration of which is not the same as the plane of incidence and is not perpendicular to it, elliptic polarisation is obtained, which is particularly well marked in the neighbourhood of the Brewster angle (i.e. the angle of incidence $\varphi = \arctan n$). Show that each of these deviations is a consequence of the other.

371. When deriving Fresnel's formulae, it is assumed that the magnetic permeability μ of the medium is unity. What is the effect on Fresnel's formulae if this assumption is not introduced?

372. Will a polarising angle exist if the magnetic permeabilities μ_1 and μ_2 of the two contiguous media are different from unity?

373. Show that the reflecting power of a medium for which $\varepsilon = \mu$ (ε is the dielectric constant, μ the magnetic permeability) is zero.

374. In most optical instruments, loss of light occurs on passage through the instrument, mainly due to reflection from the optical parts. In order to increase the surface transparency of the glass, it is coated with a thin film, the refractive index of which is less than the refractive index of the glass. Find the thickness of the film and its refractive index if the reflecting power of the glass becomes zero.

375. Two monochromatic waves, linearly polarised in mutually perpendicular planes, are propagated in the same direction. In the general case, their superposition leads to light which is elliptically polarised. Knowing the phase difference between the added waves how do we determine whether the polarisation is right-handed or left-handed.

376. Calculate the refracting angle of a Fresnel parallelepiped made of glass of refractive index $n = 1{\cdot}7$.

377. The azimuth angle of an incident linearly polarised wave is $+45°$. Is the elliptic polarisation of the reflected light at the glass–air boundary right-handed or left-handed?*

378. At what angle of incidence φ is the phase difference δ between the reflected wave component polarised in the plane of incidence and the component polarised perpendicularly to it, a maximum in the case of total internal reflection, if the incident wave is linearly polarised? What is this maximum?

379. What refractive index n must a substance have in order to be able to convert linearly polarised light into circularly polarised light with the aid of a single total internal reflection at its boundary with the air? The azimuth angle of the incident light is 45°.

380. Incident light is linearly polarised and its azimuth angle is $+45°$. Is it possible to convert it into light polarised with a right-handed rotation by means of a single reflection?

381. What is the minimum refractive index of a Fresnel parallelepiped if the departing light is polarised with a right-handed rotation when the azimuth angle of the incident light is $+45°$.

382. A linearly polarised electromagnetic wave with an azimuth angle of $+135°$ is reflected at a water–air boundary. The dielectric constant of water is $\varepsilon = 81$. What is the angle of incidence of the wave if the reflected wave is circularly polarised? Is the polarisation right-handed or left-handed?

* The azimuth angle of the incident wave can vary from $-\frac{1}{2}\pi$ to $+\frac{1}{2}\pi$. It is reckoned positive if $\mathscr{E}_p/\mathscr{E}_s > 0$, and negative if $\mathscr{E}_p/\mathscr{E}_s < 0$.

383. A linearly polarised beam with an azimuth angle $+135°$ is perpendicularly incident on the boundary AB of a glass prism $ABCD$ (Fig. 35), and after undergoing total internal reflection three times, leaves the prism. What is the refracting angle A of the prism if the departing light is circularly polarised, and the refractive index of the glass is 1·52? Is the polarisation of the departing light right-handed or left-handed?

384. What minimum refractive index is required by the prism described in the previous problem if the departing light is to be right-handed circularly polarised when the azimuth angle of the incident light is $+45°$? What is the angle A in this case?

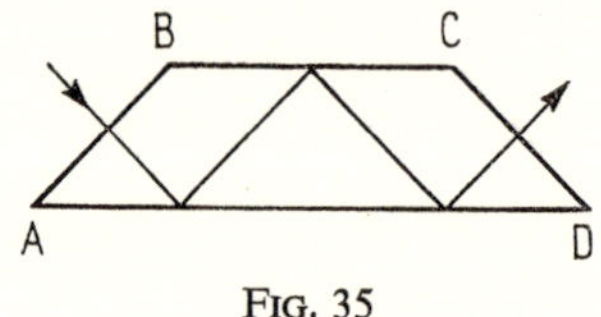

FIG. 35

385. Show with the aid of a vector diagram that the phase jump in the case of total internal reflection is more than twice the phase jump of the refracted (surface) wave.

386. What is the refractive index of a medium if the reflection coefficient of natural light has a minimum at an angle of incidence between 0° and 90°?

387. A linearly polarised electromagnetic wave with an electric vector amplitude $\mathscr{E}$ is normally incident from a medium with refractive index n_1 into a medium with index n_2. The media are separated by an intermediate layer of thickness l, in which the refractive index n varies continuously from n_1 on the upper face to n_2 on the lower face, in accordance with $n = C/(z + a)$, where C and a are constants. (The z axis is normal to the layer.) Express the refractive index n of the layer in terms of n_1, n_2, z, l. Find: (1) the electromagnetic field inside the layer; (2) the amplitudes R and D of the reflected and transmitted waves; (3) the reflection coefficient ϱ. Investigate the limiting cases of a thin and thick intermediate layer.

388. Show that, in a stratified non-absorbing medium, i.e., a medium whose refractive index $n(\omega, z)$ varies in one direction only, a monochromatic electromagnetic wave $\boldsymbol{E} = \boldsymbol{E}_0(z)\, e^{i\omega t}$, propagated in the same direction, is transverse and that the vector $\boldsymbol{E}$ satisfies the equation

$$\frac{d^2\boldsymbol{E}}{dt^2} + \frac{\omega^2}{c^2} n^2(\omega, z)\boldsymbol{E} = 0. \tag{1}$$

Show that, if the function $n(z)$ varies slowly, the approximate solution of (1) is

$$\boldsymbol{E} = \frac{\text{const}}{\sqrt{n}} \exp\left[\pm i \frac{\omega}{c} \int_{z_0}^{z} n(z) dz\right] \tag{2}$$

(the approximation of geometrical optics). Formulate the conditions in which (2) is the approximate solution of (1).

389. Show that, in the approximation of geometrical optics (i.e. when the solution is given by (2), see the previous problem), waves travelling in opposite directions (the $\pm$ signs in solution (2)) are propagated without reflection.

390. Show that the expressions

$$\boldsymbol{E} = \frac{\text{const}}{\sqrt{f(z)}} \exp\left[\pm i \int_{z_0}^{z} f(z) dz\right]$$

are exact solutions of equation (1) provided

$$n^2(z) = f^2(z) + \frac{c^2}{2\omega^2}\left[\frac{\frac{d^2 f}{dz^2}}{f} - \frac{3}{2}\frac{\left(\frac{df}{dz}\right)^2}{f^2}\right],$$

(see Problem 388). Show that, in this case, the waves travel in both directions without any reflection.

391. Two transparent layers with slowly varying refractive indices $n(z)$ are in contact along the plane $z = \text{const}$, on which the index $n(z)$ is continuous, whilst its derivative dn/dz has a jump. A plane monochromatic wave is normally incident on the boundary from the first layer. Assuming fulfilment of the conditions for applicability of geometrical optics in both media (see Problem 388), find an expression for the reflected wave amplitude and the reflection coefficient.

§ 5. Crystal Optics

392. Perform a Huygens construction for the direction of the refracted waves in a uniaxial crystal (positive and negative) for the following cases: (1) the optical axis is perpendicular to the plane of incidence and parallel to the crystal surface; (2) the optical axis lies in the plane of incidence parallel to the crystal surface; (3) the optical axis lies in the plane of incidence at an angle of 45° to the crystal surface.

393. If a distant object is viewed through a doubly refracting crystalline plate, one image is seen, and not two, as in the case of near-by objects. Why is this?

394. An observer views a near-by object through a plane-parallel doubly refracting plate of Iceland spar and sees two straight magnified images of the object, when a convergent lens is interposed between the plate and the object at a distance 4 cm from the latter. After placing an eyeglass with an optical strength of 5 diopters close against the lens, only one image of the object can be seen. Find the focal length f of the lens.

395. A trigonal prism is made from a doubly refracting crystal and is used for measuring the refractive index from the angle of deviation of the departing rays from the initial direction. Do the measured refractive indices yield the ratio of the velocity of light *in vacuo* to the normal or to the ray velocity of light in the crystal?

396. If a plate is cut arbitrarily from a uni-axial crystal, how must it be orientated in a crystal refractometer in order to obtain both the principal refractive indices of the crystal?

397. How must a prism be cut from a uni-axial crystal in order to obtain both the principal refractive indices by the method of least deviation?

398. Why are two different values d_1 and d_2 obtained for the visual thickness of a plate of Iceland spar when measured by optical means using a polarisation microscope? How must the plate be cut if d_1 and d_2 are to have extremal values? Find these extremal values if the plate thickness is 1 mm. The ordinary and extraordinary refractive indices of Iceland spare are $n_0 = 1{\cdot}658$, $n_e = 1{\cdot}486$. (See Problem 29.)

399. A narrow beam of unpolarised light is normally incident on a plate of Iceland spar, then is normally incident on a second similar plate, the principal plane of which forms an angle of 30° with the principal plane of the first plate. The light then falls on a screen. Describe the pattern obtained and find the relative intensity of the spots obtained on the screen.

Note. The plates are cut so that the optical axis of each forms an angle γ with the plane of the plate; also, $0 \leqslant \gamma \leqslant 90°$.

400. The principal planes of two Nicol prisms form an angle of 30°. What change occurs in the intensity of the transmitted light if the angle between the principal planes becomes 45°?

401. The windscreen and headlamps of cars are fitted with plates of polaroid. How must the plates be arranged so that the driver can see the road illuminated by the light from his headlamps yet not be troubled by the headlamps of oncoming traffic?

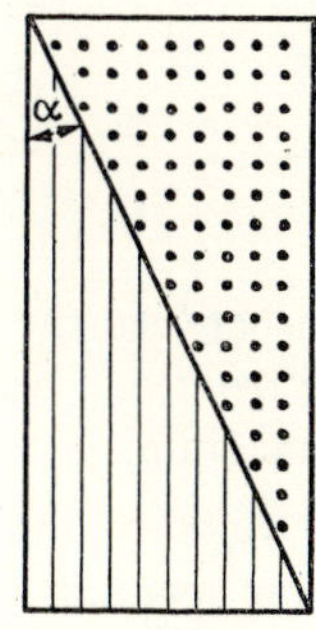

FIG. 36

402. A Wollaston prism is made of Iceland spar (Fig. 36) ($n_0 = 1{\cdot}658$, $n_e = 1{\cdot}486$). The angle $\alpha = 15°$. Find the angle φ between the ordinary and extraordinary rays.

403. A parallel light beam is normally incident on an Iceland spar plate cut parallel to the optical axis. Find the path difference between the ordinary and extraordinary rays transmitted through the plate. The plate thickness is 0·03 mm; $n_0 = 1{\cdot}658$; $n_e = 1{\cdot}486$.

404. Why does a thin doubly refracting plate placed between two Nicol prisms have a coloured tinge?

405. For what position of the analyser relative to the crystal plate is the colouration not observed in the circumstances of the previous problem?

406. The constructions of two photometers are indicated in Fig. 37. Find the law connecting the ratio of the brightnesses of the two sources compared in the photometers with the angles of rotation of the Nicol eyepiece. In the second photometer the Nicol prisms *I* and *II* are crossed, i.e. the eyepiece Nicol prism passes light only from prism *I*, if it is mounted parallel to it, and does not pass light from prism *II*.

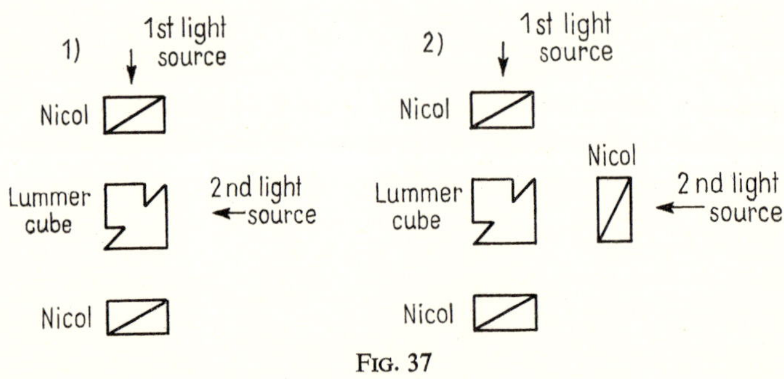

FIG. 37

407. Find the connection between the vectors $\boldsymbol{D}$, $\boldsymbol{E}$, $\boldsymbol{H}$ and the unit normal vector $\boldsymbol{N}$ to the front of a wave propagated in a transparent uniform crystalline medium.

408. Express the normal velocity v of a plane monochromatic wave in a uniform crystalline medium in terms of the vectors $\boldsymbol{D}$ and $\boldsymbol{E}$.

409. Show that the direction of the vector $\boldsymbol{D}$ (or $\boldsymbol{E}$) in a crystal uniquely determines the velocity v of a plane monochromatic wave, and also the direction of the vector $\boldsymbol{E}$ (or $\boldsymbol{D}$). Show also that the directions of the vectors $\boldsymbol{H}$ and $\boldsymbol{N}$ are in general determined, apart from the sign, by specifying the direction of the vector $\boldsymbol{E}$ (or $\boldsymbol{D}$).

410. In a system of dielectric axes, the connection between the vectors $\boldsymbol{D}$ and $\boldsymbol{E}$ is determined by

$$D_\alpha = \varepsilon_\alpha E_\alpha \quad (\alpha = x, y, z),$$

where ε_α are the principal dielectric constants of the crystal. Find the normal velocities of wave propagation in the crystal when the vector $\boldsymbol{D}$ (and hence $\boldsymbol{E}$ also) is directed along one of the dielectric axes.

Hint. See Problem 408.

411. Express the normal velocity of a plane monochromatic wave in a uniform crystal as a function of the direction of the wave normal $\boldsymbol{N}$.

412. Show that two waves, which in general have different normal velocities, can be propagated in every direction $\boldsymbol{N}$ in a crystal. If the velocities are different, each of the waves is linearly polarised, the vectors $\boldsymbol{D}$ of the two waves being mutually perpendicular.

413. The straight line along which the normal velocities of the two linearly polarised waves which can be propagated in a crystal are the same is called the optical axis of the first kind or the binormal. Show that there in general exist in a crystal two optical axes of the first kind and find their directions.

414. Investigate the cases when an optically bi-axial crystal degenerates into a uni-axial type. Find the expression for the normal velocities in these cases.

415. Show that the vectors $\boldsymbol{D}$ and $\boldsymbol{E}$ of the ordinary wave (i.e., the wave whose velocity is independent of the direction of the wave normal) are perpendicular to the optical axis of a single layer crystal.

416. A ray in a crystal is a line directed along the energy flux vector $\boldsymbol{S} = (c/4\pi)\,[\boldsymbol{E} \wedge \boldsymbol{H}]$. The wave energy is propagated along the ray (see Problem 489). The wave front velocity along the ray is called the ray velocity. Show that the ray velocity u is connected with the normal velocity v of the wave by

$$u = v(\boldsymbol{N} \cdot \boldsymbol{s}),$$

where $\boldsymbol{s}$ is the unit vector along the ray.

417. Show that any formula connecting the quantities $\boldsymbol{D}$, $\boldsymbol{E}$, $\boldsymbol{H}$, $\boldsymbol{N}$, v in a plane wave propagated in a uniform crystal remains valid if the quantities in the upper row of the series

$$\begin{array}{ccccccccc} \boldsymbol{D}, & \boldsymbol{E}, & \boldsymbol{H}, & \boldsymbol{N}, & v, & \boldsymbol{s}, & c, & \varepsilon_\alpha, & a_\alpha, \\ \boldsymbol{E}, & \boldsymbol{D}, & \boldsymbol{H}, & \boldsymbol{s}, & \dfrac{1}{u}, & \boldsymbol{N}, & \dfrac{1}{c}, & \dfrac{1}{\varepsilon_\alpha}, & \dfrac{1}{a_\alpha} \end{array}$$

are replaced by the quantities appearing below them in the lower row. The same applies to formulae connecting $\boldsymbol{D}, \boldsymbol{E}, \boldsymbol{H}, \boldsymbol{s}, \boldsymbol{u}$. (The conversion or reciprocity theorem.)

418. Show that two rays can be propagated in any given direction in a crystal. If the ray velocities of these rays are different, the rays are linearly polarised, the vectors $\boldsymbol{E}$ in them being mutually perpendicular.

419. The straight line in the direction of which the ray velocities of the two linearly polarised rays that can be propagated in a crystal are the same is called the optical axis of the second kind or the biradial. Show that there in general exist in a crystal two optical axes of the second kind and find their directions.

420. Find the optical sign of a bi-axial crystal from the three principal refractive indices.

Note. A bi-axial crystal is regarded as positive if the angle between the optical axis of the second kind and the dielectric axis of the maximum dielectric constant ε_z is less than 45°; if the angle is greater than 45°, the crystal is said to be negative.

421. Find the optical sign of a bi-axial crystal if $n_z - n_x = 0{\cdot}036$ and $n_z - n_y = 0{\cdot}019$.

422. Show that, if a crystal has two optical axes of the first kind, it also has two optical axes of the second kind, and vice versa.

423. Find an expression for the ray velocity as a function of the direction of the ray in an optically uni-axial crystal.

424. The wave or ray surface is constructed as follows. Straight lines are drawn in all directions from a given point O and points are marked off such that their distances from O are proportional to the ray velocities in the directions in question. Show that the ray surface of a uni-axial crystal degenerates into a system of two surfaces: a sphere (the ordinary wave) and an ellipsoid of revolution (the extra ordinary wave).

425. Show that all the crystals of the tri-, tetra- and hexagonal systems are uni-axial.

Hint. Consider the elements of symmetry of these crystals. Investigate the symmetry of the dielectric tensor.

426. Show that crystals of the cubic system are optically isotropic.

Hint. See the previous problem.

427. Find the maximum angle δ between the direction of the ray and the direction of the wave normal in Iceland spar, for which $n_0 = 1{\cdot}658$ and $n_e = 1{\cdot}486$.

428. When measuring the refractive indices of a crystal plate with a crystal refractometer, one index was found to be constant (1·646) whatever the rotation of the hemisphere, whilst the other varied from 1·642 to 1·646. Find the optical sign of the crystal and the orientation of the plate relative to its optical axis.

429. What are the changes in the refractive index of a plate of the same substance as in the previous problem, if the plate is cut perpendicularly to the optical axis?

430. Two thick plates of uni-axial crystal, similarly orientated and differing very slightly in thickness, separately yield white light in crossed Nicol prisms. Why can the plates give coloration when they are rotated 90° relative to one another and placed between the crossed Nicol prisms?

431. The second dark bands (i.e., the two bands, one of which corresponds to the path difference $+2\lambda$ introduced by the compensator, and the other to -2λ) for sodium light in a Babinet compensator (the Nicol prisms are crossed) are at readings of 7·34 and 27·20 on the compensator scale. What are the readings for the second dark bands in the case of lithium light? ($\lambda_{Li} = 6708$ Å, $\lambda_{Na} = 5893$ Å).

432. Find the positions of the first dark bands (i.e. the two nearest dark bands on either side of the central light band) for green mercury light in a Babinet compensator (the Nicol prisms are parallel), if the first dark bands for sodium light are at readings of 14·73 and 19·68 ($\lambda_{Na} = 5893$ Å, $\lambda_{Hg} = 5461$ Å).

433. What is the least thickness d required for a mica plate if it can be used as a $\lambda/4$ plate for sodium light, if for sodium light the refractive indices for waves travelling perpendicularly to the plate are respectively $n_1 = 1{\cdot}5941$ and $n_2 = 1{\cdot}5887$?

434. Find the least thickness d of a quartz plate cut parallel to the optical axis in order for incident plane-polarised light to leave it circularly polarised ($n_e = 1{\cdot}5533$, $n_0 = 1{\cdot}5442$, $\lambda = 5 \times 10^{-5}$ cm).

435. The principal dielectric constants of a crystal plate are ε_x, ε_y, ε_z. A linearly polarised light wave is incident in the direction of the x axis on the plate face, which is parallel to the yz plane. For what thickness l of plate does the wave leaving the plate have left-handed circular polarisation? The x, y, z axes form a right-handed system.

436. In Young's interference experiment, a piece of polaroid P is introduced between the slit S and the two slits S_1, S_2 (Fig. 38), in such a way that its principal axes are parallel or perpendicular to S_1 and S_2. What change occurs in the interference pattern on the screen if the slits S_1, S_2 are covered by half-wave plates orientated so as to be perpendicular to one another (parallel and perpendicular to the slits)? What happens if the polaroid P is turned through 90°?

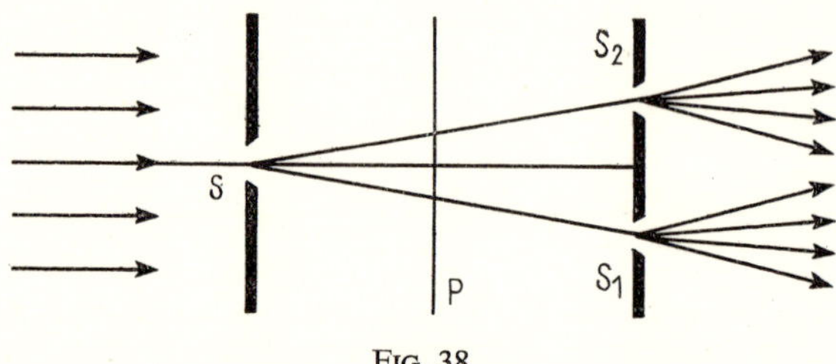

FIG. 38

What pattern is observed if the polaroid is removed? Consider the same problem, when quarter-wave instead of half-wave plates are used. The slits S_1, S_2 are assumed to be narrow (or of the order of the wavelength), whilst their distance apart is large compared with their width.

437. Given two dipoles, one of which is orientated vertically, and the other horizontally. The midpoint of the vertical dipole is on the continuation of the horizontal dipole at a distance d from the midpoint of the latter. A circularly polarised plane wave, propagated in the horizontal plane, is incident perpendicularly to the directions of the dipole. In what directions in the horizontal plane do the scattered waves possess linear polarisation?

438. Find the intensity of the transmitted light for a crystal plate mounted between two Nicol prisms, the principal planes of which form angles α and β with one of the principal directions of the plate. Investigate the cases of crossed and parallel Nicol prisms.

439. Why is it impossible to obtain interference between the ordinary and extraordinary rays leaving a plate of doubly refracting crystal which is so thin that it gives no observable separation of the rays? (See Problem 195.)

440. What is the colouration of a crystal plate mounted between crossed Nicol prisms when it gives a path difference of 6500 Å and is illuminated by white light?

441. In what circumstances does a thin crystal plate appear dark in monochromatic light when placed between crossed Nicol prisms?

442. A quartz plate, cut parallel to the optical axis, is mounted between crossed Nicol prisms. The optical axis of the plate is at 45° to the principal directions of the prisms. Calculate the minimum plate thickness for which one hydrogen line $\lambda_1 = 6563$ Å is strongly attenuated and the other $\lambda_2 = 4102$ Å possesses maximum intensity. The double refraction of quartz is $\Delta n = 0{\cdot}009$.

443. A crystal plate of thickness $d_1 = 0{\cdot}02$ mm with double refraction $\Delta n_1 = 0{\cdot}05$, is mounted between crossed Nicol prisms. A second plate with thickness $d_2 = 0{\cdot}02$ mm and $\Delta n_2 = 0{\cdot}025$ is mounted in a parallel position flat against the first. In what type of light is the field of vision coloured? In what type of light is it coloured if the upper plate and upper prism are turned 90° from their original positions?

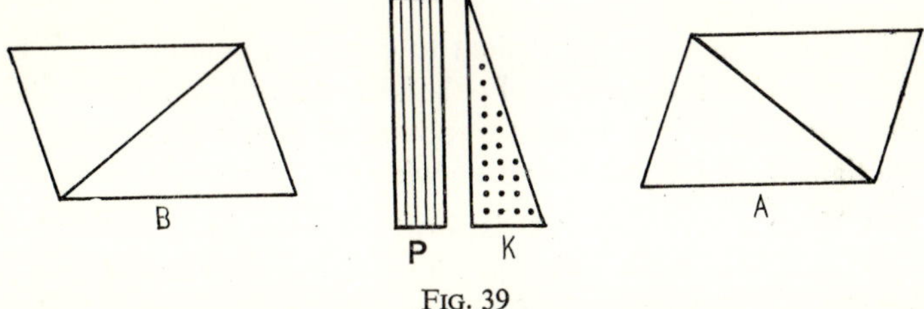

FIG. 39

Note. A parallel position is an orientation of the plates such that the direction of the wave vibration propagated with the greater (lesser) velocity in one plate coincides with the direction of the wave vibration propagated with the greater (lesser) velocity in the other.

444. The plate P and wedge K (Fig. 39) are cut from different positive uni-axial crystals and orientated so that their optical axes are perpendicular. At what distance from the wedge vertex will a dark band be observed when the system is viewed in white light between the crossed Nicol prisms A and B. The plate thickness is d, the refractive indices n_0 and n_e, the (small) angle at the wedge vertex α, the refractive indices of the wedge n_0' and n_e'. The plate and wedge are in a diagonal position relative to B and A.

445. In some instruments for analysing polarised light, the beam passes through a uniformly rotating Nicol prism, then strikes a photoelement. To what frequency should the photocurrent amplifier be tuned if the prism rotates with angular velocity ω?

446. A beam of white linearly polarised light is normally incident on a quartz plate 3 mm thick, cut parallel to the optic axis, the plane of polarisation being at 45° to the plate axis. The light leaving the plate first passes through a second Nicol prism which is crossed relative to the first (that polarises the beam), then is incident on the slit of a spectroscope. How many dark bands will be observed in the spectrum between the wavelengths $\lambda_D = 5890$ Å and $\lambda_F = 4860$ Å, if the ordinary (n_0) and extraordinary (n_e) refractive indices of quartz for these wavelengths are as follows:

wave-length	n_0	n_e
λ_D	1·5442	1·5533
λ_F	1·5497	1·5589

447. Why is it more convenient to carry out demonstration experiments on the interference of polarised rays with thin rather than thick plates? Why is it difficult to obtain an interference pattern in white light from Iceland spar even with thin plates?

448. When convergent polarised rays interfere in a crystal plate, cut perpendicular to the optical axis and orientated so that the optical axis coincides with the axis of the cone of convergent rays, a characteristic white or black cross is observed on the plate surface. What must be done with the elements of the arrangement in order to turn the cross as a whole through a given angle?

449. A quarter-wave mica plate rotates between crossed Nicol prisms. A plaster of Paris compensator, giving a sensitive tint, is introduced into the system at 45° to the principal sections of the prisms. Describe the characteristic colourations obtained. The first sensitive tint is obtained with a path difference of 5600 Å. The path difference due to the mica plate is about 1500 Å.

Hint. A sensitive tint is a violet colouration of the field of vision, observed in polarimeters when the brightest greenish–yellow rays, to which the eye is most sensitive, are extinguished in white light. Use of the sensitive tint enables a polarisation instrument to be set up very accurately, since the slightest rotation of the analyser or the introduction of an optically active substance into the path of the ray produces a sharp change in the colouration.

450. A black mica plate is mounted behind a Nicol prism. Why does the colouration of the plate vary when it is rotated relative to the prism, even in the absence of a second Nicol prism.

451. How can left-hand circularly polarised light be distinguished from right-hand polarised light?

452. How can natural light be distinguished from circularly polarised light or a mixture of natural and circularly polarised light?

453. How can the following be distinguished: (1) elliptically polarised light; (2) a mixture of natural light and linearly polarised light (partly linearly polarised light); (3) a mixture of natural light and elliptically polarised light (partly elliptically polarised light)?

454. Partly linearly polarised light is viewed through a Nicol prism. When the prism is turned 60° from the position corresponding to maximum brightness, the beam brightness is halved. Find the degree of polarisation $\Delta = (I_s - I_p)/(I_s + I_p)$ of the beam and the ratio of the intensities of the natural and linearly polarised light (I_s and I_p are the maximum and minimum intensities of the light passing through the prism).

455. A linearly polarised ray passes through a crystal plate, one of the principal directions of which is at an angle i with the principal plane of the polariser. The phase difference produced by the plate is δ. Find: (1) the ratio of the semiaxes of the ellipse of the vibrations of the elliptically polarised light obtained; (2) the angle between the principal directions of the plate and the semiaxes of the ellipse.

456. How can one determine the path difference introduced by a crystal plate by using another crystal plate, for which the path difference is unknown?

457. At what angle α to the long rib must the base of a Nicol prism be sawn off in order for the extraordinary ray alone to pass through the prism, in such a way that the wave normal corresponding to it is parallel to the long rib? In this case the angle of incidence of the ordinary ray on the Canada balsam layer exceeds the limiting angle of total internal reflection by $\delta = 1°45'$. The refractive index of the extraordinary wave for the direction in question is $n_e = 1{\cdot}516$, and of the ordinary $n_0 = 1{\cdot}658$. The refractive index of Canada balsam is $n = 1{\cdot}54$. Calculate the ratio of the length a to the width b of the prism in these conditions.

458. A polarisation prism consists of a rectangular prism sawn from Iceland spar so that its optical axis is parallel to the plane of sawing (Fig. 40, where the optical axis is perpendicular to the plane

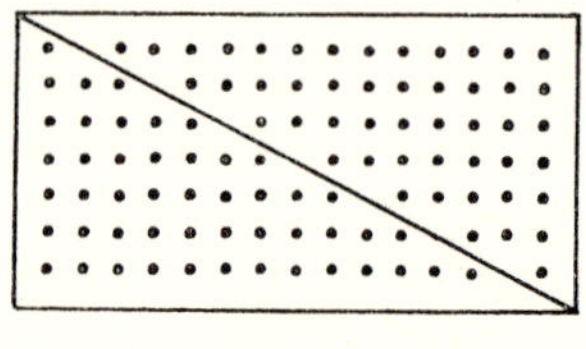

FIG. 40

of the figure). The adhesive is either Canada balsam ($n = 1{\cdot}54$) or linseed oil ($n = 1{\cdot}494$). Find the best aperture of the prism and the corresponding ratio of the length a to the width b of the prism for both adhesives.

459. Solve the previous problem on the assumption that the layer of adhesive is replaced by air.

460. For a topaz plate, the graphical picture of the variations in the refractive index obtained on a crystal refractometer consists of a circle of radius $n_z = 1{\cdot}6193$ and an ellipse inside it with semi-axes $n_x = 1{\cdot}6100$ and $n_y = 1{\cdot}6127$. Find the optical sign of topaz and the orientation of the plate relative to the dielectric axes of the crystal.

461. How must a plate of doubly refracting crystal be orientated in order to obtain three principal refractive indices on a crystal refractometer?

462. Circularly polarised light is normally incident on a crystal plate cut parallel to the optic axis. The transmitted light is viewed through an analyser. (1) Find the intensity of the light, if the principal plane of the analyser forms an angle α with one of the principal directions of the plate. (2) Find the analyser angles corresponding to maximum and minimum intensity.

463. A wedge of doubly refracting material is placed in the path of circularly polarised monochromatic light. The optical axis is parallel to the wedge rib. Describe the pattern observed through a Nicol prism, when the wedge is fixed and when it rotates about the direction of propagation of the light.

464. A quartz plate 1 mm thick is cut perpendicular to the optical axis and placed between crossed Nicol prisms. Why does it remain illuminated whatever the wavelength of the incident light?

465. How is a quartz cut perpendicular to the axis distinguished from one cut parallel to the axis, if one has at one's disposal two Nicol prisms and a source of white light?

466. Why does a quartz plate, cut perpendicular to the optical axis and placed between the Nicol prisms of an analyser, change its colouration when the analyser turns?

467. Given the circumstances of the previous problem and a rotation of the analyser in a specific direction, some quartz plates yield a certain sequence of colour changes and other plates the reverse sequence. Why is this?

468. A quartz plate 1 mm thick is cut perpendicular to the optical axis. How can one determine whether the plate is made of dextro- or laevo-rotatory quartz, having at one's disposal two Nicol prisms and a source (1) of monochromatic light, (2) of white light?

469. A quartz plate 1 mm thick, cut perpendicularly to the optic axis, is placed between two parallel Nicol prisms. For a certain wavelength the rotation of the plane of polarisation is 20°. What is the thickness d of the quartz if light of this wavelength is totally extinguished?

470. What thickness of quartz is required in order to obtain the sensitive tint: (1) in crossed, and (2) in parallel Nicol prisms, if the rotatory power of quartz is 24 deg mm^{-1} for yellow–green rays?

Note. See the note on Problem 449.

471. The dispersion of the rotation of quartz cut perpendicularly to the optical axis is characterised for the yellow region of the spectrum by the following values of the rotatory power α:

λ	α
5269 Å	27·543 deg mm^{-1}
5895 Å	21·684 deg mm^{-1}

The dependence of the rotatory power on the wavelength in a narrow spectral region can be expressed as

$$\alpha = A + \frac{B}{\lambda^2},$$

where A, B are constants. Find the least thickness d of a quartz plate, placed between two crossed Nicol prisms, if one of the two sodium lines $\lambda_1 = 5889{\cdot}953$ Å, $\lambda_2 = 5895{\cdot}923$ Å is fully extinguished and the other is completely transmitted.

472. An arrangement for separating out one of the lines of a narrow doublet and holding up the other is illustrated in Fig. 41. A

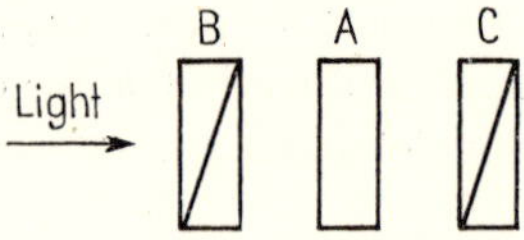

FIG. 41

plate of Iceland spar is mounted between two parallel Nicol prisms B and C, the axis of the plate A being parallel to the plane of the plate and at 45° to the plane of polarisation of the light passing through the prisms. What is the approximate thickness d of the plate if one of the lines of the sodium doublet is filtered out, and the dispersion of the refractive index of Iceland spar close to the sodium doublet is given by the following table:

λ	n_0	n_e
5876 Å	1·65846	1·48647
5893 Å	1·65836	1·48641

473. What is the minimum difference Δn in the refractive indices of right-hand and left-hand circularly polarised rays ($\lambda = 5893$ Å) that can be observed in the case of a layer of thickness $l = 30$ cm, if the angle of rotation of the plane of polarisation is measured to an accuracy of 1°?

474. What is the difference Δn between the refractive indices of left-hand and right-hand polarised light of $\lambda = 5893$ Å in quartz, if the rotation of the plane of polarisation in quartz is known to be 21·7° per 1 mm at this wavelength?

475. A polarisation device consists of two pairs of quartz wedges, cut perpendicularly to the optical axis. One pair of wedges is made from right-handed, the other from left-handed quartz. The wedges of a given pair are joined so as to form a rectangular parallelepiped. The two pairs are glued together by their triangular faces. One part of the device can be displaced relative to the other by means of a screw (as in a Babinet compensator); thus the device amounts to a bi-quartz of variable thickness. How can the device be used to determine accurately the principal directions of the plate investigated, and its dispersion?

476. Find the condition for Cherenkov radiation and describe qualitatively this phenomenon when a particle moves in a crystal. (See Problem 239.)

477. Show that, when a particle moves along the optical axis of un-axial crystal, the Cherenkov radiation can only consist of a cone of extraordinary rays.

§ 6. Velocity of Light. Optics of Moving Media and Sources. Some Problems of the Theory of Relativity

478. What is wrong with the following argument: "The aberration depends on the motion of the star relative to the earth. The angle of aberration ϑ is given by $\tan \vartheta = v/c$, where v is the transverse velocity of the star relative to the earth. Since the velocities of the different stars differ widely, the observed angles of aberration must differ widely (contrary to experimental results) even for stars which are close together on the celestial sphere".

479. (1) What is the magnitude of the aberration produced by the earth's rotation about its axis (on the equator)? (2) What fraction of this is the aberration connected with the annual motion of the earth?

480. Find an expression for the velocity c of light in Fizeau's experiment in the case when nth darkening occurs. The distance between the wheel and mirror is D, the number of revolutions per sec is N, the number of teeth is Z. Find c, if $D = 10$ km, $Z = 720$. The angular velocities at the four successive extinctions of the light were 326, 457, 588 and 719 deg sec^{-1}.

481. By considering the pulse consisting of a superposition of two harmonic waves: $\cos(\omega t - kx)$ and $\cos(\omega' t - k' x)$, find the group velocity u.

482. Express the group velocity $u = d\omega/dk$ in terms of the phase velocity v and $dv/d\lambda$, and also in terms of v and $dn/d\lambda$.

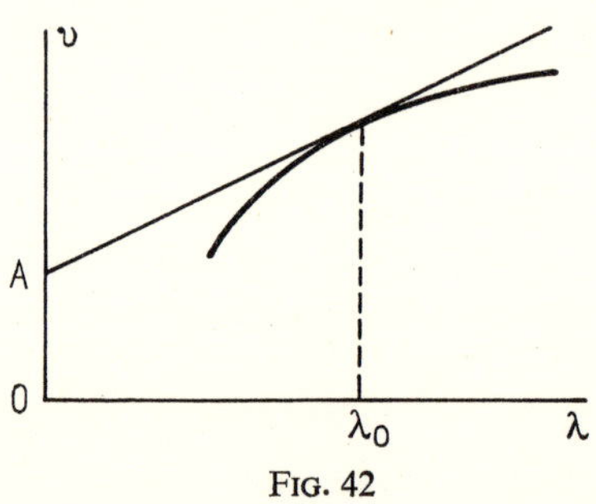

FIG. 42

483. Figure 42 illustrates the phase velocity v as a function of the wavelength λ. Show that the segment OA cut off on the v axis by the tangent to the curve at the point λ_0 is equal to the group velocity for the wavelength $\lambda = \lambda_0$. (Ehrenfest's construction.)

484. A plane wave disturbance is propagated in a medium with a linear dispersion law:

$$v = a + b\lambda,$$

where v is the phase velocity, and a, b are constants. Show that, whatever the disturbance, when it varies continuously its form will be periodically reproduced after an interval $\tau = d\lambda/dv = 1/b$. Show that the ratio of the path s travelled by the disturbance in the time interval τ to the length of the interval is equal to the group velocity.

Note. Any plane disturbance can be obtained at a given instant by a superposition of sine waves. Each of the sine waves moves with its own phase velocity in the same direction. As a result of this the shape of the disturbance is deformed continuously. The assertion of the problem will be proved if it is shown that a time τ exists, during which the initial relative disposition of the sine waves is re-established. It is sufficient to carry out the argument for three sine waves; the generalisation to a greater number is trivial.

485. Calculate the group velocity for the following dispersion laws (v is the phase velocity):

(1) $v = a$ (a = const)—a non-dispersive medium, e.g., sound waves in air.

(2) $v = a\sqrt{\lambda}$—waves on the surface of water produced by gravity.

(3) $v = a/\sqrt{\lambda}$—capillary waves.

(4) $v = a/\lambda$—transverse vibrations of a rod.

(5) $v = \sqrt{c^2 + b^2\lambda^2}$—electromagnetic waves in the ionosphere (c is the velocity of light *in vacuo*, λ is the wavelength in the medium, see Problem 557).

(6) $v = c\omega/\sqrt{\omega^2\varepsilon\mu - c^2\alpha^2}$—electromagnetic waves in a straight waveguide filled with a dispersive medium of dielectric constant $\varepsilon = \varepsilon(\omega)$ and magnetic permeability $\mu = \mu(\omega)$ (c is the velocity of light *in vacuo*, α is a constant depending on the dimensions and shape of the waveguide cross section).

486. For what law of dispersion $\varepsilon = \varepsilon(\omega)$ of a non-magnetic medium filling a straight waveguide or infinite space is the connection between the phase and group velocities of the electromagnetic waves given by $vu = c^2$?

Hint. See the previous problem.

487. Show that, given the conditions of the previous problem, as also when there is a vacuum inside the waveguide, the phase velocity of electromagnetic waves in the waveguide exceeds the velocity of light *in vacuo*.

488. The following procedure can be used for finding the density of electromagnetic energy in a non-absorbing dispersive medium. Let the material, of dielectric constant $\varepsilon = \varepsilon(\omega)$ and magnetic permeability $\mu(\omega)$, be used to fill a plane condenser of capacity $C = \varepsilon(\omega)C_0$ and a thin coil of inductance $L = \mu(\omega)L_0$, which are connected in an oscillatory circuit (Fig. 43). C_0 and L_0 are the capacity and inductance when a vacuum is present inside the condenser and the coil. In the absence of resistance the circuit performs free harmonic oscillations of angular frequency $\omega = 1/\sqrt{L(\omega)C(\omega)}$. If a small resistance R is introduced into the circuit at a certain instant, the oscillations become damped, and the electromagnetic energy initially stored will be converted into Joule heat, released in the resistance R. The total amount of heat released up to the time when the oscillations cease will be equal to the electromagnetic energy stored in the circuit prior to introducing the resistance. Find an expression for the energy density in a non-absorbing dispersive medium.

Note. See Problem 563 for the physical interpretation of the expression obtained.

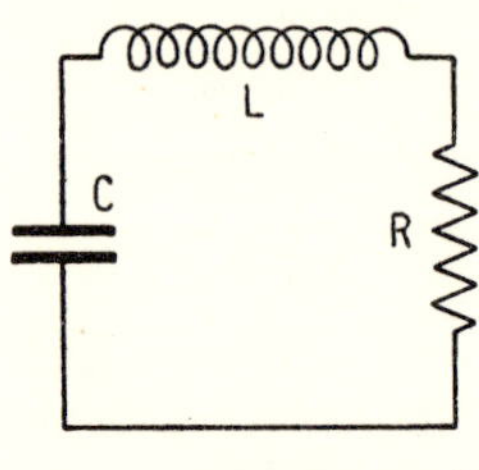

FIG. 43

489. The mean velocity u of the energy in a plane monochromatic travelling wave can be defined as the ratio of the mean density of the energy flux to the mean density of the energy itself. In an electromagnetic wave, the energy flux density is given by the vector $\boldsymbol{S} = (c/4\pi)\,[\boldsymbol{E} \wedge \boldsymbol{H}]$. Use this, and the result from the previous problem, to show that the mean velocity of the electromagnetic energy in a plane monochromatic travelling wave is the same as the group velocity.

490. Is the velocity measured by the Römer and Fizeau method the phase or the group velocity?

491. Show that, if $\varepsilon(\omega)$ and $\mu(\omega)$ are positive, the phase and group velocities in an electromagnetic wave are in the same direction.

492. The so-called dispersion relations, i.e. the relations establishing the connection between the real and imaginary parts of the dielectric constant, follow from general principles. As a result of these relations, the inequalities $\partial\varepsilon/\partial\omega \geqslant 0$, $\partial\varepsilon/\partial\omega \geqslant 2(1-\varepsilon)/\omega$ hold for a transparent isotropic medium (where $\varepsilon(\omega) > 0$ is the dielectric constant at the frequency ω).* Use these inequalities to show that the group velocity $v_{gr} \leqslant c$.

493. In an anisotropic medium the phase velocity depends on the direction of wave propagation as well as on the frequency ω. If the dispersion law is written in the form $\omega = \omega(\mathbf{k})$, it is easily shown that the group velocity in the medium is a vector with components $\partial\omega/\partial k_i$ $(i = x, y, z)$. Show that, in a transparent homogeneous crystal, the group velocity is the same, as regards both magnitude and direction, as the ray velocity $\mathbf{u}$. Neglect the dependence of the dielectric tensor $\varepsilon_{\alpha\beta}$ on the frequency ω.

494. The ray of a projector, rotating about the axis with angular velocity ω, grazes on a cylindrical screen. Is it possible to calculate the speed of the "spot" from the formula $v = \omega r$ (r is the distance from the projector to the screen), if $v > c = 3 \times 10^{10}$ cm/sec? If the "spot" velocity is greater than c, does this not contradict the theory of relativity?

495. If we confine ourselves to direct observations of Saturn's rings in the telescope, it is impossible to decide whether the rings are continuous formations or merely accumulations of a large number of small satellites in certain planes. How can the problem be decided one way or the other by using the laws of mechanics and the optical Doppler effect?

496. Derive a formula for the Doppler effect in acoustics in the case of longitudinal motion of the source and observer relative to the air.

497. Obtain an expression for the Doppler effect in acoustics when the source and observer move along the straight line joining them.

498. The optical Doppler effect differs from the acoustic one in two ways. (1) In acoustics there is a medium (air), relative to which the source and observer can move. In optics, there is no such medium when we are speaking of the propagation of light *in vacuo*—we can only speak of the relative motion of the source and observer. (2) At large velocities of the light sources in optics we have to take account of the "slowing-down of clocks" effect of relativity theory.

* L.D. Landau and E.M. Lifshitz, Electrodynamics of continuous media, Pergamon Press, Oxford, 1960.

Obtain a formula for the optical Doppler effect, taking account of these two differences. Take the frame of reference relative to which the observer is at rest. Consider the particular cases: (1) the source moves along the ray in the direction of which it is seen by the observer; (2) the source moves perpendicularly to this ray.

499. Find an approximate formula for the Doppler effect (neglecting the transverse Doppler effect), if the source velocity v forms an angle ϑ with the line of observation.

500. Obtain a formula for the relativistic Doppler effect, taking the frame of references in which the source is at rest.

501. Use the results from Problems 498 and 500 to obtain a relativistic formula for the aberration of light.

502. Obtain the relativistic formula for the Doppler effect when the source moves in the medium with velocity $\mathfrak{v}$ adn the observer is at rest in the medium.

503. A monochromatic wave of frequency ν is normally incident on a mirror, which moves uniformly in the direction of the normal. What is the connection, in the non-relativistic approximation, of the frequency ν' of the reflected wave with the velocity v of the mirror?

504. To verify experimentally the Doppler principle in terrestrial conditions, A. A. Belopol'skii used the reflection of light from mirrors subjected to rapid rotation. The light ray, before striking the eye of the observer, underwent several reflections from the moving mirrors. Assuming that the light is normally incident on the moving mirror, find the change in the frequency ν' if the mirror velocity is v and the number of reflections is N (assume that $v \ll c$, and neglect terms of the order v^2/c^2).

505. Is the velocity of light measured in the Foucault rotating mirror method the phase or the group velocity?

Hint. By Doppler's principle, the wavelength changes when light is reflected from a moving mirror. Since different points of the rotating mirror have different velocities, the wavelength changes will be different for rays reflected from different points. Hence, if the medium in which the reflected light is propagated is dispersive, the phase velocities will also be different for these rays. This leads to a rotation of the wave front of the reflected wave. This rotation has to be taken into account in Foucault's method.

506. Michelson measured the velocity of light in carbon disulphide by a rotating mirror method. The refractive index of carbon disulphide for the average wavelength of the visible spectrum is $n = 1{\cdot}64$, whilst the quantity $1 + (\lambda/n)dn/d\lambda$ is equal to 0·93. Find what value is to be expected for the ratio of the velocity of light *in vacuo* to the velocity of light in carbon disulphide measured by this method.

507. In classical theory, unlike the theory of relativity, the Doppler effect is deduced from the motion of the light source and observer relative to the ether. Suppose that the source moves relative to the ether, whilst the observer is at rest. The wavelength of the observed light now changes, and the fixed observer can discover this with the aid of a diffraction grating. But if the source is fixed relative to the ether, the motion of the grating can obviously have no effect on the wavelength of the light. Nevertheless, the diffraction grating reveals a shift of the spectral lines in accordance with the Doppler effect. Analyse the mechanism involved and calculate the amount of the shift.

508. Find the Doppler shift $\Delta\lambda$ of the hydrogen line H_β ($\lambda = 4861$ Å) when it is observed along a beam of hydrogen canal rays having a mean velocity $v = 1{\cdot}3 \times 10^8$ cm sec^{-1}.

509. Find the Doppler shift $\delta\lambda$ in the conditions of the previous problem if the observation is in a direction perpendicular to the beam.

510. Find the maximum Doppler shift $\Delta\lambda$ for the hydrogen line H_β, radiated by moving hydrogen atoms with kinetic energy 4×10^6 eV.

511. What is the transverse Doppler shift $\delta\lambda$ in the conditions of the previous problem?

512. The main difficulty in observing the transverse Doppler effect in canal rays is as follows. Since the transverse effect is a second order effect in v/c, it is very small compared to the first order effect (see Problems 508 and 509). In order to exclude the first order effect, it is necessary to produce a highly parallel beam of canal rays, moving perpendicularly to the line of observation. The slightest deviation in the direction of motion of these particles from strict perpendicularity to the line of observation leads to the appearance of a longitudinal component of the velocity and to the longitudinal

Doppler effect, which can mask the second order effect. Given the conditions of Problem 508, calculate the maximum angle of deviation of the beam from exact perpendicularity to the line of observation, for which the transverse effect is not yet masked by the longitudinal effect.

513. What is the motion of a nebula relative to the earth, if the hydrogen line H_γ (λ = 4340 Å) in the spectrum of the nebula is known to be shifted 20 Å towards the red?

514. The wavelength of a Fraunhofer line in the solar spectrum is 5900 Å when observed in the direction to the pole of the sun. When the same line is observed in the direction to the edge of the sun's disc at the equator a shift of 0·04 Å is discovered. Find the linear velocity v of the solar equator.

515. What is the maximum half-yearly change $\Delta\lambda$ in the green lines (λ = 5500 Å) of the spectra of stars lying in the plane of the earth's orbit?

516. Find the approximate value of the cathodic potential drop V in a discharge tube, if the Doppler shift of the line λ = 5016 Å, belonging to helium and observed at 145° to the canal ray, is 5 Å.

517. Find the spectral distribution of the light radiated by a rarefied gas which is in thermodynamic equilibrium at T°K. Assume that the gas atoms radiate only the spectral line whose frequency is ν_0 in the coordinate system fixed in the atom.

518. Find the half-width of the line H_α radiated by hydrogen at 50 °C. Assume that the widening of the lines is caused solely by the Doppler effect. The wavelength of the H_α line is λ = 6563 Å.

Note. The half-width of a line is $\Delta\lambda = \lambda_0 - \lambda_{\frac{1}{2}}$, where λ_0 is the wavelength corresponding to the line centre and $\lambda_{\frac{1}{2}}$ is the wavelength at which $I = \frac{1}{2}I_0$.

519. Find $\Delta\lambda/\lambda$, if the source moves with velocity v in a medium of refractive index n.

520. A radar receiver determines the speed of approach of an aeroplane from the frequency of the beats between a signal taken directly from the transmitter and a signal obtained by reflection from the aeroplane. What is the operating wavelength λ of the radar system if an aeroplane approaching at a speed v = 360 km/hr^{-1} gives a beat frequency $\Delta\nu$ = 400 c/s?

521. A space ship moves with a speed $v = 1000 \text{ km/hr}^{-1}$ towards the nearest star, situated at a distance $L = 4{\cdot}3$ light years away. On reaching the star, the ship returns in the opposite direction. By what amount Δt is a clock on the ship slow compared with a clock on earth when the ship returns to the earth?

Note. In view of the high speed of the space ship the motion of the star relative to the sun can be neglected.

522. What kinetic energy E must be communicated to a space ship of mass $m = 10^4$ kg in order for a clock on it to register half the time of terrestrial clock when the ship returns to earth. How many tons M of uranium must be burnt in order to release this amount of energy? The energy released by fission of one atom of uranium is 170 MeV. Given this kinetic energy, what is the speed v of the space ship?

523. The space ship discussed in the previous problem is a rocket powered by uranium fuel. Suppose that all the reaction products leave the rocket as gases with the constant exhaust velocity $v_0 = 10 \text{ km/hr}^{-1}$ (relative to the rocket). Estimate the amount of fuel required to communicate to the rocket the speed which was needed in the previous problem.

Note. Since we are concerned with an estimate, non-relativistic mechanics can be used.

524. Find the life τ of a μ-meson with energy $E = 10^9$ eV (in a laboratory coordinate system). The life time of a μ-meson at rest is $\tau_0 = 2{\cdot}2 \times 10^{-6}$ sec. The mass of a μ-meson is $m = 206{\cdot}7\, m_e$ (m_e is the mass of an electron).

525. According to Einstein's equivalence principle, all processes occurring in a uniform gravitational field proceed in the same way as in a reference system moving with constant acceleration relative to an inertial reference system. Use this principle to show that the frequency of light propagated in a gravitational field must change (gravitational displacement of the spectral lines). Connect the frequency change with the change of gravitational potential along a light ray.

526. The light emitted from the surface of the photosphere of a star is observed on the earth. In what direction is the gravitational shift of the spectral lines?

527. Radio signals are received on the earth from an artificial earth satellite at a height $h = 800$ km above the earth's surface. Find the relative change in the radio wave frequency due to the earth's gravitational field. Is the gravitational shift to the red or the violet end of the spectrum?

528. Find the relative frequency change due to the earth's gravitational field when the transmitter is sited on a mountain 5 km higher than the receiver.

529. Show that the gravitational shift of the frequency of a radio signal from an artificial satellite is a second order effect relative to v/c (v is the velocity of the satellite, c is the velocity of light).

530. Take account of the (linear and quadratic) Doppler effect in Problem 527. Find the total relative frequency change due to the Doppler effect and the earth's gravitational field, if (a) the satellite rotates exactly in a circle, (b) the satellite moves at an angle $\Theta = 89°$ to the vertical, approaching the earth with velocity $v = 7{\cdot}5\,\text{km sec}^{-1}$.

§ 7. Radiation Pressure

531. Starting from the proposition that light consists of photons, each of which has momentum $h\nu/c$, find the pressure P of a light wave on a plane mirror, assuming that the mirror reflection coefficient is r and the angle of incidence φ. Find also the tangential force T acting per unit surface area of the mirror from the incident radiation.

532. Solve the previous problem on the assumption that the surface on which the light wave is incident is ideally mat (satisfies Lambert's law).

533. Show that the radiation pressure when light is normally incident on an ideal mirror is equal to $2u$, and is equal to u on a completely absorbent surface, where u is the energy density of the incident radiation.

534. What is the light pressure on an ideal mirror if the radiation is isotropic?

535. Find the light pressure of the solar radiation per square metre of the earth's surface, perpendicular to the direction of the radiation. The solar constant (see the note on Problem 189) is $2\,\text{cal cm}^{-2}\,\text{min}^{-1}$.

Neglect the absorption in the earth's atmosphere. Consider three cases: (1) the earth's surface is absolutely black; (2) the earth's surface is absolutely reflecting; (3) the surface is absolutely reflecting but mat (satisfies Lambert's law).

536. P. N. Lebedev first showed experimentally the existence of light pressure on solids and gases and measured it. Lebedev's apparatus for studying light pressure on solids consisted of a light

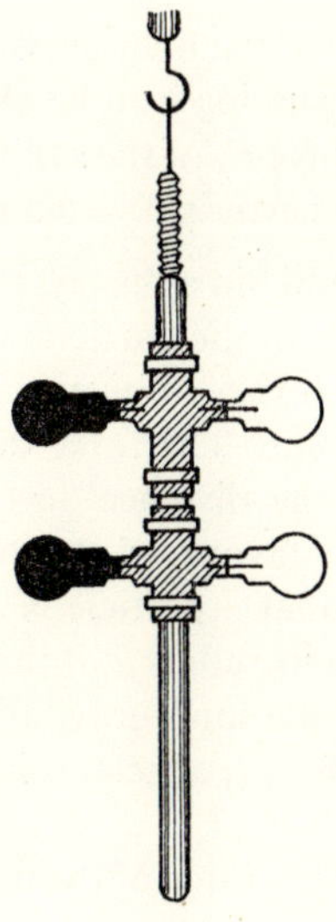

FIG. 44

suspension on a fine thread, to the edges of which very thin, light wings were attached (Fig. 44). The wings were cup-shaped, with a diameter of 5 mm. One of the wings was blackened, whilst the other was shiny. The suspension was placed in an evacuated vessel and formed a very sensitive torsion balance. A beam of light energy with a power of 1·2–1·8 cal/min was directed on to the wings by special means. Find the force exerted by the light pressure on the blackened wing when the power of the light pressure beam incident on it is $Q = 1{\cdot}5$ cal/min.

537. A plane light wave is incident on the surface of a sphere, which is large compared with the wavelength. Assuming that the surface is either (1) absolutely black, or (2) absolutely reflecting, or (3) absolutely mat (satisfying Lambert's law), express the force of the light pressure on the sphere in terms of the density of the incident radiation.

538. In which case is the light pressure on a sphere of a plane unpolarised wave the greater: when the surface of the sphere is ideally reflecting or when it partially reflects light, the remainder of the light being absorbed inside the sphere? The sphere is large compared with the wavelength.

539. Find the force F_1 of the light pressure of the solar radiation on the earth's surface, assuming it to be absolutely black. Find the ratio of this force to the force F_2 of the sun's gravitational attraction. The mean density of the earth is $\delta = 5{\cdot}5\ \mathrm{g\,cm^{-3}}$.

540. According to Bredikhin's theory, the form of a comet's tail is explained by the action on the particles of the comet of repulsive forces from the sun, which vary in inverse proportion to the square of the distance from the sun. The force due to the solar radiation pressure decreases with the distance according to the same law, which is an argument in favour of the two forces being equal.* Assuming for simplicity that a particle is a small sphere, calculate the order of magnitude of its radius a, if the solar radiation pressure on it exceeds the force of the sun's gravitational attraction. Assume that the surface of the sphere (particle) is absolutely black, and that its density is $\delta = 1$.

Hint. Since the ratio of the force of the light repulsion to the force of gravitational attraction is independent of the distance from the sun, it can be assumed that the small sphere (particle) is at the same distance from the sun as the earth, and the solar radiation energy density can be taken to be the same as close to the earth.

541. Using the fact that the light pressure at normal incidence on an ideally reflecting mirror is twice the incident wave energy density, find the law of variation of the light energy density on reflection from a slowly moving ideal mirror.

542. An intense light beam is incident on a solid situated in a vacuum. Is it possible, and if so under what conditions, for the momentum acquired by the solid to exceed the momentum which it

* Obviously, in the majority of cases the repulsion of the comet's tail is due not so much to light pressure as to other cases, for instance the sun's corpuscular radiation.

receives as a result of the light pressure in the case of mirror reflection (this latter momentum is equal, at normal incidence, to $2uSt$, where u is the energy density in the beam, S is the cross-sectional area of the beam and t is the time of illumination).

§ 8. Molecular Optics

543. Determine the polarisability α of a CO_2 molecule, if the refractive index of carbon dioxide in standard conditions is $n = 1{\cdot}000449$, and the number of molecules per cm^3 (Loschmidt's number) is $N = 2{\cdot}687 \times 10^{19}$.

544. Show that J.J.Thomson's model of the atom leads to the relationship $\alpha = a^3$, where a is the radius of the Thomson atom.

Note. According to Thomson, the atom consists of a sphere, the total positive charge of which is $+e$, uniformly distributed throughout the volume of the sphere. Inside the sphere there is a point negative electron with a charge $-e$.

545. Find the maximum velocity of a free electron during its forced oscillations in the field of the solar radiation close to the earth's surface (see Problem 189). Find also the ratio of the maximum force F_m acting on the electron due to the magnetic field, to the maximum force F_e due to the electric field. Replace the solar radiation field with the monochromatic field $\mathbf{E} = \mathbf{E}_0 \cos \omega t$, with wavelength $\lambda = 5500$ Å.

Hint. To a first approximation the action of the magnetic field of the wave can be neglected. Having found the motion of the electron, the force on it from the magnetic field can be calculated.

546. Find the average force of the light pressure on an oscillating electron in the field of a plane monochromatic light wave of frequency ω. In addition to the field of the wave, two further forces act on the electron: (1) the quasi-elastic force $-m\omega_0^2 x$, under the action of which it would perform free harmonic oscillations with natural frequency ω_0; (2) the "friction force" $-m\gamma\dot{x}$, as a result of which the electron absorbs light. Calculate also the average energy ε absorbed by the electron per sec, and express the average force of the light pressure in terms of this. Show that, if there were no absorption of light, the average force of the light pressure would be zero.

547. The constant dipole moment of a polar molecule p_0 is of the order 10^{-18} (in e.s.u.), and the polarisability α of a molecule is of the order 10^{-24} cm^3.* Compare the constant dipole moment with (1) the moment induces in the field of the solar radiation light wave, if the electric field-strength of the solar radiation at the earth's surface is approx. 7 V cm^{-1}; (2) the moment induced in a field of intensity 10,000 V cm^{-1}.

548. Explain why there is such a sharp divergence from the relationship $n = \sqrt{\varepsilon}$, where n is the refractive index and ε is the dielectric constant, for water in the optical region of the electromagnetic spectrum.

549. The density of hydrogen at 0 °C and pressure 760 mm Hg is 0·0000896 g cm^{-3}, and its refractive index is 1·000138. The density of liquid hydrogen is 0·068 g cm^{-3}. Assuming that the Lorentz–Lorenz relation is applicable to this case, find the refractive index of liquid hydrogen. (The experimental value is $n = 1{\cdot}12$.)

550. Obtain the formula for the dielectric constant $\varepsilon(\omega)$ of an ionised gas in a monochromatic electric field $\boldsymbol{E} = \boldsymbol{E}_0 \cos \omega t$. Neglect the collisions of electrons and ions.

551. Is it possible for a refractive index to be less than unity?

552. In the region of anomalous dispersion, $dv/d\lambda < 0$ (v is the phase velocity, λ the wavelength in the medium). In this region it is possible for the group velocity $u = v - \lambda dv/d\lambda$ to be greater than the velocity c *in vacuo*. How does this conform to the proposition

* The following table gives the values of α and p_0 for a number of substances. In the case of an anisotropic molecule α is taken to be the mean of the values of the three principal polarisabilities.

Substance	$\alpha \cdot 10^{25}$ cm^3	$p_0 \cdot 10^{18}$ e.s.u.
Hydrogen H_2	7·9	0·0
Nitrogen N_2	17·6	0·0
Carbon monoxide CO	19·5	0·11
Carbon dioxide CO_2	26·5	0·0 ± 0·02
Water vapour H_2O	—	1·79
Chloroform $CHCl_3$	82·3	1·05
Methyl chloride CH_3Cl	42·3	1·86
Acetone CH_3COCH_3	63·3	2·73
Benzene C_6H_6	103·2	0·0
Nitrobenzene $C_6H_5NO_2$	129·2	3·8

of relativity theory that it is impossible for signals to be propagated with velocity greater than c?

553. The dielectric constant $\varepsilon(\omega)$ of a plasma (see Problem 550) is negative if $\omega < \omega_0$. In this case the refractive index $n = \sqrt{\varepsilon}$ is purely imaginary. Explain the physical meaning of a purely imaginary refractive index.

554. A radio wave is propagated upwards. What frequencies can pass through the ionosphere, and what are totally reflected?

555. A radio signal of given frequency $\nu = \omega/2\pi$ is transmitted upwards and is reflected at a certain height. Find the electron concentration at the point of reflection.

556. The electron concentration in the sun at a distance $r = 0{\cdot}06\,R$ from the edge of the photosphere ($R = 6{\cdot}95 \times 10^{10}$ cm is the sun's radius) is roughly $N = 2 \times 10^8$ cm^{-3}. Is it possible for radio waves from this region of the sun to reach the earth, if the wavelength *(in vacuo)* is (1) $\lambda = 1$ m, (2) $\lambda = 10$ m, (3) $\lambda = 50$ m?

557. Obtain an expression for the phase velocity of a radio wave in the ionosphere as a function of the wavelength λ in the ionosphere. (See Problem 485.)

558. In what conditions can longitudinal electric field oscillations exist in a plasma? What are the phase and group velocities of the corresponding waves?

559. The outer surface of a charged spherical condenser or any charged body of spherical shape oscillates (without destroying the spherical shape of the surface) at a frequency ω_0. Will these oscillations give rise to electromagnetic waves, if the condenser is in a vacuum? Can waves be excited, and if so, what type, if the condenser is in a medium?

560. The spatial dispersion of the dielectric constant is the dependence of ε on the wave vector $\boldsymbol{k}$ (in the absence of absorption $k = 2\pi/\lambda$, where λ is the wavelength in the medium) of the electromagnetic field (the frequency dispersion of ε is the dependence of ε on the frequency ω; in any electromagnetic field produced by sources the variables ω and $\boldsymbol{k}$ can be regarded as independent). The natural optical activity is a spatial dispersion effect of the order a/λ, where a is a characteristic dimension, of the order of magnitude of the lattice constant or the size of a molecule. The natural optical activity is zero in a medium with a centre of symmetry.

What is the order of magnitude of the effect of the spatial dispersion in such media (in the optical part of the spectrum)? Can a cubic crystal (with a centre of symmetry) remain optically anisotropic when the spatial dispersion is taken into account?

561. When account is taken of the spatial dispersion, the frequency of plasma waves depends on the wave number $k = 2\pi/\lambda$. As follows from the solution of the kinetic equation, in this case $\omega^2 = \omega_0^2 + 3k_B Tk^2/m$ (the wave damping is assumed to be small and this formula can only be used when $3k_B Tk^2/m \ll \omega_0^2 \equiv 4\pi e^2 N/m$, where k_B is Boltzmann's constant). Find the phase and group velocities of plasma waves and the corresponding refractive index.

562. The plasma wave damping in an isotropic plasma (in the absence of collisions) is a reverse Cherenkov effect, i.e., Cherenkov absorption. Write down the absorption condition and consider qualitatively when the absorption is strong and when weak (in a plasma with a Maxwell velocity distribution, neglecting the disturbance produced by the wave itself).

563. The electromagnetic energy density in a dispersive medium is easily determined in the case of a gas. It is made up in this case from (1) the energy density of the electromagnetic field itself (i.e. the field *in vacuo*) and (2) the energy density of the particles in the field. This latter energy in turn consists of (a) the kinetic energy of the oscillating particles and (b) the potential energy of the deformed quasi-elastic dipoles. On the basis of this, find an expression for the electromagnetic energy density in a non-absorbent dispersive medium (see Problem 488). Consider also the particular case of a plasma.

564. What pattern is observed on a spectroscope if a system of horizontal interference bands obtained from a source of white light is focused on its slit? How does the pattern change if a glass plate is introduced into one of the arms of the interferometer? Neglect the dispersion of the refractive index of the glass plate.*

* D.S. Rozhdestvenskii developed an elegant and accurate method of investigating anomalous dispersion, which has come to be known as the method of Rozhdestvenskii hooks. Problems 564–567 are intended to explain the idea of this method.

565. What change occurs in the pattern observed in a spectroscope crossed with a Jamin interferometer (see the previous problem) if the thickness and dispersion of the glass plate introduced into one of the interferometer arms are varied? What is the change in pattern when the plate is transferred from one arm to the other?

566. What is the shape of the interference pattern (see Problem 564) is a layer of sodium vapour is introduced into one of the interferometer arms and a glass plate into the other? (1) Consider the shape of the bands close to the sodium absorption band; (2) Find an expression for $(dn/d\lambda)_{\mathrm{Na}}$ at the vertex of the hook (λ is the wavelength *in vacuo*), if the thickness of the glass plate is l_g, the thickness of the sodium vapour layer is l_{Na}, and their respective refractive indices are n_g and n_{Na}.

Note. The vertex of the hook is the point at which the tangent to the interference band is horizontal.

567. The distance in wavelengths between the vertices of the hooks on either side of the resonance line is $2\Delta\lambda$, the thickness of the glass plate and the gas layer under study are l_g and l respectively, and the refractive index of the glass is n_g. Find the oscillator strength f_0 corresponding to the given line.

Note. To bring the classical theory of dispersion into agreement with experiment it is necessary to replace in the formulae the number of scattered electrons N_0 by the number $f_0 N_0$, where f_0 is called the oscillator strength. When solving the problem it should be remembered that the refractive index of a gas is close to unity.

568. Will an oscillator on which a light wave of frequency ω is incident, radiate light of this frequency after the wave has been shut off, if ω is not equal to the natural frequency ω_0 of the oscillator?

569. A beam of electrons travels *in vacuo* under the action of Coulomb forces. Will the motion be accompanied by dipole radiation?

570. It is well known that a linear oscillator does not radiate in the direction of its axis. Use this fact to give a molecular explanation of the existence of a polarisation angle (Brewster's angle) when light is reflected from a solid with $n > 1$. The molecules of the solid are assumed isotropic.

Hint. See Problem 24.

571. Deviations from Fresnel's formulae (see Problem 370) are usually connected with the presence on the surface of the reflecting body of an intermediate layer, the refractive index of which differs from the refractive index of the reflecting body, and the thickness of which is small compared with the wavelength. Use molecular considerations to explain why Brewster's law is not observed in the presence of an intermediate layer.

572. Experiment shows that Brewster's law is applicable not only to an isotropic medium, the molecules of which are themselves isotropic, but also to an isotropic medium consisting of anisotropic molecules. How does this accord with molecular theory if the direction of the induced dipole moment is in general not the same, for an anisotropic molecule, as the direction of the exciting electric field? For in this case, when the light is polarised perpendicularly to the plane of incidence, the excited dipole moments of the molecules will not be parallel to the direction of the reflected ray. Hence the molecules will radiate in this direction, and we must expect the appearance of reflected light in spite of Brewster's law.

573. The propagation of light in a medium amounts to the following from the molecular point of view. Under the influence of the incident light wave, as also under the influence of the radiations of neighbouring molecules and atoms, each molecule (or atom) acquires a dipole moment, which varies in time, and hence itself becomes a source of secondary light waves. These secondary waves are propagated in the space between the molecules and atoms with the velocity c of light *in vacuo*. Since the secondary waves are excited in the long run by the same incident wave, they are coherent and interfere with one another. The result of this interference outside the medium is reflection of the wave, and inside the medium is refraction of the wave. When studying the reflection of light we are interested in the field at distances from the boundary of the medium which are large not only compared with the interatomic and intermolecular distances, but also compared with the wavelength. When calculating the radiation field at such distances, the discrete radiating centres – molecules or atoms – can be replaced by sources with a continuously distributed polarisation vector: each volume element dV of the medium (the size of which is small compared with λ^3) radiates as a dipole with moment $\boldsymbol{P}dV$ ($\boldsymbol{P}$ is the polarisation vector of the medium). Let the medium be bounded on a plane face by a vacuum, and let a plane monochromatic wave be incident on it. In the steady state $\boldsymbol{P} = \boldsymbol{P}_0 \exp i[\omega t - (\boldsymbol{k} \cdot \boldsymbol{r})]$. The medium can be divided into layers, parallel to its face. Each layer will radiate a plane wave into the vacuum in the direction of the reflected light. We choose the thickness l of the layers so that two neighbouring layers radiate plane waves in opposite phase. Show that the field strength of the wave radiated into the vacuum by the medium as a whole is equal to half the field strength of the wave radiated by the first layer. Find also the layer thickness l.

574. A uniform electromagnetic wave, and a corresponding uniform wave of polarisation, can be propagated in an infinite isotropic medium. This can be used in the following way to derive Fresnel's formula for the reflection of light from the medium bounded by a vacuum. Let a uniform wave of polarisation $\boldsymbol{P} = \boldsymbol{P}_0 \exp i[\omega t - (\boldsymbol{k} \cdot \boldsymbol{r})]$, where $k_z > 0$ (the z axis is directed vertically downwards), be propagated in the infinite medium. We split the medium into two halves by the plane $z = 0$. The effect of the upper on the lower half amounts to its radiating downwards a plane wave (propagated with the velocity of light *in vacuo*) with wave vector $\boldsymbol{f}$ whose components are

$$f_x = k_x; \quad f_y = k_y; \quad f_z = +\sqrt{\frac{\omega^2}{c^2} - k_x^2 - k_y^2}\,.$$

If we dispense with the part of the medium above the $z = 0$ plane, but preserve its radiation field, the state of the medium below the $z = 0$ plane remains unchanged. But we obtain this state in the lower half-plane if a plane monochromatic wave is transmitted from the vacuum into the medium filling the lower half-plane. Thus the incident wave is equivalent to the wave radiated in the lower half-space by the fictitious medium filling the upper half-space. Use this discussion and the result from the previous problem to obtain Fresnel's formula for the reflection of light.

575. An elementary oscillating dipole of moment $\boldsymbol{p}$ situated in a medium of refractive index $n = \sqrt{\varepsilon}$ gives a radiation field $\boldsymbol{E}$. What will be the radiation from the same dipole (i.e., a dipole with the same moment $\boldsymbol{p}$) if it is situated in a narrow slit so as to be (a) parallel to, (b) perpendicular to the slit. The slit width is small compared with the wavelength. The slit is filled with a homogeneous substance of dielectric constant ε'.

Hint. Use the reciprocity theorem of electrodynamics. It can be stated as follows. Suppose we have two elementary dipoles of moments $\boldsymbol{p}_1$ and $\boldsymbol{p}_2$. Let the field of dipole 1 at the position of dipole 2 be $\boldsymbol{E}_1(2)$, and the field of dipole 2 at the position of dipole 1 be $\boldsymbol{E}_2(1)$. Then, by the reciprocity theorem, $(\boldsymbol{p}_1 \cdot \boldsymbol{E}_2(1)) = (\boldsymbol{p}_2 \cdot \boldsymbol{E}_1(2))$. The theorem is applicable to any medium in which there is magnetic rotation of the plane of polarisation (Faraday effect). (See Problems 595 and 596.)

576. Solve the previous problem for a cylindrical cavity, when the dipole $\boldsymbol{p}$ is mounted (a) parallel to the cavity axis, (b) perpendicular to the axis. The radius of the cavity is small compared with the wavelength.

577. The same for a spherical cavity.

578. A particle with charge e, moving with the non-relativistic velocity $\boldsymbol{v}$, crosses normally a vacuum-metal boundary. This leads to so-called transition radiation. Explain its nature and characteristics.

579. Consider the motion of an elastically bound electron in an external magnetic field and show that the motion in the presence of the field differs from the motion in its absence by the superposition of a uniform rotation about the field direction with frequency $\omega = -eH/2mc$. It is assumed that the frequency ω is small compared with the natural frequency of the elastically bound electron.

580. When placed in a magnetic field the energy of an electron moving in an orbit of given radius r with a frequency ω_0 changes as a result of Larmor precession. Describe the mechanism of the energy change and find its value.

581. The constant R of the magnetic rotation of the plane of polarisation of CS_2 is 0·04347 minutes of arc/oersted cm (at 0°C and $\lambda = 5890$ Å). Find the angle through which the plane of polarisation is rotated when light passes through a CS_2 layer 1 cm thick in a field of 10,000 oersted.

Note. The angle of rotation of the plane of polarisation in a magnetic field H when light passes through a layer of substance of thickness l is given by $\alpha = RlH$, where R is a constant.

582. Find the constant R for iron, given that a 10^{-3} cm layer of iron rotates the plane of polarisation through 130° in a field of 10,000 oersted at $\lambda = 5890$ Å.

583. Express the constant R in terms of the refractive indices n_- and n_+ for right-hand and left-hand polarised light, travelling along the lines of the magnetic field.

584. Show that $n_- - n_+ \approx 2\omega_L \partial n/\partial\omega$, where $\omega_L = -eH/2mc$ is the angular velocity of precession of the electron orbits in the magnetic field, n_- and n_+ are the refractive indices for light rays with right-hand and left-hand circular polarisation respectively. Obtain from this a formula for the constant R.

585. Find the sign of the rotation of the plane of polarisation in a magnetic field when light is propagated in a transparent medium (i.e., in a medium with small absorption).

Hint. See the two previous problems.

586. Find the ratio of the charge to the mass e/m of an electron, given that the angle α of magnetic rotation for hydrogen at a pressure of 85 atm is 0·063′; $\lambda_0 \partial n/\partial\lambda_0 = 0{\cdot}0625 \times 10^{-4}$ ($\lambda = 5890$ Å), $l = 1$ cm; $H = 10{,}000$ oersted.

587. When studying the normal Zeeman effect, the direction of observation is opposite to the direction of the lines of force. Which of the components has right circular polarisation, and which left?

588. An electromagnetic wave is propagated in a plasma (ionised gas), situated in a magnetic field $\boldsymbol{H}$. The direction of wave propagation is the same as the direction of $\boldsymbol{H}$. Neglecting particle collisions (i.e. absorption), determine the type of polarisation of the wave and the corresponding refractive index.

589. Linearly polarised radiation from one of the radiogalaxies passes through the region of ionised interstellar gas in conditions when the field $H \approx 10^{-4}$ oersted and is parallel to the line of sight, the mean electron concentration $N = 1\ \text{cm}^{-3}$ and the diameter of the region is $L = 10^{18}$ cm. Find the angle α of rotation of the plane of polarisation for radiation of wavelength $\lambda = 10$ cm.

590. A free electron moves in a magnetic field along a helix and thus has an orbital magnetic moment. It would therefore seem that an electron gas placed in a vessel with ideally reflecting walls (a crude model of a metal) will possess diamagnetism. However, in the equilibrium state the diamagnetic moment of a vessel containing a gas is actually zero (within the framework of classical theory). Give a qualitative explanation of this result.

Hint. Take account of the reflection of the electrons from the vessel walls.

591. Consider qualitatively the influence of an external magnetic field on the polarisation of the radiation of a damped oscillator in the case when, prior to switching on the field, (1) the direction of the oscillations is parallel to the direction of the field, whilst the direction of observation is perpendicular to the field; (2) the direction of the oscillations is perpendicular to the field, whilst the direction of observation is either parallel to or perpendicular to the field.

Note. Consideration of the effect of a field on the radiation of a damped oscillator gives the classical theory of the effect of a magnetic field on resonance fluorescence.

592. The width of the resonance line of mercury $\lambda = 2537$ Å corresponds to a lifetime of the mercury atom in the excited state equal to $T = 10^{-7}$ sec. Find the order of magnitude of the magnetic field producing almost complete depolarisation of the resonance emission of mercury when it is observed along the field. The direction of the oscillations in the absence of a field is perpendicular to the direction of observation.

593. Show that, in the case of forced vibrations of an oscillator with small damping, described by the equation

$$\ddot{x} + 2\lambda\dot{x} + \omega_0^2 x = f_0 \cos \gamma t = f;$$

$$|\lambda| \ll \gamma; \quad |\lambda| \ll \omega_0, \quad f_0 > 0, \quad \gamma > 0,$$

where λ can be positive or negative ($\lambda < 0$ corresponds to the case of negative friction), the work done by the force is positive when $\lambda > 0$, i.e. energy is transferred to the oscillator. In the opposite case, when $\lambda < 0$, the reverse process occurs.

594. Is it possible for a constant electric field to produce a change in the frequency of the oscillations of a harmonic oscillator? Take as the model of a harmonic oscillator an electron acted on by a quasi-elastic force.

595. Given two Nicol prisms N_1 and N_2 (Fig. 45), the principal planes of which are at 45° to one another. A layer of a substance, which rotates the plane of polarisation (Faraday effect) is placed between the prisms in a longitudinal magnetic field. What is the angle through which the layer should turn the plane of polarisation in order for light to pass through the system in one direction only (for example, from the body A to B)? (Optical valve.)

596. What is the behaviour of the optical valve described in the previous problem if the direction of the magnetic field is reversed whilst the mutual arrangement of the prisms and the field-strength magnitude remain the same?

597. Is it possible for the arrangement described in Problem 595 to act as an optical valve, if a layer of naturally active material is interposed between the prisms and there is no magnetic field?

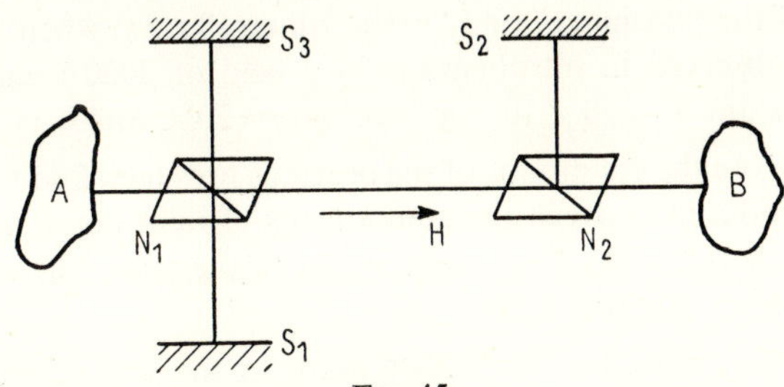

FIG. 45

598. Explain the following paradox (Wien's paradox). Two identical heated bodies A and B (Fig. 45), with an optical valve between them, are placed in an adiabatic envelope. The light, radiated by A, is incident on the Nicol prism N_1. Half of the incident energy I, i.e., $\frac{1}{2}I$, passes through the prism, whilst the other half undergoes total internal reflection and returns via the mirror S_1 to the body A (when using the mirror, the heating of the prism can be neglected). The other half $\frac{1}{2}I$ of the energy, having passed through N_1, is completely transmitted by the prism N_2 and is absorbed by the body B. Meantime, the light from B does not pass through the valve. Half the energy I, i.e., $\frac{1}{2}I$, radiated by B undergoes total internal reflection in the Nicol prism N_2 and after reflection from the mirror S_2 returns to the body B. The other half of the energy, having passed through N_2 and the rotating medium, undergoes a 45° rotation of the plane of polarisation and hence cannot pass through N_1, and instead undergoes total internal reflection. This part of the energy will be reflected in the reverse direction by the additional mirror S_3 and after total internal reflection in N_1 returns to the body B. Thus the body A acquires an energy $\frac{1}{2}I$, and B the energy $3I/2$, so that B

becomes hotter, in contradiction to the second law of thermodynamics.

599. The Cotton–Mouton effect is observed in acetone. Calculate the phase difference δ produced between the components of light polarised in the direction of the magnetic field and perpendicular to the field (the light is propagated perpendicularly to the field). The Cotton–Mouton constant for acetone at $t = 20\,°\text{C}$ and for $\lambda_0 = 5780$ Å is $C = 37{\cdot}6 \times 10^{-13}$ deg oersted^{-2} cm^{-1}. The field-strength $H = 20{,}000$ oersted, the layer thickness is 2 cm.

600. Find the difference $n_0 - n_e$ (n_0 and n_e are the refractive indices of the "ordinary" and "extraordinary" rays) when the Kerr effect is observed in nitrobenzene in a field of 3000 V cm^{-1}. The Kerr constant $B = 220 \times 10^{-7}$ g^{-1} sec^2 (at $t = 20\,°\text{C}$ and $\lambda_0 = 5890$ Å).

601. Given the conditions of the previous problem, find the phase shift δ produced between the components of light polarised in the direction of the field and at right angles to the field. The length of the condenser plates is 4 cm.

602. What must be the field-strength in the conditions of the previous problem in order for $\delta = \frac{1}{2}\pi$?

603. Light polarised at 45° to the field is incident on a Kerr cell. The phase shift produced by the cell is $\frac{1}{2}\pi$. What is the intensity I of the light passing through a Nicol prism placed behind the Kerr condenser and passing light whose plane of polarisation is perpendicular to the plane of polarisation of the incident light?

604. Indicate qualitatively the orientation of the ellipsoid of optical polarisability of a polar molecule relative to its constant dipole moment, if the substance behaves as follows when introduced into an electric field: (1) like a positive crystal, (2) like a negative crystal. Which of the possible orientations is the most suitable for observing the Kerr effect?

605. Consider a gas consisting of completely anisotropic molecules* (in such molecules the electron can only vibrate in one fixed

* Completely anisotropic molecules do not actually exist. The polarisability α of an anisotropic molecule is a tensor. If α_1, α_2, α_3 are the principal values of this tensor, total anisotropy would imply that two of these values vanish. The results of the solutions of Problems 605 and 606 can be applied approximately to molecules for which one of the quantities α_1, α_2, α_3 is large compared with the other two. These problems should be regarded as basically qualitative. Their aim is to explain the basic theory of the Kerr effect by reference to a simple model.

direction relative to the molecule axis). Calculate the refractive indices n_z and n_y for waves whose electric fields are directed along the z and y axes, as a function of the angular disposition of the molecule axes; assume that $n_z - n_y \ll n_0$ and n_0 is close to unity (n_0 is the refractive index for an isotropic disposition of the molecules). Assume further that the distribution of the molecule axes depends only on their angle to the z axis.

606. Calculate the Kerr constant $B = (n_z - n_y)/\lambda_0 E_0^2$ for a gas consisting of completely anisotropic molecules without a constant dipole moment. The constant electric field E_0 is directed along the z axis. The quantity $\beta = \alpha E_0^2/2kT$ can be assumed small compared with unity.

607. Calculate the Kerr constant B for a gas consisting of completely anisotropic molecules with constant dipole moment p_0, the direction of which is the same as the direction of polarisability of the molecules. Assume that the moment induced by the constant external field is small compared with p_0 (i.e. neglect the induced moment), and that $\beta = p_0 E_0/k_B T$ is small compared with unity.

608. The time-average of the light energy radiated by a linear oscillator in the solid angle $d\Omega$ in unit time is

$$I(\vartheta)\, d\Omega = \frac{\overline{\ddot{p}^2} \sin^2 \vartheta}{4\pi c^3}\, d\Omega,$$

where ϑ is the angle between the electric moment $\boldsymbol{p}$ of the oscillator and the direction of observation. Use this formula to consider the scattering of light by a free electron and find the cross section σ of this process.

Note. The cross section σ is the ratio of the energy scattered by the electron in unit time to the energy flux density of the incident light wave.

609. What is the relationship between the cross section σ for scattering of light by a proton and by an electron?

610. Unpolarised light is incident on an electron; observation of the scattered radiation is carried out at an angle ϑ to the direction of the primary beam. Find the light intensity $d\Phi(\vartheta)$ scattered in the solid angle $d\Omega$ in the direction towards the observer.

611. An elastically bound electron, whose natural angular frequency is ω_0, is illuminated by polarised light with frequency ω differing substantially from ω_0. Find the scattering cross section σ, and $I(\vartheta)$.

Hint. See Problem 608.

612. Solve the previous problem, taking account of the oscillator damping. Assume that the "friction force" is $R = -m\gamma\dot{x}$. Find the approximate value of σ close to resonance.

613. Find the ratio Σ of the energy flux of the radiation scattered by a gas to the energy flux of the incident plane wave for normal pressure p and temperature $T = 273\,°\text{K}$. The gas molecules can be regarded as linear oscillators, i.e. assume that there is only one natural frequency for the molecules. The length of the scattering volume along the beam is $l = 10$ cm. The frequency of the incident light is $\omega = 3 \times 10^{15}\ \text{sec}^{-1}$; the natural frequency of the oscillators is $\omega_0 = 6 \times 10^{15}\ \text{sec}^{-1}$.

614. Solve the previous problem on the assumption that the wavelength of the incident light is $\lambda_1 = 7000\ \text{Å}$ in one case, and $\lambda_2 = 4000\ \text{Å}$ in the other. What is the ratio $A = \Sigma(\lambda_1)/\Sigma(\lambda_2)$? Compare A with the ratio $B = (\lambda_2/\lambda_1)^4$.

615. Explain qualitatively the blue colour of the sky and the red of the setting sun.

616. Linearly polarised light is scattered by a gas, the molecules of which are isotropic. Assuming that the molecules scatter the light independently of one another, and that their radiation does not interfere, calculate the ratio $d\Sigma$ of the energy flux of the scattered radiation in the solid angle $d\Omega = \sin\vartheta\, d\vartheta\, d\varphi$ (ϑ is the angle between the direction of observation and the vector $\boldsymbol{E}_0$ of the incident light), to the energy flux of the incident radiation. The volume of the scattering region is V ($V \ll r^3$, where r is the distance from the scattering volume to the observer); the number of molecules per unit volume is N; the refractive index of the gas is n; the wavelength of the light is λ.

617. Observation of scattered light is carried out in the plane perpendicular to $\boldsymbol{E}_0$ (see the previous problem). (1) Find the scattered radiation flux $d\Phi$ over the solid angle $d\Omega$; (2) find the same flux if the incident light is natural.

618. Discuss the scattering of light in a gas, the molecules of which are completely anisotropic (see Problem 605). Remembering that the different molecules are distributed randomly and scatter the light independently of one another, calculate the flux I of the scattered radiation for light with electric field vibrations along the x and z axes, if the observation is along the y axis; the incident light is propagated along the x axis and is linearly polarised, the vector $\mathbf{E}_0$ being directed along the z axis. Find also the degree of depolarisation $\Delta = I_x/I_z$ of the scattered light.

619. Solve the previous problem on the assumption that the incident light is natural, i.e. $\overline{E_z^2} = \overline{E_y^2}$.

620. Find the ratio Σ of the energy flux of the radiation scattered by air to the energy flux of the incident plane wave at $T = 273\,°\mathrm{K}$ and normal pressure. The refractive index is 1·00029. The wavelength is $\lambda = 5000$ Å, the length of the scattering volume along the ray is $l = 1$ m.

621. Solve the same problem for carbon disulphide (CS_2). The length of the scattering volume is $l = 10$ cm; $n = 1{\cdot}628$. The density of CS_2 is 1·264 $\mathrm{g\,cm^{-3}}$.

622. On the average about 2 cal solar energy is incident per min per cm^2 on the surface of the atmosphere. Assuming that the density of the atmosphere is constant and equal to the air density at the earth's surface, and that its height is $h = 10$ km ("equivalent atmosphere"), calculate the energy flux S arriving at the earth's surface, for the two cases: (1) $\lambda = 6000$ Å and (2) $\lambda = 4000$ Å.

Hint. See Problem 620.

623. A parallel beam of linearly polarised rays passes through a tall tube filled with a slightly muddied sugar solution. In the case of white light, a series of helices of different tinges is observed from the side. (1) Explain their occurrence; (2) discuss the dependence of the pitch of the helix on the concentration of the solution and on the colour.

Note. Sugar is an optically active substance, i.e. when linearly polarised light travels through the solution the plane of polarisation is rotated.

624. Circularly polarised light is scattered in a gas, the molecules of which are optically isotropic. Consider the polarisation of the scattered light as a function of the angle ϑ between the directions of propagation of the incident and scattered light. In the case when the scattered light is elliptically polarised find the orientation of the ellipse of vibrations and the ellipticity ϱ, i.e. the ratio of the minor to the major axis of the ellipse.

625. Natural light travels in a gas, the molecules of which are optically isotropic. Show that the scattered light can be resolved into linearly polarised and natural light. Consider the inclination of the plane of polarisation of the linearly polarised component of the scattered light. Find the ratio of the intensity of the linearly polarised component to the intensity of the unpolarised component, as a function of the angle ϑ between the directions of propagation of the incident and scattered light.

626. L.I. Mandel'shtam and G.S. Landsberg carried out their first experiments on Raman scattering (independent of and simultaneous with Raman) on quartz crystals. The source was a quartz mercury lamp. The investigations were carried out in ultraviolet light. The lamp spectrum consists of three distinct waves of wavelengths 2536 Å, 3126 Å, and 3650 Å. The scattered light was photographed by a quartz spectrograph. Mandel'shtam and Landsberg found that all the mercury lines in the scattered light are accompanied by secondary lines. In order to show that the secondary lines are not "false", i.e. are not obtained as a result of random reflections of the spectral pattern as a whole, it was necessary to show that their wavelengths were different from those of the basic lines. One proof consisted in placing a quartz vessel filled with mercury vapour between the scattering crystal and the spectrograph slit. Describe the pattern that would be expected on heating up the vessel containing the mercury, if the wavelengths of the secondary lines were the same as those of the basic lines, and the pattern to be expected if we assume that these wavelengths are different.

627. Find the frequency ν of the natural vibrations of a bromine molecule, yielding on Raman scattering of the line $\lambda = 3131{\cdot}6$ Å the secondary line of wavelength $\lambda_1 = 3164{\cdot}0$ Å.

628. Find the wavelengths of the Raman lines of the Cl_2 molecule, obtained from the exciting line with $\lambda = 4358{\cdot}3$ Å, if the vibration frequency of the molecule corresponds to the wave number 556 cm^{-1}.

Note. The wave number $N = 1/\lambda$.

629. The distance between the violet ($\lambda = 4046{\cdot}8$ Å) and blue ($\lambda = 4358{\cdot}3$ Å) lines of the mercury spectrum on a photographic plate is $a_1 = 8{\cdot}680$ mm, between the blue and the blue-green ($\lambda = 4916{\cdot}0$ Å) $a_2 = 9{\cdot}124$ mm. In series with the blue there are four Raman lines of CCl_4 at distances 0·903; 1·300; 1·865; 3·083 mm from it. Find the normal frequencies of CCl_4 in cm^{-1}.

Hint. The positions of the spectral lines can be found by using the following formula, which connects the frequencies of two spectral lines with the distance between them: $\nu - \nu_0 = a/(x - x_0)$.

630. What must be the resolution of a prism in order to resolve the Raman doublet 1500 cm^{-1} and 1530 cm^{-1}, obtained from the exciting line with $\lambda = 4358{\cdot}3$ Å?

631. Find the ratio of the intensities of the violet and red secondary lines in the Raman scattering spectrum of CCl_4 at 27°C, if the frequencies of the normal vibrations of CCl_4 are 217 cm^{-1}, 315 cm^{-1}, 457 cm^{-1} and 774 cm^{-1}.

632. Estimate, using the classical theory, the order of magnitude of the frequency of rotation ω_0 of an H_2 molecule at $T = 300$°K. The moment of inertia of the H_2 molecule is of the order 5×10^{-40} g cm².

633. Find the distance $\Delta\nu$ between the lines of the rotation structure of the Raman line of N_2, given that the moment of inertia of N_2 is $I = 13{\cdot}8 \times 10^{-40}$ g cm².

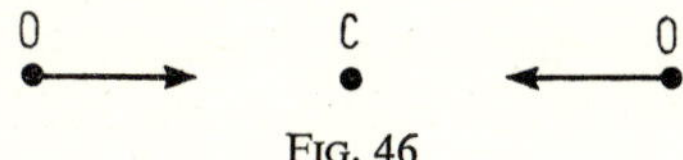

FIG. 46

634. Show by using classical theory that the symmetric normal vibration of the CO_2, illustrated in Fig. 46, does not give bands in the infrared absorption spectrum.

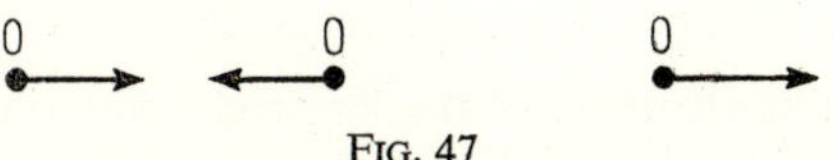

FIG. 47

635. Show by using classical theory that the frequency of the normal vibration, antisymmetric with respect to the centre, of the CO_2 molecule, illustrated in Fig. 47, corresponds to the Raman scattering spectrum.

636. Show by using classical theory that the distance in Å between the lines of the rotation structure of the combination scattering of a molecule is twice the distance between the lines of the rotation structure of the infrared absorption spectrum.

637. Given an isotropic medium with weak optical non-uniformity, i.e. with a dielectric constant of the form $\varepsilon = \varepsilon_0 + \delta\varepsilon$, where ε_0 is the mean value of ε, and $\delta\varepsilon$ is the deviation from the mean value. Show that, in an approximation linear in $\delta\varepsilon$, the problem of light scattering can be reduced to the problem of light propagation in a uniform medium with dielectric constant ε_0, in which there are additional sources in the form of vibrating dipoles, distributed in the medium. Show that, if we write $\delta\varepsilon$ as $\delta\varepsilon = \Sigma\delta_i\varepsilon$, the scattered radiation can be obtained in this approximation by simple superposition of the fields scattered at the non-uniformities $\delta_i\varepsilon$.

638. A plane light wave:

$$\boldsymbol{E}_0 = \boldsymbol{A} \exp i[\omega t - (\boldsymbol{k} \cdot \boldsymbol{r})], \quad \boldsymbol{H}_0 = \boldsymbol{B} \exp i[\omega t - (\boldsymbol{k} \cdot \boldsymbol{r})],$$

is propagated in a medium with small optical non-uniformity of the form $\delta\varepsilon = a \exp[-i(\boldsymbol{K} \cdot \boldsymbol{r})]$ (a and $\boldsymbol{K}$ are constants). At what wavelengths $\lambda = 2\pi/k$, and in what directions, will scattered radiation be observed?

639. Assuming that the dielectric constant ε of a medium is a function of its density ϱ only, find the wavelengths of the scattered radiation due to heat fluctuations of the density, as a function of the angle ϑ between the directions of the incident and scattered waves. The incident wave is monochromatic.

640. Describe qualitatively the fine structure of the Rayleigh light scattering lines in amorphous solids.

641. What fine structure of the Rayleigh scattering lines of unpolarised light is to be expected in crystals?

642. What fine structure of the Rayleigh scattering lines is to be expected in liquid helium II?

643. When the light of the resonance line of a mercury lamp ($\lambda = 2536{\cdot}5$ Å) is scattered in a diamond crystal at an angle $\vartheta = 90°$ to the direction of the incident beam, two pairs of displaced components with $\delta\lambda = 0{\cdot}52$ Å and $\delta\lambda = 0{\cdot}32$ Å are found. (We are speaking of displacement relative to the central—undisplaced—component.) Find the velocities of the longitudinal and transverse acoustic waves in the diamond. The refractive index of diamond is $n = 2{\cdot}42$.

644. An experimental investigation has recently been carried out into the back scattering of short radio waves in the ionosphere. Assuming that this effect is determined by the scattering at free electrons, calculate the frequency spectrum of the scattered radiation.

645. A charge moving with constant velocity in a vacuum is well known not to radiate. Is radiation obtained when a charge moves in a medium with randomly arranged non-uniformities of the dielectric constant ($\varepsilon = 1 + \Delta\varepsilon(\boldsymbol{r})$, and $\Delta\varepsilon \ll 1$) and what are the special features of the radiation when the charge velocity approaches the velocity of light?

ANSWERS AND SOLUTIONS

§ 1. Geometrical Optics

1. The distance $x = 2rd/(r_1 + r_2 - 2r)$; the source radius is $y = r(r_2 - r_1)/(r_1 + r_2 - 2r)$.

2. The eclipse is total when the distance d from the centre of the moon to the earth's surface is less than 376,000 km; it is annular when $d > 376{,}000$ km.

4. When the screen is close to the mirror the illuminated part has a quadrilateral shape. When the screen is remote from the mirror, an elliptic image of the sun is obtained.

5. (a) A system of horizontal light and dark bands is obtained on the screen. When the slit is turned through 90° the bands become vertical. When turned through 45°, the bands vanish in the case of Fig. 1(a); in the case of Fig. 1(b), bands appear inclined at 45° to the horizontal. The distance between the bands in the last case is reduced $\sqrt{2}$ times compared with the distance between the horizontal or vertical bands. The bands are parallel to the slit in all these cases.

When slit and mesh are interchanged, the nature of the pattern is unchanged, but the bands become somewhat narrower.

6. $\delta = 2\alpha$.

This formula embraces all the possible conditions provided that the angles α and δ are measured in a well-defined and identical manner. It is assumed that the light ray is first reflected from the first mirror, then from the second mirror. α is the angle through which the first mirror must be turned in order to make it coincide with the second. Similarly, δ is defined as the angle through which the initial direction of the ray must be turned in order for it to coincide with the direction of the ray reflected from the second mirror. The directions of rotation are arbitrary, but they must be the same in both cases (for instance, clockwise or counter-clockwise). This point should be borne in mind whenever solving problems of this type.

7. $\boldsymbol{r}_1 = \boldsymbol{r}_0 - 2(\boldsymbol{r}_0 \cdot \boldsymbol{N})\boldsymbol{N}$;

$$n_2\boldsymbol{r}_2 = n_1\boldsymbol{r}_0 - \boldsymbol{N}\left\{n_1(\boldsymbol{r}_0 \cdot \boldsymbol{N}) + \sqrt{n_2^2 - n_1^2 + n_1^2(\boldsymbol{r}_0 \cdot \boldsymbol{N})^2}\right\}.$$

8. Let N_1, N_2, N_3 be the unit vectors of the normal to planes of the mirrors, $\boldsymbol{r}_0$ the unit vector of the ray incident on the first mirror, $\boldsymbol{r}_1, \boldsymbol{r}_2, \boldsymbol{r}_3$ the unit vectors of the ray after reflection from the first, second and third mirrors.

Now,

$$\boldsymbol{r}_1 = \boldsymbol{r}_0 - 2(\boldsymbol{r}_0 \cdot N_1)N_1,$$

$$\boldsymbol{r}_2 = \boldsymbol{r}_1 - 2(\boldsymbol{r}_1 \cdot N_2)N_2,$$

$$\boldsymbol{r}_3 = \boldsymbol{r}_2 - 2(\boldsymbol{r}_2 \cdot N_3)N_3.$$

Hence it easily follows that $\boldsymbol{r}_3 = -\boldsymbol{r}_0$.

11. If m is even, the number of images is $m - 1$. If m is odd, the number of images is m; when the object is arranged symmetrically with respect to the mirrors, two of these images merge into one, and the total number of images is reduced to $m - 1$.

12. If the rays departing from the prism are collected by an achromatic lens, there will be no spectral resolution. If the departing rays are immediately incident on a screen, a white spot is obtained with a coloured edge; $\delta = 2\alpha$.

14. The image diameter is about 7·5 cm.

15. The image is real and magnified twice when the object is 30 cm from the mirror. The image is virtual and magnified twice when the object is 10 cm away.

16. $f = 7{\cdot}5$ cm.

18. The convex surface of a paraboloid of revolution, the axis of which is parallel to the rays.

19. $f = \dfrac{g}{2\omega^2} = 490$ cm.

20. *Solution.* It follows from the laws of reflection of light that the continuation of the reflected ray CB (Fig. 48) cuts the perpendicular AA' to the plane of the mirror at the point A', which is at the same distance from the plane as the point A. Thus $A'C = AC$, and the length of the light path ACB is equal to the length of the straight line $A'B$. If the light travelled along the path $AC'B$, the length of this path would be equal to the length of the step line $A'C'B$. Equating the length of the step line $A'C'B$ to the length of the straight line $A'CB$ gives the solution.

21. Since the angles of incidence and reflection are equal, it follows from the property of the bisector of the angle of a triangle that, in the approximation of paraxial optics, the positions of the point—the object P—and its image P' in the spherical mirror are connected by

$$\frac{OP}{OP'} = \frac{CP}{P'C},$$

i.e. the points P, P', C, O are four harmonic points. At the same time, the construction given in the text reduces to the familiar theorem of projective geometry on the complete quadrangle.

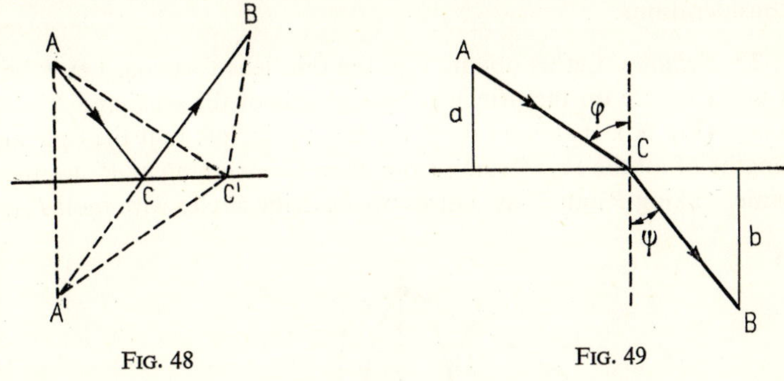

FIG. 48 FIG. 49

22. *Solution.* It can be assumed without loss of generality that the refractive index of the first medium is unity. We have for the optical length L of the step line joining the points A and B (Fig. 49):

$$L = \frac{a}{\cos\varphi} + \frac{nb}{\cos\psi}.$$

We must add the auxiliary relationship

$$a\tan\varphi + b\tan\psi = \text{const},$$

which expresses the constancy of the length of the projection of the step line ACB on the boundary plane between the media. We must have, for a minimum:

$$\frac{dL}{d\varphi} = \frac{a\sin\varphi}{\cos^2\varphi} + \frac{nb\sin\psi}{\cos^2\psi}\frac{d\psi}{d\varphi} = 0.$$

It follows from the auxiliary condition that

$$\frac{a}{\cos^2 \varphi} + \frac{b}{\cos^2 \psi}\frac{d\psi}{d\varphi} = 0.$$

On comparing this relationship with the previous one, we get

$$\sin \varphi - n \sin \psi = 0,$$

i.e. the law of refraction of light. To show that this law actually expresses the condition for a minimum of the optical path of the ray, and not simply an extremum of it, we can either investigate the sign of the second derivative $d^2L/d\psi^2$ or use directly geometrical considerations.

23. *Solution.* Let us obtain, e.g. the thin lens formula. Let P be a point source on the principal optical axis of the lens, and P' its image (Fig. 50). It follows from Fermat's principle that the optical lengths of all the rays issuing from P and converging at P' are the same. Taking P and P' as centres, we describe circles with radii PA,

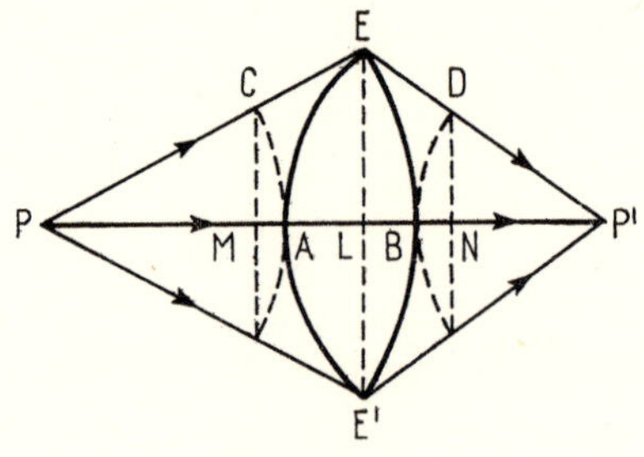

FIG. 50

$P'B$ respectively. We can now write, since the optical lengths of the rays are the same:

$$(CED) = (AB).$$

If the rays PE and EP' are paraxial, the length of the step line CDE can be taken as approximately equal to the length MN of its projection on the principal optical axis. The previous relationship can be written in this approximation as

$$MN = nAB$$

or

$$AM + BN = (n - 1)(AL + LB), \tag{1}$$

where L is the projection of the point E on the principal axis. We have approximately for a thin lens:

$$AL = \frac{(EL)^2}{2R_1}, \quad LB = -\frac{(EL)^2}{2R_2},$$

where R_1, R_2 are the radii of curvature of the spherical surfaces of the lens. Similarly, if the paraxial condition is satisfied, we have

$$AM = -\frac{(EL)^2}{2x_1}, \quad BN = \frac{(EL)^2}{2x_2},$$

where x_1, x_2 denote the lengths PA, BP' respectively. On substituting these expressions in (1), we get

$$\frac{1}{x_2} - \frac{1}{x_1} = (n - 1)\left(\frac{1}{R_1} - \frac{1}{R_2}\right).$$

24. $\varphi = \text{arc tan } n$.

26. The lateral displacement is $l = d \sin(\varphi - \psi)/\cos\psi = 6{\cdot}6$ cm.

27. $h' = \dfrac{h}{n}\dfrac{\cos^3\varphi}{\cos^3\psi} = 0{\cdot}215$ m.

28. $x = \dfrac{d}{n} = 10$ cm.

29. $n = 1{\cdot}5$.

30. $f = l + \dfrac{d}{n} = 18$ cm.

31. The focus moves back $d(n - 1)/n = 2$ mm.

34. $n = \dfrac{\sin\frac{1}{2}(A + \delta)}{\sin\frac{1}{2}A}$.

35. $\delta = 48°\,12'$.

37. $n = \sqrt{2} = 1{\cdot}41$.

38. $\sin\frac{\alpha}{2} \geqslant \frac{1}{n} = 0{\cdot}752; \quad \alpha \geqslant 97°30'.$

40. $\delta = A(n-1)\left\{1 + \frac{n(n+1)}{24}A^2\right\}.$

41. $$D = \frac{d\delta}{d\lambda} = 2\frac{\sin\psi}{\cos\varphi}\frac{dn}{d\lambda} = 2\frac{\sin\frac{A}{2}}{\sqrt{1 - n^2\sin^2\frac{A}{2}}}\frac{dn}{d\lambda};$$

$$\Delta\delta = 2\frac{\sin\frac{A}{2}}{\sqrt{1 - n^2\sin^2\frac{A}{2}}}\Delta n = 5'12''.$$

42.

Intervals	1	2	3	4	5	6
Angular dispersion in sec/Å	0·9	1·7	2·9	8	13	36

43. Linear dispersion: 0·0022; 0·0042; 0·0071; 0·0195; 0·032; 0·088.

44. The yellow ray travels without deviation, the blue is deviated towards the vertex of the prism, the red towards the prism base.

45. *Solution.* Let AB be a piece of the wave front of the incident plane wave (Fig. 51). After passing through the optical system it occupies the position $A'B'$. By the definition of wave front, the optical lengths of the rays AA' and BB' must be equal: $(AA') = (BB')$. We turn the wave front through a small angle α about the point A, so that it occupies the position AC. The wave is now turned through an angle β and occupies the position $A''C''$. The magnification given by the telescope will be equal to β/α.

Obviously, $(AA'') = (CC'')$. We choose the point A'' so that it lies on the plane of the wave front $A'B'$. Since the rays are perpendicular to the front, the optical lengths (AA') and (AA'') will be equal up to terms of order α^2. To the same accuracy, $(BB') = (CC'')$. We draw through the point C'' a plane parallel to the plane $A'B'$. It cuts the position of the ray BB' at the point C'. We again conclude, from the fact that the rays are perpendicular to the wave front, that $(CC') =$

(CC'') up to terms in α^2. We compare this with the equation $(BB') = (CC'')$, and find that $(BB') = (CC')$. Hence, $(BC) = (B'C')$ or $n \cdot AB \cdot \alpha = n'A'B' \cdot \beta$, where n is the refractive index in the object space, and n' in the image space. Thus

$$\frac{\beta}{\alpha} = \frac{AB}{A'B'} \frac{n}{n'}.$$

For the telescope, $n = n'$, so that $\beta/\alpha = AB/A'B'$.

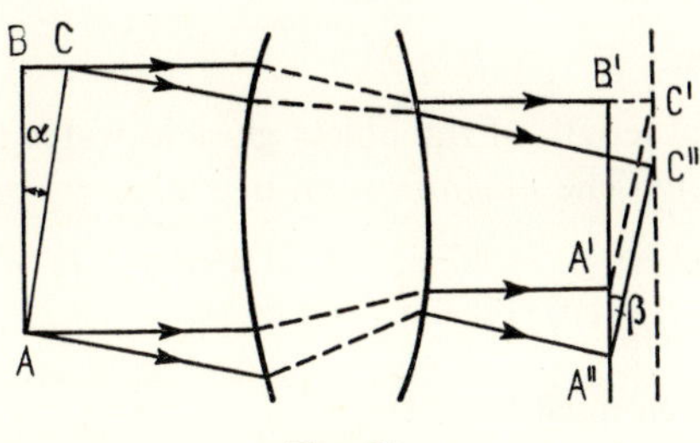

FIG. 51

46. The prism must be mounted so that rays undergo minimum deviation on passing through it.

Solution. The magnification of the prism is generally different in different directions. It is unity in the direction parallel to the refracting edge, since the transverse dimensions of a parallel light beam are unchanged after passing through the prism in this direction (see the solution of the previous problem).

Conversely, in the direction perpendicular to the refracting edge, the transverse dimensions generally undergo a change. In this direction the magnification can be both greater than and less than unity. This explains the lengthening or flattening of the image shape. It is only when the path of the beam through the prism is symmetrical that its transverse dimensions remain unchanged in all directions. In this case the magnification is unity and independent of the direction.

47. The prisms must be arranged at right angles, by turning them about their edges so that the magnifications in the two perpendicular directions are the same.

49. The image is first situated at a distance $X = D/(2-n) = 15\,\text{cm}$ from the nearer end of the diameter in the same direction as the grain. When the grain moves along the diameter its image moves in the same direction and merges with the grain when the latter reaches the nearer end of the diameter.

50. $d \approx 2$ cm.

51. $f = 30{\cdot}8$ mm.

52. $f' = 40$ cm.

53. The focal length is increased 8·64 times; the convergent lens becomes divergent and vice versa.

54. $f = 9$ cm.

55. The focal length of the object glass in water must be 48 cm, and in air 12 cm. The magnification is $\times 3$.

56. $f'_1 = 36$ cm; $f'_2 = 4$ cm; $f_1 = 45$ cm; $f_2 = 5$ cm.

57. $\Delta l = 0{\cdot}5$ cm.

58. The cornea must be flat.

59. $f = +20$ cm (convergent lens).

60. The system is telescopic.

61. The image is 5 cm to the right of the extreme right-hand lens of the system.

62. $d = 1{\cdot}06$ cm from the objective; the linear magnification is 126.

65. $h = \sqrt{ab}$.

66. $f = \dfrac{L^2 - l^2}{4L} = 12$ cm.

67. $l > \dfrac{100 + p}{p} f$.

68. $f = -2$ m.

69. $f = 1{\cdot}5$ m.

70. $R = 72$ cm, $a = 108$ cm.

71. A convergent lens of focal length 30 cm.

72. The optical length of the ray must be reckoned positive in the direction of propagation and negative in the reverse direction. Hence the optical lengths of all the rays joining the source P to its image P' in a plane mirror are zero.

73. We take the axis of revolution as the x axis, and its point of intersection with the required surface as the origin. The equation of the aplanatic surface is now

$$(n'^2 - n^2)x^2 + n'^2(y^2 + z^2) - 2n'(n' - n)qx = 0,$$

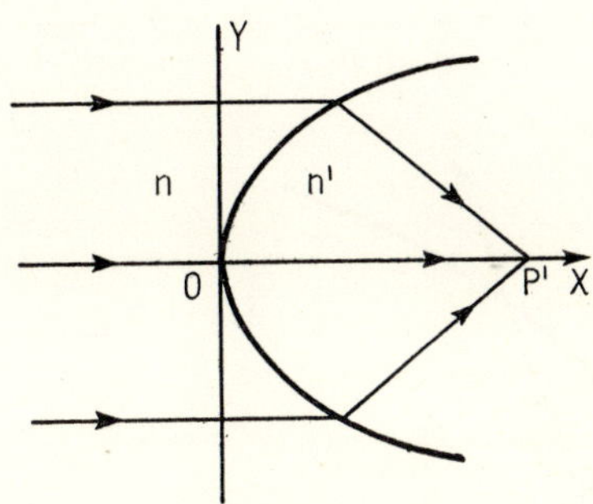

FIG. 52

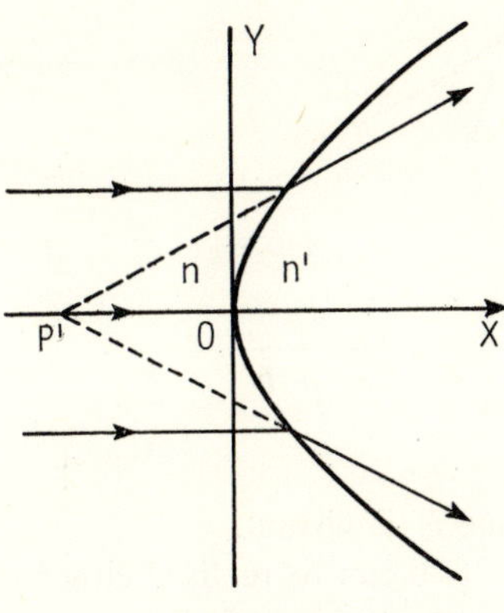

FIG. 53

where q is the abscissa of the point P'. When $n'^2 > n^2$ a prolate ellipsoid of revolution is obtained (Fig. 52), with the semi-axes

$$a = \frac{n'}{n' + n} q; \quad b = q\sqrt{\frac{n' - n}{n' + n}}$$

and eccentricity

$$e = \frac{\sqrt{a^2 - b^2}}{a} = \frac{n}{n'} < 1.$$

When $n'^2 < n^2$ a hyperboloid of revolution of two sheets is obtained (Fig. 53), with semiaxes

$$a = \frac{n'}{n' + n} q; \quad b = q\sqrt{\frac{n - n'}{n' + n}}$$

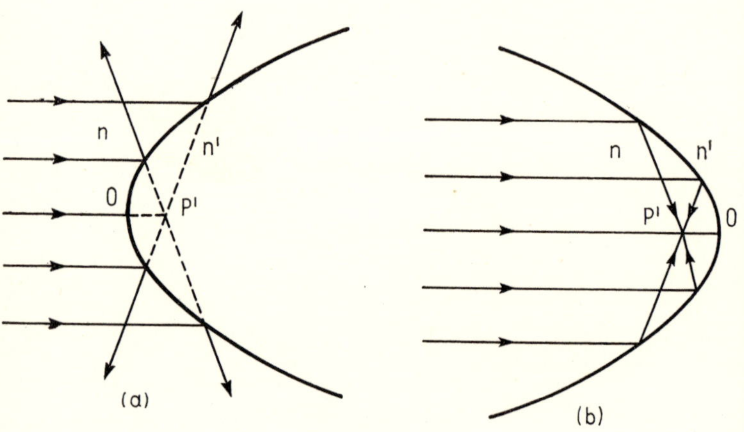

FIG. 54

and eccentricity

$$e = \frac{\sqrt{a^2 + b^2}}{a} = \frac{n}{n'} > 1.$$

In this case the image P' is virtual.

The case $n'^2 - n^2 = 0$ can be realised either with $n' = n$, which is of no interest, or with $n' + n = 0$. The second possibility corresponds to reflection. In this case the aplanatic surface

$$y^2 + z^2 = 4qx$$

is a paraboloid of revolution with parameter $p = 2q$ (parabolic mirror). When $q > 0$ the image P' is virtual (Fig. 54(a)), when $q < 0$ it is real (Fig. 54(b))

74. *Solution.* Let us take, e.g. case (a). Case (b) can be considered in the same way.

We draw an arbitrary straight line CD parallel to the major axis AB of the ellipse (Fig. 55). Its point of intersection D with the ellipse is joined to the foci F_1, F_2. If DN is the normal to the ellipse, then $\angle F_1DN = \angle F_2DN$. Further, $\angle DNF_2 = \varphi$. Hence we have from the triangles F_1DN and F_2DN, by the sines theorem:

$$\frac{F_1D}{F_1N} = \frac{\sin\varphi}{\sin\psi}; \qquad \frac{F_2D}{F_2N} = \frac{\sin\varphi}{\sin\psi}.$$

Thus

$$\frac{\sin\varphi}{\sin\psi} = \frac{F_1D + F_2D}{F_1N + NF_2} = \frac{AB}{F_1F_2}.$$

It is now obvious that the refractive index of the ellipsoid relative to the surrounding medium is $n = AB/F_1F_2 = 1/e$, and if the incident ray is along CD, the refracted ray departs along DF_1.

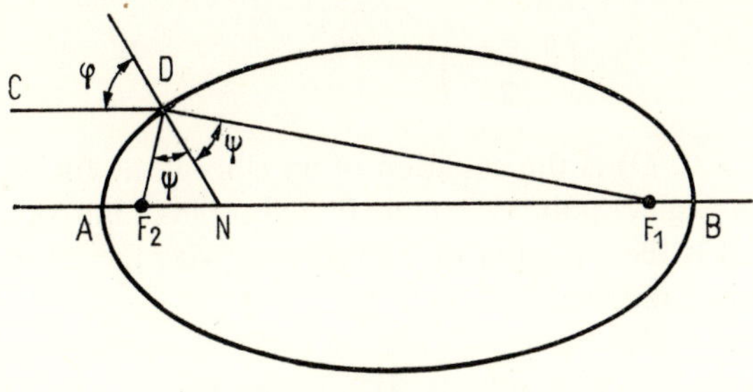

FIG. 55

77. *Solution.* We take the x axis along PP', and the y axis perpendicular to it. We place the origin at the point of intersection of the Cartesian oval with its axis along the x axis. Let q, q' denote the abscissae of the points P, P'. The Cartesian oval is an aplanatic surface relative to the pair of points PP', so that the equation of its intersection with the xy plane is

$$n\sqrt{(x-q)^2 + y^2} + n'\sqrt{(x-q')^2 + y^2} = n'q' - nq,$$

or (after getting rid of the radicals):

$$(n^2 - n'^2)(x^2 + y^2) + 4(n^2 - n'^2)(n'^2q' - n^2q)(x^2 + y^2)x$$
$$+ 4nn'(nq - n'q')(nq' - n'q)(x^2 + y^2) + 4(n'^2q' - n^2q)x^2$$
$$+ 8nn'(n' - n)(nq - n'q')qq'x = 0. \tag{1}$$

If $n^2 - n'^2 = 0$, this equation becomes a second order equation. This can occur either with $n - n' = 0$, which is of no interest, or with $n + n' = 0$. In the second case (1) becomes

$$4qq'x^2 + (q + q')y^2 - 4qq'(q + q')x = 0. \tag{2}$$

If we introduce new coordinates ξ and η, with the origin at the midpoint of PP', we have

$$x = \xi + \frac{q + q'}{2}, \quad y = \eta,$$

and the equation of curve (2) becomes

$$\frac{\xi^2}{\left(\frac{q + q'}{2}\right)^2} + \frac{\eta^2}{qq'} = 1. \tag{3}$$

When $qq' > 0$, (3) is the equation of an ellipse, the foci of which are the conjugate points P and P' (ellipsoidal mirror). When $qq' < 0$, (3) is the equation of a hyperbola with foci at P and P' (hyperboloidal mirror).

Equation (1) also becomes a second order equation when one of the points P or P' is at infinity. If, for instance, $q = \infty$, we only retain the highest terms in q in (1) and cancel by $4q^2n^2$, and obtain

$$(n'^2 - n^2)x^2 + n'^2y^2 - 2n'(n - n')q'x = 0. \tag{4}$$

This case was considered in Problem 72.

When $qn = q'n'$, (1) becomes

$$[(n + n')(x^2 + y^2) - 2qnx]^2 = 0$$

and is the equation of two coincident circles. The equation of one circle is

$$(n + n')(x^2 + y^2) - 2qnx = 0. \tag{5}$$

The aplanatic surface in this case is a sphere of radius

$$R = \frac{qn}{n + n'} = \frac{q'n'}{n + n'} \tag{6}$$

(see the next problem).

There is a further (trivial) case when (1) must reduce to a second order equation. If $q = q'$, both the conjugate points P and P' coincide, i.e. light rays are not refracted at the aplanatic surface. In this case, provided $n \neq n'$, the Cartesian oval must degenerate to a sphere or to a system of two concentric spheres. This requirement can serve as a criterion for the validity of the calculations. On putting $q = q'$ in (1), we find that

$$(x^2 + y^2 - 2qx)\,[(n + n')^2\,(x^2 + y^2 - 2qx) + 4nn'q^2] = 0,$$

which is the equation of a system of two concentric spheres with centres at the point P.

79. If P and Q are the aplanatic points of the spherical surface

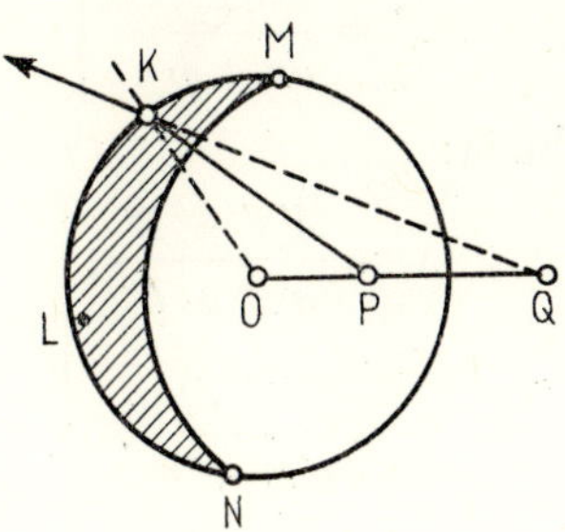

FIG. 56

KL, they will also be aplanatic points of the lens bounded by the surface KL and the sphere MN, centre at the point P (Fig. 56).

80. $f = \dfrac{r_1 r_2}{2(n-1)r_2 + 2nr_1}$.

81. $\dfrac{f_1}{f_2} = \dfrac{n}{n-1}$.

82. A convex meniscus: $r_1 = 20$ cm, $r_2 = 10$ cm, $n = 1{\cdot}53$. The object is on the side of the concave surface of the meniscus.

83.

$$x' = \frac{n'Rx}{(n' - n)x + nR};$$

$$y' = \frac{nRy}{(n' - n)x + nR};$$

$$z' = \frac{nRz}{(n' - n)x + nR}.$$

85. *Solution.* On solving the equations

$$\left.\begin{aligned} x' &= \frac{Ax + B}{ax + b}; \\ y' &= \frac{Cy}{ax + b}; \\ z' &= \frac{Cz}{ax + b} \end{aligned}\right\} \tag{1}$$

for x and y, we obtain:

$$\left.\begin{aligned} x &= \frac{A'x' + B'}{a'x' + b'}; \\ y &= \frac{C'y'}{a'x' + b'}; \\ z &= \frac{C'z'}{a'x' + b'}, \end{aligned}\right\} \tag{2}$$

where

$$A' = -b; \quad B' = B; \quad a' = a; \quad b' = -A; \quad C' = \frac{aB - Ab}{C}. \tag{3}$$

If $ax + b = 0$, in general x', y', z' become infinite. This means that rays issuing from any point of the plane $ax + b = 0$ become parallel after passing through the optical system. We call $ax + b = 0$ the focal plane of the object space. We call $a'x' + b' = 0$ the focal plane of the image space: a parallel pencil of rays incident on the system is convergent to a point of this plane. The points of intersection F and F' of the focal planes with the principal optical axis are called the focal points or principal foci of the system. We have for the coordinates of these points:

$$x_F = -\frac{b}{a}; \quad x'_{F'}, = -\frac{b'}{a'} = \frac{A}{a}. \tag{4}$$

The conjugate planes, the coordinates of the conjugate points of which are connected by $y' = y$, $z' = z$, are called the principal planes of the optical system. They are reflected into one another with transverse magnification $+1$. The points of intersection H and H' of the principal planes with the principal optical axis are called the principal points of the system. Their coordinates are

$$x_H = \frac{C-b}{a}; \quad x'_{H'} = \frac{C'-b'}{a'} = \frac{aB + A(C-b)}{Ca}. \tag{5}$$

The distances of the principal points from the corresponding principal foci are called the focal lengths of the system. We have for the focal lengths:

$$f = x_H - x_F = \frac{C}{a}; \quad f' = x'_{H'} - x'_{F'} = \frac{C'}{a'} = \frac{aB - Ab}{Ca}. \tag{6}$$

The nodes K and K' are defined as the conjugate points, possessing the following property: a light ray passing through K at a given angle to the optical axis passes through K' at the same angle and in the same direction. This means that the equation of the ray

$$y = \alpha(x - x_K)$$

becomes

$$y' = \alpha(x' - x'_{K'}),$$

i.e.

$$\frac{y'}{y} = \frac{x' - x'_{K'}}{x - x_K}.$$

On using formulae (1) and bearing in mind that the last equation must hold for any x, we easily obtain

$$x_K = x_F - f'; \quad x'_{K'} = x'_{F'} - f.$$

86. In case (1) we have to put $x_H = x'_{H'} = 0$, and in case (2), $x_F = x'_{F'} = 0$. Hence we obtain, after a coordinate transformation:

$$\left.\begin{aligned} &\frac{f}{\xi} + \frac{f'}{\xi'} = -1, \\ &\frac{\eta'}{\eta} = \frac{f}{f+\xi} = \frac{f'+\xi'}{f'} = -\frac{f\xi'}{f'\xi}; \end{aligned}\right\} \quad (1)$$

$$\left.\begin{aligned} &XX' = ff', \\ &\frac{Y'}{Y} = \frac{f}{X} = \frac{X'}{f'}. \end{aligned}\right\} \quad (2)$$

87. The principal planes coincide and are tangential to the refracting surface at its point of intersection with the principal optical axis:

$$f = \frac{nR}{n'-n}; \quad f' = -\frac{n'R}{n'-n}.$$

90. *Solution.* We put the origin of each component system at its focal point. Let X_1, Y_1 be the coordinates of the point object, and X'_1, Y'_1 the coordinates of its image in the first system. Then

$$X_1X'_1 = f_1f'_1; \quad \frac{Y'_1}{Y_1} = \frac{f_1}{X_1}.$$

We take the image given by the first system as the object for the second system. The coordinates of this "object" will be

$$X_2 = X'_1 - \delta; \quad Y_2 = Y'_1.$$

The coordinates of its image, given by the second system (relative to F'_2) are denoted by X'_2, Y'_2. Now

$$X_2X'_2 = f_2f'_2; \quad \frac{Y'_2}{Y_2} = \frac{X'_2}{f'_2}.$$

On eliminating the coordinates of the intermediate image, we obtain

$$X'_2 = \frac{f_2f'_2}{f_1f'_1 - \delta X_1}X_1; \quad Y'_2 = \frac{f_1f_2}{f_1f'_1 - \delta X_1}Y_1.$$

Hence we can find by the usual method (see Problem 84) the coordinates of the focal and principal points of the compound system:

$$x_F = \frac{f_1 f_1'}{\delta}; \quad x'_{F'} = -\frac{f_2 f_2'}{\delta};$$

$$x_H = \frac{f_1 f_1' - f_1 f_2}{\delta}; \quad x'_{H'} = \frac{f_1' f_2' - f_2 f_2'}{\delta},$$

where we take as origin in the object space the forward focus of the first system, and as origin in the image space the rear focus of the second system. We find for the focal lengths of the compound system:

$$f = -\frac{f_1 f_2}{\delta}; \quad f' = \frac{f_1' f_2'}{\delta}.$$

91. $\dfrac{1}{f} = \dfrac{1}{f_1} + \dfrac{1}{f_2} - \dfrac{1}{f_1 f_2}; \quad f = \dfrac{f_1 f_2}{f_1 + f_2 - l}.$

The distances of the principal planes of the system H and H' from the first and second lens are

$$O_1H = -\frac{f_1 l}{l - f_1 - f_2}; \quad O_2H' = \frac{f_2 l}{l - f_1 - f_2}.$$

92. The "equivalent" lens must be placed at the forward principal plane of the two-lens system:

$$f = \frac{f_1 f_2}{f_1 + f_2 - l}.$$

93. $f = \dfrac{f_1 f_2}{f_1 + f_2 - \dfrac{l}{n}}$, where n is the refractive index of water.

94. $f = -n_1 n_2 \dfrac{R_1 R_2}{D}; \quad f' = n_2 n_3 \dfrac{R_1 R_2}{D},$

where

$$D = d(n_2 - n_1)(n_3 - n_2) + n_2[R_1(n_2 - n_3) + R_2(n_1 - n_2)],$$

$d = OO'$ (Fig. 57) is the lens thickness. On taking O and O' as origin, we have for the coordinates of the principal points H and H':

$$h = OH = -n_1(n_3 - n_2)\frac{R_1 d}{D};$$

$$h' = O'H' = n_3(n_2 - n_1)\frac{R_2 d}{D}.$$

95. The two principal planes coincide and pass through the centre of the sphere.

(1) $$f = -f' = \frac{R}{2}\frac{n}{n-1} = 2R,$$

the focal points lie outside the sphere at a distance R from its surface;

(2) $f = 1{\cdot}5R$; the focal points lie outside the sphere at a distance $\frac{1}{2}R$ from its surface.

The focal points do not lie outside for $n \geqslant 2$.

96. (1) $x' = 15$ cm. (2) The magnification is $y'/y = 1{\cdot}5$.

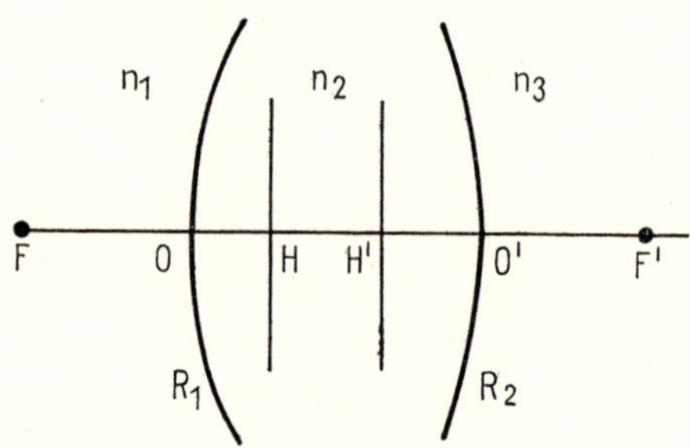

FIG. 57

97. For a plano-convex and plano-concave lens, i.e. when R_1 or $R_2 = \pm\infty$. If the light is incident from the side of the spherical surface, the position of the focus in the image space relative to the lens depends on the lens thickness; if incident from the plane side, it is independent of the thickness.

98. When the lens thickness $d > n(R_1 + R_2)/(n-1) = 3(R_1 + R_2)$, where R_1 and R_2 are the numerical values of the radii of curvature of the lens surfaces.

99. When the lens thickness $d = n(R_1 + R_2)/(n - 1)$, where R_1 and R_2 are the numerical values of the radii of curvature of the lens surfaces.

101. The principal points coincide with the lens centre. The focal planes are 28·2 cm from the lens in air and 37·5 cm from the lens in water. The nodal points coincide, and in water, are 9·3 cm from the lens.

102. $f = 50$ cm. (1) 148 cm from the plane surface; (2) 143 cm from the convex surface. In both cases the image is at the opposite side of the lens to the object.

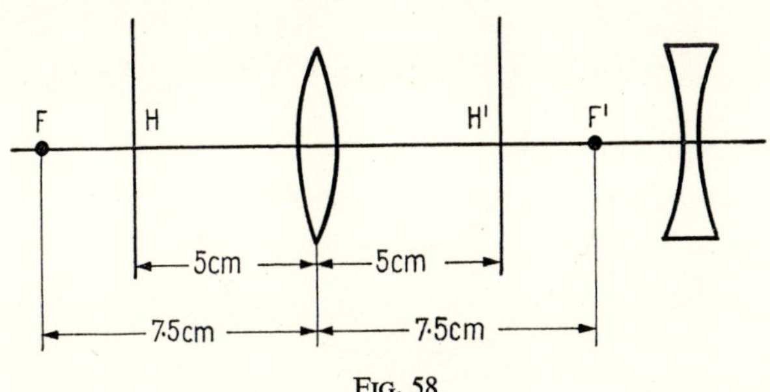

FIG. 58

103. $f = 6$ cm. The principal planes lie inside the lens at 1 cm and 1·6 cm from the lens surface with the greater radius of curvature.

104. $f = 2{\cdot}5$ cm. The positions of the focal points and principal planes are illustrated in Fig. 58.

105. No. This is only true when the nodal points coincide with the optical centre.

106. Convergent. The principal planes lie on the side of the convex surface at a distance d from one another. The first principal plane is a distance $R/(n - 1)$ from the convex surface. The second principal plane is at the same distance from the concave surface. $f = nR^2/(d(n - 1)^2)$.

107. Divergent. The principal planes coincide and pass through the common centre of curvature of the lens surfaces.

$$f = -\frac{nR(R - d)}{d(n - 1)}.$$

108. The object must be placed at one of the nodal inverse nodal points of the system.*

109. *Solution.* Let a small object, perpendicular to the cylinder generator, be placed at the outer surface of the cylinder at the point P (Fig. 59). After refraction of the rays at the inner cylindrical surface in the neighbourhood of the point A, an intermediate image of the object is obtained at some point P'. By using the formulae

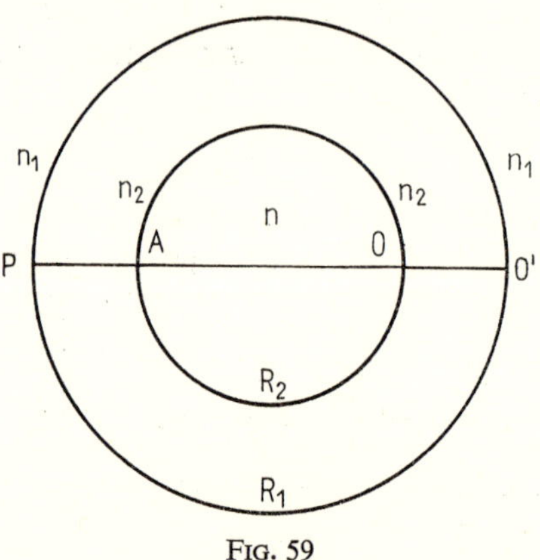

FIG. 59

derived in the answer to Problem 83, we can easily find the abscissa x' of the point P' (relative to the origin A), and also the transverse magnification y'/y:

$$x' = \frac{nR_2(R_2 - R_1)}{(n_2 - n)R_1 + nR_2};$$

$$\frac{y'}{y} = \frac{n_2R_2}{(n_2 - n)R_1 + nR_2}.$$

The remaining two refracting surfaces with vertices at O and O' act like a lens, for which

$$f = -nn_2\frac{R_1R_2}{D}; \quad h = n(n_1 - n_2)\frac{R_2(R_1 - R_2)}{D},$$

* If a light ray issues from a point of the optical axis at an angle u to it, and on leaving the system passes through the conjugate point at the angle $u' = -u$, these two conjugate points are called inverse nodal points of the system. By using the formulae of paraxial optics, it is easily shown that a centralised system has one pair of inverse nodal points.

where

$$D = n_1 R_1 (n_2 - n) + n R_2 (n_1 - n_2).$$

The point P' plays the role of object relative to this lens. Its abscissa relative to the focus F of the lens is

$$X = FP' = FH + HO + OA + AP' = f - h - 2R_2 + x'.$$

Further,

$$\frac{y_1}{y'} = \frac{f}{X},$$

so that

$$\frac{y}{y_1} = \frac{(n_2 - n)R_1 + nR_2}{n_2 R_2} \frac{X}{f},$$

whence the required result easily follows.

112. *Solution.* Obviously, $A = \xi' + e - \xi$, where ξ and ξ' are the coordinates of the object and its image relative to the corresponding principal planes. On eliminating ξ' from this and from the lens equation, we get

$$\xi^2 + (A - e)\xi + (A - e)f = 0.$$

If $A - e > 4f$, the equation has two real roots ξ_1 and ξ_2, and there are two positions of the object as mentioned in the problem. The distance between them is positive:

$$a = |\xi_1 - \xi_2| = \sqrt{(A - e)^2 - 4f(A - e)},$$

whence

$$f = \frac{(A - e)^2 - a^2}{4(A - e)} \approx \frac{A^2 - a^2}{4A} - \frac{A^2 + a^2}{4A^2} e.$$

To determine e, the experiment is repeated with another distance A_1 between the object and the screen.

113. $1/v + 1/u = 2/r + (1/r - 1/u)^2 h^2/r$. The distance h can be measured either along the arc, or along the perpendicular to the axis of the mirror, since the difference between these two distances can only affect higher order terms (namely, terms in h^4).

114. The longitudinal aberration is $(1/r - 1/u)^2 h^2/[r(2/r - 1/u)^2]$.

115. 0·2 mm; 0·8 mm; 1·8 mm; 3·2 mm.

116. 3·1 mm.

117. $\approx$ 0·3 mm.

119. The longitudinal spherical aberration is

$$v' - v = -\frac{n-1}{n^2}\left\{\left(\frac{1}{r_1} - \frac{1}{u}\right)^2\left(\frac{1}{r_1} - \frac{n+1}{u}\right) - \left(\frac{1}{r_2} - \frac{1}{v}\right)^2\left(\frac{1}{r_2} - \frac{n+1}{v}\right)\right\}\frac{v^2h^2}{2},$$

where v and v' are the coordinates of the points on the optical axis at which it is cut by the paraxial ray and the ray meeting the lens at a height h.

120. (1) $-0{\cdot}292$ cm; $-0{\cdot}0147$ cm. (2) $-1{\cdot}125$ cm; $-0{\cdot}056$ cm.

121. $f_{\text{red}} = 1015$ mm, $f_{\text{yel}} = 1000$ mm, $f_{\text{blue}} = 982$ mm, $\Delta f = 33$ mm.

122. $d_{\text{red}} = 0{\cdot}75$ mm, $d_{\text{blue}} = 0{\cdot}90$ mm.

123. $N = X'L/(f(X' - a)) = L(f + aX/f)$. The magnification is independent of the position of the eye and is equal to $N = L/f$, if $X = 0$, i.e. the object is placed at the principal focus of the magnifying glass; in this case the eye must be accommodated to infinity. The magnification is independent of the position of the object and is also equal to $N = L/f$, if $a = 0$, i.e. the eye is at the rear focus of the glass. When the eye is accommodated to the least distance for distinct vision, $X' = a - L$, $N = (L - a)/f$. The object is usually very close to the principal focus, so that in practice we always have $N = L/j$.

125. *Solution.* The focal length f of the system of two thin lenses at a distance l from one another is given by

$$\frac{1}{f} = \frac{1}{f_1} + \frac{1}{f_2} - \frac{l}{f_1 f_2}. \tag{1}$$

Here,

$$\frac{1}{f_1} = (n-1)A_1; \quad \frac{1}{f_2} = (n-1)A_2, \tag{2}$$

where A_1 and A_2 are constants that depend only on the curvatures of the lens surfaces. The achromatisation condition is

$$\delta\left(\frac{1}{f}\right) = \delta\left(\frac{1}{f_1}\right) + \delta\left(\frac{1}{f_2}\right) - \frac{l}{f_2}\delta\left(\frac{1}{f_1}\right) - \frac{l}{f_1}\delta\left(\frac{1}{f_2}\right) = 0.$$

On substituting in this

$$\delta\left(\frac{1}{f_1}\right) = A_1\delta n, \quad \delta\left(\frac{1}{f_2}\right) = A_2\delta n.$$

the solution is easily obtained.

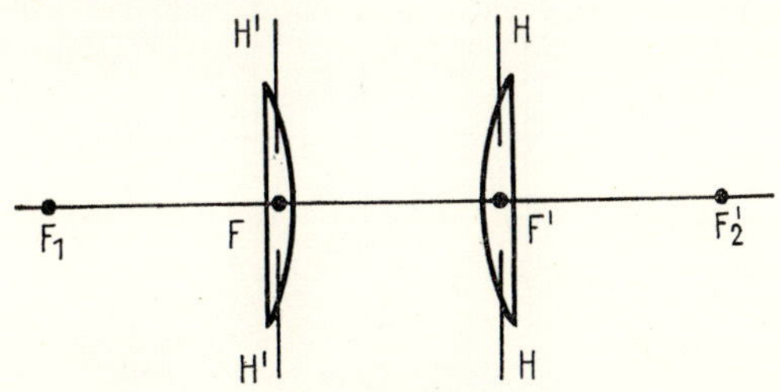

FIG. 60

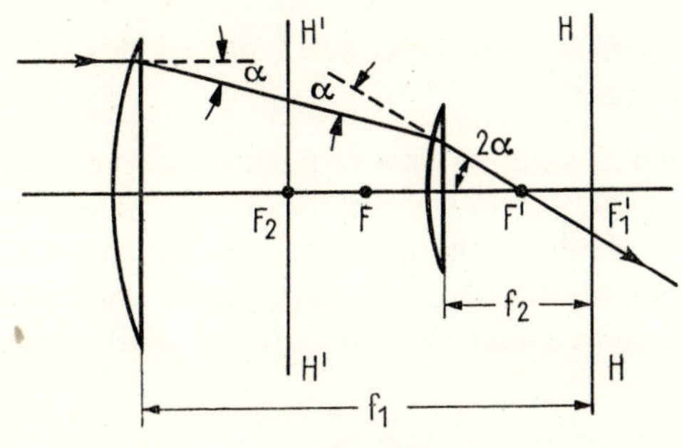

FIG. 61

126. $f = f_1 = f_2$. The positions of the principal planes and focal points are shown in Fig. 60.

127. $f_1 = 3f_2$; $l = \frac{1}{2}(f_1 + f_2) = 2f_2 = \frac{2}{3}f_1$; $f = \frac{3}{2}f_2 = \frac{1}{2}f_1$. The positions of the principal planes and focal points are shown in Fig. 61. The figure also shows the path of a ray incident on the Huygens eyepiece parallel to the principal optical axis.

129. $f = \frac{3}{4} f_1$. The positions of the principal planes and focal points are shown in Fig. 62. The cross-hair lines must be in front of the first lens at a distance $\frac{1}{4} f_1$ from it.

130. $$\frac{1}{f_1} \frac{\delta n_1}{n_1 - 1} + \frac{1}{f_2} \frac{\delta n_2}{n_2 - 1} = 0.$$

The focal lengths of the two components always have opposite signs. If the system as a whole is convergent, the lens with the greater dispersion is divergent, and that with the lesser dispersion is convergent. Conversely, if the system is divergent, the lens with the greater dispersion must be convergent, and that with the lesser dispersion divergent.

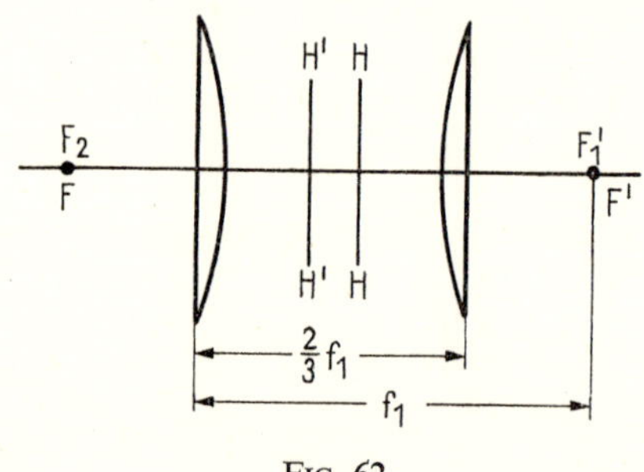

FIG. 62

131. *Solution.* The object glass of a telescope, binocular, ... is always a convergent system. Hence the double convex lens of the system must be made of the material with the smaller dispersion (i.e. crown glass), and the plano-concave of material with the greater dispersion (i.e. flint glass) (see the solution of the previous problem).

132. The first lens: $r_1 = 41{\cdot}6$ cm; $r_2 = -41{\cdot}3$ cm; the second lens: $r_1 = -41{\cdot}3$ cm; $r_2 = \infty$.

133. This is possible for a thick lens because the formula for its focal length contains n^2. Thus there can be two values n_1 and n_2 corresponding to one value of f. The lens thickness should be equal to $d = n^2(R_1 - R_2)/(n^2 - 1)$, where $n = \sqrt{n_1 n_2}$ is the geometric mean of n_1 and n_2. Since the thickness is essentially positive, the necessary condition for achromatisation is that $R_1 - R_2 > 0$. This condition is only satisfied by double convex and convexo-concave lenses. No other thick lens can be achromatised.

134. The result follows from the formula

$$f = -f' = (n+1)R_1R_2/(n-1)(R_2 - R_1),$$

giving the focal lengths of the lens for the refractive index $n = \sqrt{n_1 n_2}$.

135. $d = 31{\cdot}42$ cm; $f = -f' = +20{\cdot}2$ cm.

137. The plate must be turned through the angle

$$\beta = (n_F - n_C)/\alpha(n-1) + \tfrac{1}{2}\alpha = 1{\cdot}8°,$$

so that the violet end of the spectrum is closer to the object than the red.

138. *Solution.* If a light ray AB is incident on the surface of the sphere at an angle φ and is refracted at the angle ψ (Fig. 63), the angle of incidence BCO of the refracted ray BC at this surface is equal to ψ. It follows from this that the ray leaves the sphere at an angle φ to the normal OC.

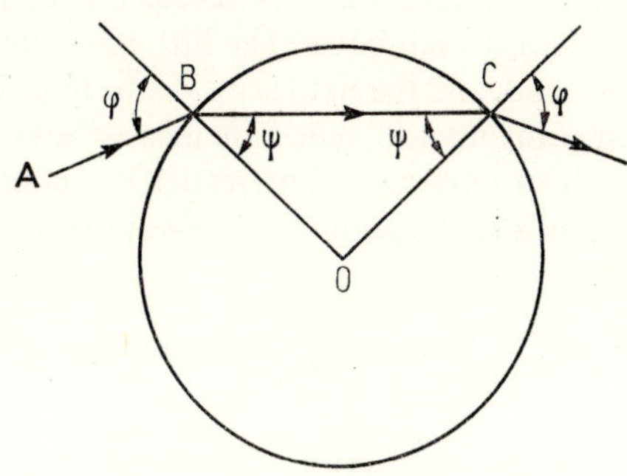

FIG. 63

139. In the case of a single reflection,

$$\cos\varphi = \sqrt{\frac{n^2-1}{3}}; \quad \alpha = 4\psi - 2\varphi,$$

where ψ is the angle of refraction in the drop, $\alpha_{red} = 42°42'$; $\alpha_{viol} = 40°44'$. In the case of double reflection,

$$\cos\varphi = \sqrt{\frac{n^2-1}{8}}; \quad \alpha = 180° + 2\varphi - 6\psi;$$

$$\alpha_{red} = 49°46'; \quad \alpha_{viol} = 53°29'.$$

140. $\cos\varphi = \sqrt{\dfrac{n^2 - 1}{N(N+2)}}$; $\delta = N\pi + 2\varphi - 2(N+1)\psi$.

The rainbows of orders 3–6 have the following characteristic data:

Order of rainbow	φ	ψ	δ	α
3	76°55′	47°04′	317°20′	42°40′
4	79°41′	47°42′	42°20′	42°40′
5	81°29′	48°02′	126°30′	53°30′
6	82°40′	48°14′	210°00′	30°00′

The third and fourth rainbows are behind the observer when his face is turned to the first rainbow. If a cloud comes between the observer and the sun, he sees the drops as strongly illuminated by the rays which are refracted in the drop without internal reflection. The intensity of these rays substantially exceeds the intensity of the rays of the third and fourth rainbows. The fifth bow almost exactly coincides with the second, and the sixth is inside the first. These bows are never visible since any internal reflection means that the intensity is reduced as a result of refraction. The reader is recommended to make accurate diagrams of the path of the ray in the drop for bows of the first six orders.

141. 21°52′; 45°44′. In both circles the outer edge is bluish, and the inner reddish.

142. *Solution.* We imagine a series of plane-parallel layers with constant refractive indices $n_1, n_2, n_3, \ldots,$ (Fig. 64). In view of the law of refraction, the following relations hold when light travels in a stratified medium of this type:

$$n_1 \sin\alpha_1 = n_2 \sin\alpha_2 = n_3 \sin\alpha_3 = \cdots$$

Now let the number of layers increase indefinitely and the thickness of each diminish indefinitely. We obtain in the limit a non-uniform medium with constantly varying refractive index. If the change in the refractive index is small over the light wave, the effects of reflection at the layer boundaries can be neglected. The light travels along curved rays in such a medium. We take as the z axis a straight line perpendicular to the layers, and write α for the angle between the z axis and the tangent to the ray, whilst N denotes the normal to the ray (Fig. 65). Now,

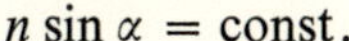

$$n \sin \alpha = \text{const.}$$

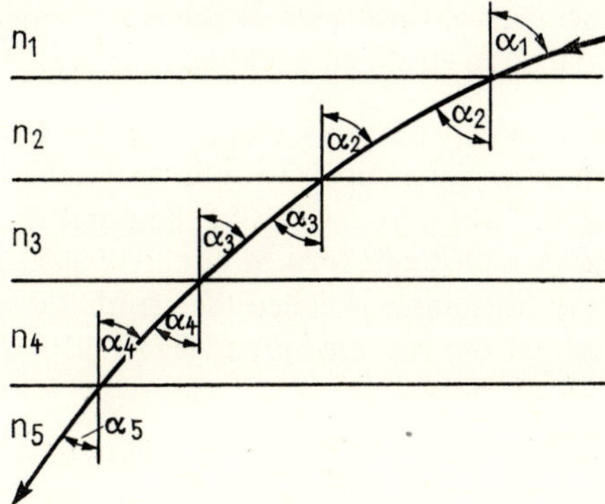

FIG. 64

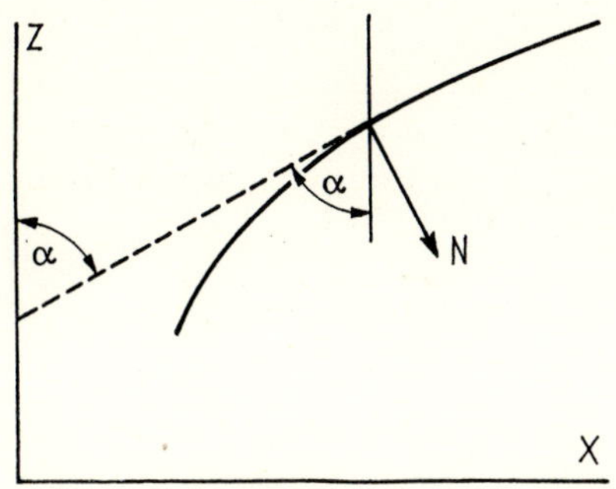

FIG. 65

On differentiating this relationship with respect to the length of arc s of the ray and recalling that $1/\varrho = d\alpha/ds$, we get

$$\frac{1}{\varrho} = -\frac{\sin \alpha}{n \cos \alpha} \frac{dn}{ds}.$$

Since

$$\frac{dn}{ds} = \frac{dn}{dz} \cos \alpha, \qquad \frac{dn}{dN} = -\frac{dn}{dz} \sin \alpha,$$

we have

$$\frac{1}{\varrho} = \frac{1}{n}\frac{dn}{dN} = \frac{d}{dN}(\ln n).$$

The formula has been obtained for a stratified medium. But it still holds in the general case, since a small volume of any medium can be regarded as part of a stratified medium. (See also Problem 152.)

143. *Solution.* If n depends only on r, the path AM of the light ray (Fig. 66) will be a plane curve, lying in the plane which passes through the star and the vertical MZ at the point of observation. Let α denote the variable angle formed by the vertical MZ with the tangent to the ray (this angle is called the zenithal distance). Let s denote the length of the ray measured from the point M. Now:

$$\frac{1}{\varrho} = \frac{d\alpha}{ds} = \frac{d}{dN}(\ln n); \quad \frac{d\alpha}{ds} = \frac{d\alpha}{dr}\frac{dr}{ds} = \frac{d\alpha}{dr}\sin\gamma = \frac{d\alpha}{dr}\cos(\alpha - \beta);$$

$$\frac{d}{dN}(\ln n) = -\frac{d}{dr}(\ln n)\cos\gamma = -\frac{d}{dr}(\ln n)\sin(\alpha - \beta).$$

Hence

$$\frac{d\alpha}{dr}\frac{1}{\tan(\alpha - \beta)} = -\frac{d}{dr}(\ln n). \tag{1}$$

Further, from Fig. 66:

$$d\beta = \frac{ds}{r}\cos\gamma = \frac{ds}{r}\sin(\alpha - \beta),$$

whence

$$\frac{d\beta}{ds} = \frac{d\beta}{dr}\frac{dr}{ds} = \frac{d\beta}{dr}\cos(\alpha - \beta) = \frac{1}{r}\sin(\alpha - \beta).$$

Thus

$$\frac{d\beta}{dr}\frac{1}{\tan(\alpha - \beta)} = \frac{1}{r}. \tag{2}$$

On subtracting (2) from (1), we find that

$$\frac{d(\alpha - \beta)}{\tan(\alpha - \beta)} = -d\ln(nr).$$

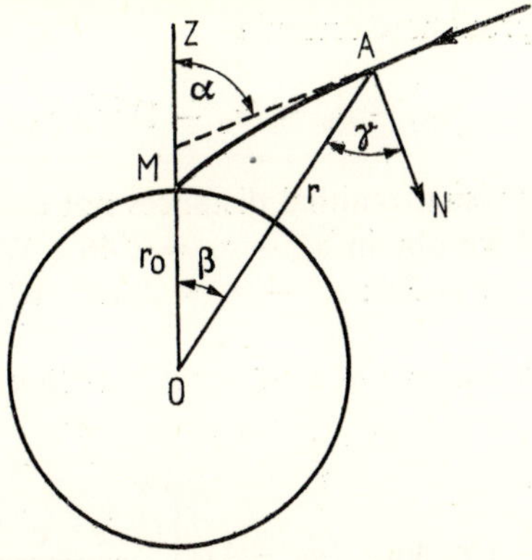

FIG. 66

Integration of this equation gives

$$\frac{\sin(\alpha - \beta)}{\sin \alpha_0} = \frac{n_0 r_0}{nr}, \tag{3}$$

where r_0 is the radius of the terrestrial sphere, n_0 is the refractive index of the air at the earth's surface, α_0 is the visual zenithal distance of the star when observed from the point M. On calculating $\tan(\alpha - \beta)$ from (3) and substituting the result in (1), we find after integration:

$$\alpha_\infty - \alpha_0 = -n_0 r_0 \sin \alpha_0 \int_{r_0}^{\infty} \frac{d \ln n}{dr} \frac{dr}{\sqrt{n^2 r^2 - n_0^2 r_0^2 \sin^2 \alpha_0}}. \tag{4}$$

Here α_∞ is the angle formed by the asymptote to the ray with the vertical at the point of observation. The difference $\alpha_\infty - \alpha_0$ gives the angle of deviation of the direction of the ray on passing through the earth's atmosphere and is known as the refraction. If we know the law of variation of the refractive index n with the height and measure the visual zenithal distance α_0 of the star, we can calculate from (4) the refraction $\alpha_\infty - \alpha_0$.*

* All the accurate tables of refraction have been compiled by using (4). The refractive index of the air has to be known as a function of the height. It is determined from the variation of the air density δ with the height. In the older theories, the formula $n^2 - 1 = A\delta$ was used, where A is a constant. In more recent theories, the formula $n - 1 = A\delta$ is used, since experiment shows that it leads to a more accurate dependence of n on ϱ. The first refraction tables were compiled by Bessel, who took the law $n^2 - 1 = A\delta$. At the present time the Pulkovo tables compiled by Gil'den are used almost exclusively throughout the world.

145. The approximate formula

$$\alpha_\infty - \alpha_0 = (n_0 - 1)\tan\alpha_0$$

can be used for visual zenithal distances not exceeding about 75°. When $\alpha_0 = 70°$ we obtain $\alpha_\infty - \alpha_0 = 2'46''$. We find in the Pulkovo tables for $\alpha_0 = 70°$: $\alpha_\infty - \alpha_0 = 2'45'' \cdot 673$.

146. *Solution.* Since $(n - 1) \ll 1$, we have $\ln n = \ln[1 + (n-1)] \approx n - 1$.

Now,

$$\alpha_\infty - \alpha_0 = \frac{Mg}{RT} n_0 r_0 \sin\alpha_0 (n_0 - 1) \int_{r_0}^{\infty} \frac{e^{-\frac{Mg}{RT}(r - r_0)}}{\sqrt{n^2 r^2 - n_0^2 r_0^2 \sin^2\alpha_0}}\, dr,$$

where M is the molecular weight of air, R is the gas constant, T the absolute temperature. The expression under the square root can be replaced by the approximate expression:

$$n^2 r^2 - n_0^2 r_0^2 \sin^2\alpha_0 = (nr + n_0 r_0 \sin\alpha_0)(nr - n_0 r_0 \sin\alpha_0)$$

$$\approx n_0^2 r_0 (1 + \sin\alpha_0)(r - r_0 \sin\alpha_0).$$

Now,

$$\alpha_\infty - \alpha_0 = 2(n_0 - 1) x_0 \tan\alpha_0 \int_{x_0}^{\infty} e^{-(x^2 - x_0^2)}\, dx,$$

where

$$x_0^2 = \frac{Mgr_0}{RT}(1 - \sin\alpha_0).$$

The values of

$$\Phi(x_0) = \frac{2}{\sqrt{\pi}} \int_0^{x_0} e^{-x^2}\, dx,$$

which is known as the error function, may be found in special tables.

147. $\alpha_\infty - \alpha_0 = \sqrt{\dfrac{\pi M g r_0}{2RT}}\,(n_0 - 1) = 35'29''.$

148. 33000 km; $1{\cdot}6 \times 10^{-9}$ cm^{-1}.

149. *Solution*. Let the circle K of radius ϱ (Fig. 67) be the path of the light ray in the medium, the refractive index n of which depends only on the distance r from the point O. Now,

$$\frac{1}{\varrho} = \frac{d}{dN}(\ln n) = -\frac{d}{dr}(\ln n) \cos \vartheta .$$

Let b denote the distance OA between the point O and the centre A of the circle K. Now,

$$b^2 = r^2 + \varrho^2 - 2r\varrho \cos \vartheta .$$

If we find $\cos \vartheta$ from this and substitute the result in the previous equation, we get

$$d(\ln n) = -\frac{2rdr}{r^2 + \varrho^2 - b^2},$$

whence

$$n = \frac{C}{r^2 + \varrho^2 - b^2}, \tag{1}$$

where C is an arbitrary constant.

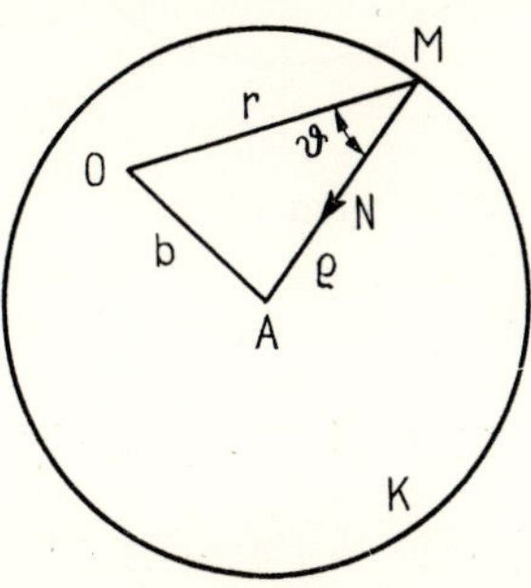

Fig. 67

We take an arbitrary point P on the circle K and continue the straight line PO to its intersection with the circle K at the point P' (Fig. 68). We erect a perpendicular CD to the straight line PP' through its mid-point A_0. Taking an arbitrary point A_1 of this perpendicular as centre, we describe a circle K_1 of radius ϱ_1 through the point P (and hence also through P'). In order for the light ray to describe the circle K_1, the refractive index of the medium must vary in accordance with the law:

$$n = \frac{C_1}{r^2 + \varrho_1^2 - b_1^2}, \tag{2}$$

where b_1 denotes the distance A_1O, and C_1 is an arbitrary constant. Let us show that formulae (1) and (2) are identical. We show first of all that

$$\varrho^2 - b^2 = \varrho_1^2 - b_1^2.$$

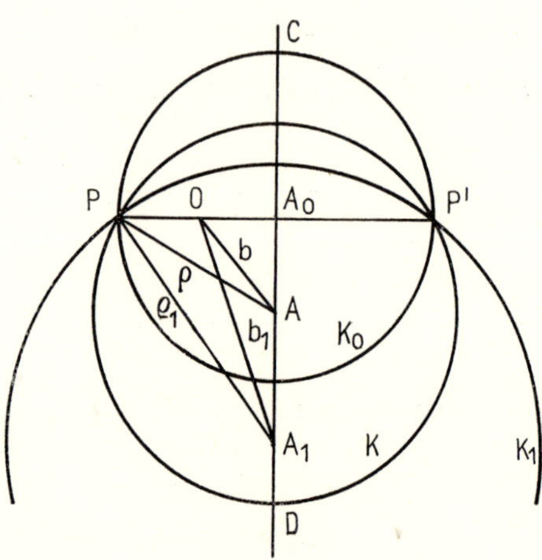

FIG. 68

We have from the right-angled triangles AOA_0 and APA_0:

$$\varrho^2 = PA_0^2 + AA_0^2; \quad b^2 = A_0O^2 + AA_0^2,$$

whence

$$\varrho^2 - b^2 = PA_0^2 - A_0O^2.$$

Similarly, from the right-angled triangles A_1PA_0 and A_1OA_0:

$$\varrho_1^2 - b_1^2 = PA_0^2 - A_0O^2.$$

On comparing this with the previous expression, we obtain the required result. We can therefore put

$$\varrho^2 - b^2 = \varrho_1^2 - b_1^2 = a^2.$$

We now explain the physical meaning of the constants C, C_1.

On putting $r = 0$ in (1) and (2) and writing n_0 for the refractive index of the medium at the point O, we find that $C = C_1 = n_0 a^2$. This means that (1) and (2) are identical, and can be rewritten as

$$n = \frac{n_0}{1 + \frac{r^2}{a^2}}. \tag{3}$$

If the refractive index varies according to (3), the ray issuing from P describes a circle whose centre lies on the straight line CD. The position of the centre on this line depends on the direction of the ray at P. But whatever the direction of the ray at P, it always passes through P'. Thus all the rays issuing from P converge at P'. In other words, P' is the stigmatic image of the point P. Any point of the medium possesses the same properties. For we can take as the circle K any circle of the family with centres on CD that pass through P, whilst we can take P wherever we like on the circle K. The magnification given by the "fish eye" for any object may easily be found from the construction.

150. $\varrho = a$.

151. No.

Solution. Formally, the motion of a particle in a conservative field of force is like the propagation of a light ray in a non-uniform isotropic medium. The role of the refractive index is played by the particle velocity v. Thus, if the "fish eye" were to be realisable in electron optics, the electron velocity v in the field would have to be given by

$$v = \frac{v_0}{1 + \frac{r^2}{a^2}}.$$

On the other hand, by the law of conservation of energy,

$$\frac{mv^2}{2} + eV = \text{const},$$

where V is the field potential. Using this and the previous relationship, we can express V as a function of r. It turns out that this function does not satisfy Laplace's equation

$$\nabla^2 V \equiv \frac{\partial^2 V}{\partial x^2} + \frac{\partial^2 V}{\partial y^2} + \frac{\partial^2 V}{\partial z^2} = 0.$$

It follows from this that it is impossible to obtain a "fish eye" by means of electrostatic field in a vacuum. The presence of a space charge is required for this.

152. *Solution.* The radius of curvature ϱ of the particle trajectory is found from the expression for the centripetal acceleration:

$$\frac{mv^2}{\varrho} = F_N,$$

where F_N is the component of the force along the principal normal to the trajectory. If U is the potential energy of the particle, we have $F_N = -\partial U/\partial N$. On the other hand, by the law of conservation of energy,

$$\frac{mv^2}{2} + U = \text{const},$$

whence

$$mv\frac{\partial v}{\partial N} = -\frac{\partial U}{\partial N}.$$

Consequently,

$$\frac{1}{\varrho} = \frac{1}{v}\frac{\partial v}{\partial N}.$$

If we replace the particle velocity v here by the refractive index n of the medium, we obtain the required formula for the curvature of the ray:

$$\frac{1}{\varrho} = \frac{1}{n}\frac{\partial n}{\partial N} = \frac{\partial}{\partial N}(\ln n).$$

153. *Solution.* On replacing n by v in the formula for the ray curvature, we obtain:

$$\frac{1}{\varrho} = \frac{\partial}{\partial N}(\ln v).$$

By the law of conservation of energy,

$$\frac{mv^2}{2} + eV = \text{const}, \quad e < 0, \quad V > 0,$$

where, since the potential is normalised, const = 0, inasmuch as $v = 0$ at $V = 0$. Hence,

$$2 \ln v = \ln V + \text{const}, \qquad \frac{1}{\varrho} = \frac{1}{2}\frac{\partial}{\partial N}(\ln V) = \frac{1}{2V}\frac{\partial V}{\partial N} = -\frac{E_N}{2V}.$$

154. *Solution.* The input pupil of the system will be a reduced image of the pupil of the eye, located at the aplanatic point P'. The limiting aplanatic point P will be the centre of the input pupil. Let the plane AB, perpendicular to the optical axis, be situated in front of the aplanatic point P at a distance a from the latter, which is large compared with the input pupil diameter. We consider the image of the plane AB, given by the objective. A cone of rays of only very small angle, determined by the size of the input pupil, can pass through the optical system from every point of the plane AB. Since these rays are not paraxial, but in general are inclined at large angles to the optical axis, the beams will be astigmatic. In what follows we shall neglect the astigmatism, and also the distortion of the image plane. In this approximation the plane AB has as its image the conjugate plane $A'B'$, perpendicular to the optical axis, and the image of a point can be constructed in the following way:

We draw from the point A of the plane AB the ray AP through the centre of the input pupil, at an angle u to the optical axis. The conjugate ray $A'P'$ now passes through the second aplanatic point P' at an angle u', the value of which is given by the sines condition: $nl \sin u = n'l' \sin u'$. The point of intersection of this ray with the plane $A'B'$ is in fact the image of the point A. Let y and z be the coordinates of A in the plane AB, and y', z' the coordinates of A'. In this case

$$\sin u = \sqrt{\frac{y^2 + z^2}{a^2 + y^2 + z^2}}, \qquad \sin u' = \sqrt{\frac{y'^2 + z'^2}{a'^2 + y'^2 + z'^2}},$$

where a' is the distance of the point P' from the plane $A'B'$. On substituting these expressions in the sines condition and introducing the notation $\alpha = nl/n'l'$, we get

$$\alpha^2(y^2 + z^2)(a'^2 + y'^2 + z'^2) = (y'^2 + z'^2)(a^2 + y^2 + z^2).$$

In view of the axial symmetry of the system, $z'/y' = z/y$. On eliminating z' with the aid of these relationships, we find that

$$[\alpha^2(a'^2 + y'^2) - y'^2]y^2 - y'^2(1 - \alpha^2)z^2 = a^2y'^2.$$

Let us take the straight line $y' = \pm p$, parallel to the z axis, in the plane $A'B'$. It corresponds in the plane AB to the curve

$$[\alpha^2 a'^2 - p^2(1-\alpha^2)]y^2 - p^2(1-\alpha^2)z^2 = a^2 p^2,$$

the image of which is the straight line in question. Since α is small for microscope objectives, we can neglect α^2 by comparison with unity; if we do this and introduce the notation $\omega = p/\alpha a' = pl'n'/a'ln$, we get

$$\frac{y^2}{\dfrac{a^2\omega^2}{1-\omega^2}} - \frac{z^2}{a^2} = 1. \tag{1}$$

If $\omega^2 < 1$, (1) is the equation of a family of hyperbolas. Similarly, the family of straight lines $z' = \pm p$ parallel to the y axis corresponds to the family of hyperbolas

$$-\frac{y^2}{a^2} + \frac{z^2}{\dfrac{a^2\omega^2}{1-\omega^2}} = 1, \tag{2}$$

which may be obtained from (1) by a rotation through 90° about the optical axis. If the two families (1) and (2) are drawn on a sheet of paper and the sheet placed at a distance a in front of the forward aplanatic point P of the objective, the image given by the objective is a rectangular net of straight lines. When $\omega = 1/\sqrt{2}$, (1) becomes $y^2 - z^2 = a^2$, whilst (2) becomes $z^2 - y^2 = a^2$. These hyperbolas have as asymptotes the bisectors of the coordinate quadrants. Thus a is the distance from the origin to the vertex of the hyperbola whose asymptotes coincide with the bisectors of the coordinate quadrants.

155. $a \approx 7$ mm.

156. *Solution.* The necessity is obvious. We shall prove the sufficiency. We join P and P' by an arbitrary ray. Let l_1, l_2 be two infinitesimal non-colinear vectors through the point P, for which the cosines condition is satisfied. The differences

$$n'(s' \cdot l_1') - n(s \cdot l) = H_1, \quad n'(s' \cdot l_2') - n(s \cdot l_2) = H_2 \qquad (1)$$

are now independent of the direction of the ray joining P, P'; but they can evidently be dependent on the directions of the vectors l_1,

l_2. An arbitrary vector $\boldsymbol{l}$ through P in the object plane can be resolved along vectors $\boldsymbol{l}_1$ and $\boldsymbol{l}_2$; $\boldsymbol{l} = a\boldsymbol{l}_1 + b\boldsymbol{l}_2$, where a and b are naturally independent of s. We introduce the vector $\boldsymbol{l}' = a\boldsymbol{l}_1' + b\boldsymbol{l}_2'$, multiply (1) by a and b and add. We get

$$n'(\boldsymbol{s}' \cdot \boldsymbol{l}') - n(\boldsymbol{s} \cdot \boldsymbol{l}) = H, \tag{2}$$

where $H = aH_1 + bH_2$. It is clear from this that the difference (2) is independent of s, i.e. the cosines condition is satisfied for any vector $\boldsymbol{l}$ through P in the object plane. Thus the optical system gives a stigmatic image of this (plane) object.

157. *Solution.* We take the directions of $\boldsymbol{l}_1, \boldsymbol{l}_2$ as the x and y axes in the object space, and their point of intersection as the origin. A similar role is played in the image space by the conjugate segments $\boldsymbol{l}_1', \boldsymbol{l}_2'$. The coordinates x, y of any point of the object area will now be connected with the coordinates x', y' of the conjugate point of the image area by formulae of the form

$$x' = Ax, \quad y' = By, \tag{1}$$

where A and B are constants. For, inasmuch as the areas are infinitesimal, the coordinates x', y' must be linearly expressible in

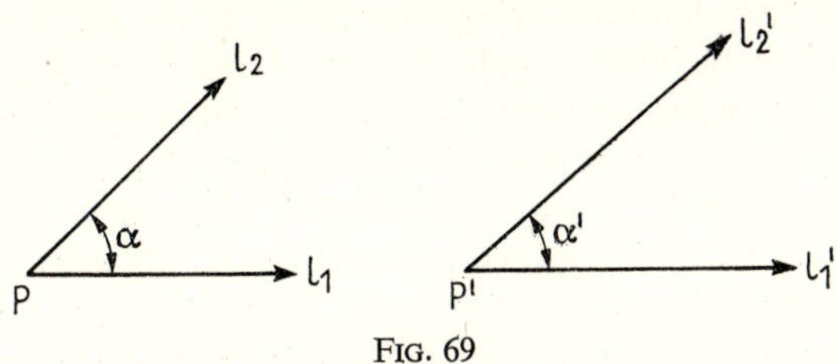

FIG. 69

terms of x and y. This connection must be of the form (1), since the x' axis is the image of the x axis, and the y' axis the image of the y axis.

By hypothesis, rays issuing from P (Fig. 69) in the directions $\boldsymbol{l}_1, \boldsymbol{l}_2$ lie in the field of the instrument. In the image space they travel in the directions of the conjugate segments $\boldsymbol{l}_1', \boldsymbol{l}_2'$. Let us first take the image of segment $\boldsymbol{l}_1$. We take two rays issuing from B in the directions $\boldsymbol{l}_2$ and $\boldsymbol{l}_1$. We can write on the basis of the cosines theorem:

$$nl_1 \cos \alpha - n'l_1' \cos \alpha' = nl_1 - n'l_1', \tag{2}$$

where α is the angle between $\boldsymbol{l}_1$ and $\boldsymbol{l}_2$, and α' is the angle between the conjugate segments $\boldsymbol{l}'_1$, $\boldsymbol{l}'_2$. Similarly, by considering the image of $\boldsymbol{l}_2$, we obtain

$$nl_2 \cos \alpha - n'l'_2 \cos \alpha' = nl_2 - n'l'_2. \tag{3}$$

Suppose that $l_1 = l_2$. We show that now $l'_1 = l'_2$. In fact, on subtracting (3) from (2), we get

$$n'l'_1(1 - \cos \alpha') = n'l'_2(1 - \cos \alpha'). \tag{4}$$

Since $\alpha \neq 0$ by hypothesis, α' is also $\neq 0$. Hence, by (4), $l'_1 = l'_2$, which is what we wished to prove. It follows from what has been proved that $\boldsymbol{l}_1$ and $\boldsymbol{l}_2$ are equally magnified by the optical system. Thus, in the case in question, $A = B$ in (1), so that the magnification of any segment in the object plane is independent of its direction. Hence it follows that similitude is preserved in forming the image.

But this latter means that angles are preserved. Hence $\alpha = \alpha'$, and (2) gives $nl_1 = n'l'_1$. All in all, for any segment l in the plane of the object,

$$nl = n'l', \quad \frac{l'}{l} = \frac{n}{n'}, \tag{5}$$

and the second part of the theorem is proved.

Thus the fact that areas lying tangentially to the instrument field produce stigmatic images implies a fully defined magnification n/n'. In particular, when the refractive indices of the object and image spaces are the same, this magnification is unity. But if the areas are not tangential to the instrument field, it is possible to obtain stigmatic images with different magnifications. To quote an example, an area forms an image by refraction at the surface of a sphere, and the area is perpendicular to the optical axis and passes through one of the aplanatic points of the sphere (see Problem 78).

158. The theorem is an immediate consequence of the theorem proved in the previous problem.

159. The theorem is proved in the same way as the similar theorem stated in Problem 156.

160. *Solution.* In the case when spatial elements give stigmatic images, there always exist three segments $\boldsymbol{l}_1$, $\boldsymbol{l}_2$, $\boldsymbol{l}_3$, not coplanar and tangential to the instrument field. On repeating the arguments adduced in the case of surface elements (Problem 157), we arrive at the conclusion that these three segments form images with the same magnification. The theorem in question easily follows from this, on the same lines as when solving Problem 157.

161. *Solution.* Let P, P' be a pair of conjugate points. We first prove the theorem for the particular case when the other pair of conjugate points Q, Q' lie on one of the rays joining P and P', for instance the ray PQP' (Fig. 70). We join P and P' by an arbitrary ray PAP'. Since P, P' are conjugate points, we have $(PAP') = (PQP')$. But since $P'Q'$ is obviously the optical image of PQ, it follows from the theorem proved in the previous problem that $(PQ) = (P'Q')$. On combining these two equations, we get $(PAP') = (QP'Q')$, which is what we wanted to prove.

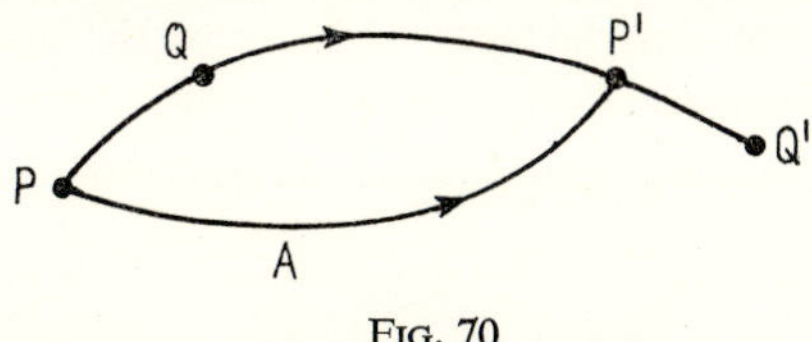

FIG. 70

The general case can be reduced to the above particular case if we notice that the arbitrary points P, Q can always be joined by a piecewise smooth curve, the individual parts of which are rays. This last assertion follows at once from the Heine–Borel lemma, if we use the fact that any point of space in an absolute optical instrument corresponds to a cone of rays of finite angle, convergent to the conjugate point.

162. Through an arbitrary point O of the object space we draw three non-coplanar rays lying in the instrument field. In the image space these three rays intersect at the conjugate point O'. We take these rays as the coordinate axes in the object and image spaces. The axes of one coordinate system are now the images of the axes of the other coordinate system. It can be assumed without loss of generality that the x axes are conjugates, and similarly for the y and z axes. In this case, given a suitable choice of the positive directions of the axes, the coordinates of conjugate points will be related by

$$x' = \frac{n}{n'}x, \quad y' = \frac{n}{n'}y, \quad z' = \frac{n}{n'}z$$

(see the solutions of Problems 157 and 160). When n, n' are constant, these relations must hold not only for infinitesimal regions, but also for the entire object space and the entire image space. We conclude from this that the instrument is a telescopic system, in which the image of a straight line is always a straight line.

163. *Solution.* We take the case of one refracting surface. If the point-object is on this surface, its image will be at the same point. We conclude from this, and the theorem proved in Problem 161, that the optical length of the ray joining any two conjugate points P, P' must be zero (thus if P is a real luminous point, its image will be virtual). The only case when this condition is satisfied for any position of the point P is that of reflection from a plane mirror.

The case of several refracting surfaces, or of a combination of refracting and reflecting surfaces, reduces to the above case of a single refracting surface.

164. See the proof of the previous theorem.

§ 2. Photometry

165. $h = \dfrac{\sqrt{2}}{2}$ m.

166. The exact value of the illumination is $E = I/(R^2 + d^2)$, where I is the intensity of the disc and d the distance from the disc. When $d = 10R$, $E = I/1{\cdot}01d^2$.

167. $I_\vartheta = I_0/\cos^3\vartheta$, where ϑ is the angle between the ray and the vertical.

168. The surface brightness of the sphere is the same everywhere, except at the place where the parallel pencil is incident.

169. The image brightness is roughly proportional to the ratio of the mirror aperture area to the focal length.

170. *Solution.* Let S be the visual area of the headlamp, B its surface brightness, and r the distance of the lamp from the observer's eye. The light flux transmitted by the lamp to the eye is given by

$$\Phi = \frac{BS\sigma}{r^2},$$

where σ is the pupil area. If S' is the area of the image on the retina, the illumination E of the retina is

$$E = \frac{\Phi}{S'} = B\frac{\sigma}{r^2}\frac{S}{S'}.$$

The ratio S'/S is the square of the magnification given by the eye, and is equal to $(d/nr)^2$, where d is the depth of the eye, and n is the refractive index of the vitreous humour. Thus

$$E = B\frac{\sigma}{r^2}\left(\frac{nr}{d}\right)^2 = B\frac{\sigma n^2}{d^2},$$

i.e. the illumination of the retina is independent of the distance from the lamp (see the solution of Problem 184). We judge the surface brightness of the lamp from the retina illumination. Since the latter is independent of the distance from the lamp, identical lamps at different distances from the eye must appear equally bright. This conclusion holds if absorption of the light in the air can be neglected, as has been done in the above working. When there is absorption, the lamp appears brighter, the closer to the eye.

When the lamp is fairly remote from the eye, the size of its image on the retina is independent of the distance away because of diffraction. Thus (neglecting absorption) the illumination of the retina now varies inversely with the square of the distance from the lamp.

171. $E = \pi B$.

172. $\alpha_1 = \arctan\frac{k_2}{k_1}, \quad \alpha_2 = \arctan\frac{k_1}{k_2}$.

173. $B = \frac{4}{\pi}\left(\frac{R}{D}\right)^2 E = 1{\cdot}5 \times 10^5$ stilb.

174. $E = \frac{\pi B}{k} = 11 \times 10^4$ lux.

175. $E = E_0\frac{\pi D^2}{4f^2\alpha^2} = 2{\cdot}58 \times 10^8$ lux.

176. The illumination is reduced 16/9 times.

177. Roughly $(1 - 2h/D)n/(n - \sqrt{n^2 - 1}) = 3{\cdot}4$ times.

178. $B = B'$ (see the solution of Problem 184).

179. The image brightness in the first case is independent of the lens diameter, and in the second case is proportional to the square of the diameter (for paraxial rays).

180. (1) 1; (2) 1; (3) 0·25. In general, the brightness $B = 1$ for $N \leqslant D/d$ and $B = (D/Nd)^2$ for $N \geqslant D/d$, where N is the magnification of the telescope, D is the diameter of the object glass, and d the diameter of the pupil of the eye.

181. $D = 100$ mm.

182. (1) Fourteenth; (2) sixty times; (3) ninth-tenth.

183. Twentieth.

184. *Solution.* We take any optical system, the final element of which is the eye. Let the system satisfy the sines condition

$$ny \sin u = n'y' \sin u'. \tag{1}$$

where y and y' are the linear dimensions of the object and its image on the retina, n and n' are the refractive indices of the object space

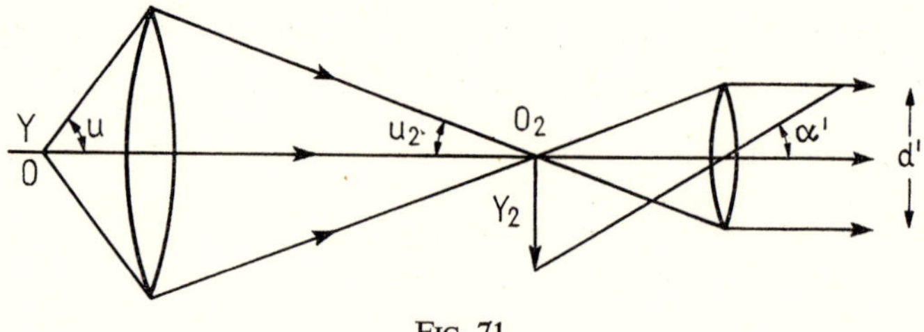

FIG. 71

and the vitreous humour (the eye and the image on the retina are not shown in Fig. 71). Condition (1) must be satisfied for any ray of slope u, but in future we shall understand by u the angle between the optical axis and the extreme rays capable of passing through the system and striking the retina.

If the object brightness B is constant, the light flux passing through the system is

$$\Phi = BS \int_0^u \cos\vartheta \, 2\pi \sin\vartheta \, d\vartheta = \pi BS \sin^2 u,$$

where S is the area of the object. The light flux incident on the eye is

$$\Phi' = B'S' \int_0^{u'} \cos\vartheta \cdot 2\pi \sin\vartheta \, d\vartheta = \pi B'S' \sin^2 u',$$

where B' is the image brightness, and S' is the image area. If we neglect the light lost in passing through the system, we have $\Phi = \Phi'$. Since $S \sim y^2$, $S' \sim y'^2$, we obtain from this and (1):

$$\frac{B}{n^2} = \frac{B'}{n'^2}. \tag{2}$$

A subjective or visual estimate of the brightness is determined by the illumination of the retina:

$$E = \frac{\Phi'}{S'} = \pi B' \sin^2 u' = \pi B \frac{n'^2}{n^2} \sin^2 u'. \tag{3}$$

Let us find the width d' of the beam issuing from O at the angle u, directly behind the eyepiece. (The image y_2 is usually obtained at the front focus of the eyepiece, so that the beam of light rays behind the eyepiece is parallel.) Since the angle u_2 is always small, we have

$$d' = 2au_2 = 2a \sin u_2 = \frac{2an \sin u}{y_2} y,$$

where a is the distance from the point O_2 to the front principal plane of the eyepiece, and we have made use of the sines condition for the points O and O_2. We introduce the magnification N of the microscope equal by definition to the ratio of the angle α' subtended at the eye by the object in the microscope, to the angle α subtended at the naked eye if the object were placed at the least distance L for distinct vision. (For the average eye, $L \approx 25$ cm.) Assuming that these angles are small, we can write

$$\alpha = \frac{y}{L}; \quad \alpha' = \frac{y_2}{a},$$

whence

$$\frac{y}{y_2} = \frac{\alpha}{\alpha'} \frac{L}{a} = \frac{1}{N} \frac{L}{a}.$$

Consequently,

$$d' = \frac{2Ln \sin u}{N}. \tag{4}$$

We have to distinguish three cases.

Case 1. The light beam just fits the pupil of the eye, i.e. d' is equal to the pupil diameter d, but the angle u is less than the limiting angle u_{max} permitted by the microscope aperture. In this case the angle u' is determined by the pupil diameter only, and is independent of the magnification. By (3), the retina illumination E, and hence also the visual estimate of the brightness, is independent of the magnification. The present case corresponds to relatively small magnification. This magnification is not worth using, since it does not use the full aperture of the microscope objective. The naked eye is an example of the present case. Here the visual estimate of the brightness is independent of the distance: objects with the same surface brightness are perceived by the eye as having the same brightness although situated at different distances.

Case 2. The pupil and the objective frame equally limit the light beams: $d' = d$, $u = u_{max}$. By (4), the magnification in this case is

$$N = N_{norm} = \frac{2Ln \sin u_{max}}{d} \tag{5}$$

and is called the normal magnification. The use of larger magnifications cannot lead to an increase in the resolution of the microscope-eye optical system. On putting $d = 2$ mm, $L = 25$ cm, we get

$$N_{norm} = 250n \sin u_{max}. \tag{6}$$

Case 3. The maximum boundary of the light beams just fits the objective frame: $d' < d$. The angle u' (proportional to d') is reduced in the ratio (d/d'). By (4), N is increased in the same ratio.

Equation (3) gives for the retina illumination:

$$E = E_{norm} \left(\frac{N_{norm}}{N}\right)^2, \tag{7}$$

where E_{norm} is the illumination when the magnification is normal or less.

Thus, if $N \leqslant N_{\text{norm}}$, the retina illumination is independent of the magnification; if $N > N_{\text{norm}}$, it is inversely proportional to the square of the magnification.

This illumination is (1) 0·16; (2) 0·0625.

185. $E = \pi B$.

187. 0·13%.

188. About 2%.

189. $\overline{E^2} = 5{\cdot}8 \times 10^{-4}$ e.s.u.; $\overline{E} \approx 0{\cdot}024$ e.s.u. $= 7{\cdot}2\ \text{V cm}^{-1}$.

190. $\overline{H^2} = 5{\cdot}8 \times 10^{-4}$ e.m.u.; $\overline{H} \approx 0{\cdot}024$ oersted.

191. $H \approx 0{\cdot}85$ oersted.

§ 3. Interference and Diffraction of Light

192. $\Psi = \varphi\left[t - \dfrac{(\boldsymbol{n}\cdot\boldsymbol{r})}{v}\right] = \varphi\left(t - \dfrac{\alpha x + \beta y + \gamma z}{v}\right)$.

For a monochromatic wave,

$$\Psi = \Psi_0 \cos\,[\omega t - (\boldsymbol{k}\cdot\boldsymbol{r}) + \delta],$$

where $\boldsymbol{k} = \omega\boldsymbol{n}/v$ is the wave vector.

193. (1) $\Psi = \dfrac{\varphi\left(t - \dfrac{R}{c}\right)}{R}$; (2) $\Psi = \dfrac{\varphi\left(t - \dfrac{r}{c}\right)}{\sqrt{r}}$.

195. When the planes of vibration of the two waves are perpendicular.

Solution. We consider the addition of the vibrations corresponding to the two waves at a point of space. Let the first vibration be given by

$$\boldsymbol{E}_1 = \boldsymbol{A}_1 \cos \omega t,$$

and the second by

$$\boldsymbol{E}_2 = \boldsymbol{A}_2 \cos(\omega t + \delta).$$

The resultant vibration is given by

$$\boldsymbol{E} = \boldsymbol{E}_1 + \boldsymbol{E}_2 = \boldsymbol{A}_1 \cos \omega t + \boldsymbol{A}_2 \cos(\omega t + \delta),$$

whence

$$E^2 = A_1^2 \cos^2 \omega t + A_2^2 \cos^2 (\omega t + \delta) + 2(A_1 \cdot A_2) \cos \omega t \cos (\omega t + \delta).$$

In order to obtain the intensity I, we have to average this expression over time. This gives:

$$I = \frac{1}{2} A_1^2 + \frac{1}{2} A_2^2 + 2(A_1 \cdot A_2) \overline{\cos \omega t \cos (\omega t + \delta)},$$

where the bar denotes time averaging. By hypothesis, the last term must vanish, whatever the angle δ. This is only possible when $(A_1 \cdot A_2) = 0$, i.e. the vibrations must be mutually perpendicular.

196. *Solution.* The interfering waves can be written as

$$\Psi_1 = \Psi_0 \cos [\omega t - (k_1 \cdot r) + \delta_1],$$

$$\Psi_2 = \Psi_0 \cos [\omega t - (k_2 \cdot r) + \delta_2].$$

Hence

$$\Psi = \Psi_1 + \Psi_2 = 2\Psi_0 \cos \left[\left(\frac{\Delta k}{2} \cdot r \right) + \frac{\delta_1 - \delta_2}{2} \right] \cos [\omega t - (k \cdot r)],$$

where

$$\Delta k = k_1 - k_2; \quad k = \frac{k_1 + k_2}{2}.$$

The intensity maxima are obtained where

$$\cos \Phi = \cos \left[\left(\frac{\Delta k}{2} \cdot r \right) + \frac{\delta_1 - \delta_2}{2} \right]$$

is a maximum. Since $k_1 = k_2$ and the angle φ between the vectors k_1 and k_2 is small, we can write approximately:

$$|\Delta k| \approx k\varphi = \frac{2\pi}{\lambda} \varphi,$$

whence the expression given in the problem follows for Δx.

197. We take as the x axis the line of intersection of the plane of incidence with the plane of the screen. Now,

$$\Phi = \frac{\pi \varphi x}{\lambda} \cos \vartheta + \frac{\delta_1 - \delta_2}{2},$$

where ϑ is the angle of incidence. On moving along the x axis over the bandwidth Δx, φ must change by π, i.e.

$$\Delta x = \frac{\lambda}{\varphi \cos \vartheta}.$$

198. $\lambda = \frac{pd}{a} = 5 \times 10^{-5}$ cm $= 5000$ Å.

199. $n_{\text{Cl}} = n + N\frac{\lambda}{l} = 1{\cdot}000865$. The interference bands are displaced towards the telescope.

200. $\alpha \approx \frac{\lambda(a+r)}{2r\Delta p} \approx 9'10''$.

201. $p \approx \frac{n\lambda(a+r)}{2r\alpha} \approx 2{\cdot}8$ mm.

202. $I = I_0 \cos^2 \frac{2\pi p r \alpha}{\lambda(a+r)}$.

203. The surfaces of equal intensity are: (1) hyperboloids of revolution; (2) hyperbolic cylinders.

204. $p = m\lambda \frac{a+b}{2a(n-1)\alpha}$.

205. No. The light beams issuing from the two halves of the bilens do not overlap.

206. $a = \frac{f\lambda}{\Delta x} = 0{\cdot}6$ mm.

207. The interference bands vanish if the screen is moved away from the bilens through a distance not less than $L = Df/a = 50$ m. The maximum number N of bands $= D/2\Delta x = 60$ is obtained when the screen is moved away a distance $\frac{1}{2}L = 25$ m from the bilens.

208. $\Delta x = \frac{\lambda}{2(n-1)\alpha} = 0{\cdot}5$ mm; $\quad N = \frac{4D(n-1)^2\alpha^2}{\lambda} = 10$.

209. The maximum number of bands $N = l(n-1)\alpha/\lambda = 40$ is obtained when the screen is moved $D = l/4(n-1)\alpha = 20$ m away from the biprism. The bands vanish when the screen is at a distance not less than $2D = 40$ m from the biprism.

210. $N = \dfrac{4ab}{a+b} \cdot \dfrac{(n-1)^2 \alpha^2}{\lambda}$.

211. A thinner plate of the same material as P should be placed on the path SCM of the ray. Experiment shows that the achromatic band remains dark in this case, as before.

212. (1) $l < \lambda/\varphi$, where l is the size of the source in the direction parallel to the line joining its image to the Fresnel mirrors, φ is the angle subtended by these images at the points of the screen where interference bands should be obtained. (2) The size of the source in the direction perpendicular to the plane of the mirror should be small by comparison with the distance of the source from the mirror.

213. $D < \dfrac{\lambda}{\alpha} \approx 0{\cdot}05$ mm.

214. $l > \dfrac{fD\alpha}{\lambda} \approx 100$ cm.

215. The antinode: $\lambda/4 = 1{\cdot}25 \times 10^{-5}$ cm; the node: $\frac{1}{2}\lambda = 2{\cdot}5 \times 10^{-5}$ cm.

216. In the first.

217. So that the lens gives an image of the film on the screen.

218. *Solution.* If the plate were absolutely transparent and the light strictly monochromatic, the intensity of the reflected light would change very sharply with a variation of the order λ in the plate thickness. It would be determined by the path difference between the waves reflected from the upper and lower surfaces of the plate. Thus in the case of strictly monochromatic light and an absolutely transparent plate, the intensity of the reflected light would actually change periodically with the thickness on indefinite increase of the latter. In nature, however, neither absolutely transparent media nor strictly monochromatic waves exist.

If the medium possesses absorption, even though very small, a wave travelling in the plate would never reach its lower surface if it were sufficiently thick, but would be absorbed in it. In this case, the intensity of the wave reflected from the plate will be determined by Fresnel's formulae.

The paradox disappears for a transparent plate if we assume that the light incident on the plate is not strictly monochromatic. For, in order to observe interference between the waves reflected from the upper and lower surfaces of the plate, it is necessary for the spectral region $\Delta\lambda$ occupied by the incident light not to exceed $\delta\lambda = \lambda/N$, where N is the order of the interference. On increasing the plate thickness the order N of the interference increases, whilst $\delta\lambda$ diminishes. Thus, since $\Delta\lambda$ is finite, when the thickness is sufficiently great, interference of the waves reflected from its upper and lower surfaces will not be observed. Hence, on further increase of the thickness, the intensity of the wave reflected from the plate will remain unchanged, although it is not defined by Fresnel's formulae, since the light waves inside the plate undergo multiple reflections from its faces.

It has been tacitly assumed in our discussion that the incident wave is plane in the strict sense of the word. It may easily be shown that the paradox disappears if we just renounce this assumption, and allow the assumptions that the wave is strictly monochromatic and the plate absolutely transparent.

219. Dark.

Solution. The path difference between a ray reflected from the lower face of the film and a ray reflected from its upper face is equal to $2dn\cos\psi \pm \frac{1}{2}\lambda$. The term $\frac{1}{2}\lambda$ takes care of the "half-wave loss", i.e. the phase rotation through π on reflection from the film-air boundary. The first term has a maximum $2dn$ for normal incidence ($\psi = 0$). On putting $d = \lambda/10$; $n = 1{\cdot}3$, we obtain for the path difference at normal incidence $(0{\cdot}26 \pm \frac{1}{2})\lambda$. This corresponds to a phase difference of approximately $(90° \pm 180°)$. If the film thickness is further reduced, the phase difference will tend to $\pm 180°$; the rays in question will interfere and virtually extinguish one another.

220. For roughly $d < \lambda/4n = 10^{-5}$ cm.

221. If the film is to acquire a greenish tint, it is obviously necessary for the blue and red wavelengths (about 0·4 and 0·6 micron in air) to be attenuated. This corresponds to a film thickness of about 0·00050 mm.

222. When light is reflected at a glass-air boundary the electric vector undergoes no phase change, but on reflection at an air-glass boundary the phase change is 180°.

223. *Solution.* Whatever the arrangement of the lens, the light either loses half-waves or nothing on reflection at the two oil-lens boundaries. Thus the path difference between the rays reflected from the lens surfaces at the place where they are in contact is zero. These rays reinforce one another when they interfere. Thus the centre of the ring is light in reflected light, and dark in transmitted light.

224. $\Delta l = 0{\cdot}32$ mm.

225. $f = 137$ cm.

226. $R = 1$ m; $\lambda_{\text{red}} = 0{\cdot}7$ micron.

227. $f = \dfrac{x_1^2 x_2^2}{x_1^2 + x_2^2} \cdot \dfrac{1}{(n-1)m\lambda} = 54$ cm.

228. $r = 0{\cdot}63$ mm.

229. In both cases two systems of half-rings that touch one another will be observed. In one system the centre is dark, in the other light. The pattern in transmitted light will be the complement of the pattern in reflected light. (See the solution of Problem 222.)

230. $r_m = \sqrt{\dfrac{m\lambda}{\dfrac{1}{R_1} + \dfrac{1}{R_2}}}$. **231.** $r_m = \sqrt{\dfrac{m\lambda}{\dfrac{1}{R_1} - \dfrac{1}{R_2}}}$.

232. *Solution.* Every Newton's ring can be defined as a line along which the path difference between the interfering rays is constant. It may easily be seen that, when the lens moves away from the plate, the "rings of constant path difference" will be displaced towards the centre of the pattern, whilst when it comes nearer, they move away from the centre. The pattern centre will be alternately light and dark.

233. *Solution.* The two wavelengths correspond to two systems of Newton's rings with negligibly different dimensions. If the lens touches the plate surface, at the centre of the pattern the light (dark) rings of one system virtually coincide with the light (dark) rings of the other system. Thus the rings are almost as distinct towards the centre as in monochromatic light. But further away from the centre the light ring of one system may coincide with the position of the dark ring of the other system. The Newton's rings will not be visible here, and will be only indistinctly visible in the neighbourhood on either side.

Let us find the number N of the light ring for the wavelength λ_2 which coincides in position with the $(N+1)$th dark ring for the wavelength λ_1. Corresponding to the first dark ring (more precisely, the central dark spot) we have the path difference $\frac{1}{2}\lambda_1$, to the second dark ring $\lambda_1 + \frac{1}{2}\lambda_1, \ldots$, and finally, to the $(N+1)$th dark ring $N\lambda_1 + \frac{1}{2}\lambda_1$. This path difference $N\lambda_1 + \frac{1}{2}\lambda_1$ must obviously be equal to $N\lambda_2$, since we require the Nth light ring for the wavelength λ_2 to be imposed on the $(N+1)$th dark ring for λ_1. Thus

$$N\lambda_1 + \frac{\lambda_1}{2} = N\lambda_2,$$

whence

$$N = \frac{\lambda_1}{2(\lambda_2 - \lambda_1)} = \frac{5890}{12} \approx 490.$$

It follows from this that the rings coincide in the neighbourhood of the four hundred and ninetieth ring. It may easily be seen that they will again be sharp in the neighbourhood of the $2 \times 490 = 980$th ring. When the lens moves away from the plate the rings contract towards the centre (see the solution of the previous problem). If the lens is shifted by $490\lambda_1$, 490 rings pass through the field of vision, and the rings disappear at the centre of the pattern. When the lens shifts through $2 \times 490\lambda_1 = 980\lambda_1$, the rings at the centre will again be sharp, when shifted through $3 \times 490\lambda_1 = 1470\lambda_1$ they again coincide and so on.

234. $\dfrac{\Delta\lambda}{\lambda} = \dfrac{1}{980}$, $\Delta\lambda = 6{\cdot}02$ Å.

235. $\alpha = \dfrac{\lambda}{2n\Delta x} \approx 8''$.

236. $N \approx \left(\frac{L}{d}\right)^2 = 2500; \quad \frac{\Delta\lambda}{\lambda} \approx \frac{1}{N} = 4 \times 10^{-4}.$

237. $N \approx \left(\frac{nL}{d}\right)^2 = 5625.$

239. Let V denote the velocity of the electron relative to the medium, and v the phase velocity of the light in the medium. The field produced by the electron disturbs the molecules or atoms of the medium, as a result of which they become sources of light waves. Let A and B be any two points of the medium on the path of the electron, and P a sufficiently remote observation point (Fig. 72). Let the light wave excited by the electron depart from A at the instant $t = 0$. It arrives at the observation point P at the instant $t_1 = AP/v$. A similar wave leaves B AB/V sec later. It arrives at P at the instant $t_2 = AB/V + BP/v$. The time difference is thus

$$t_2 - t_1 = \frac{AB}{V} - \frac{AP - BP}{v}.$$

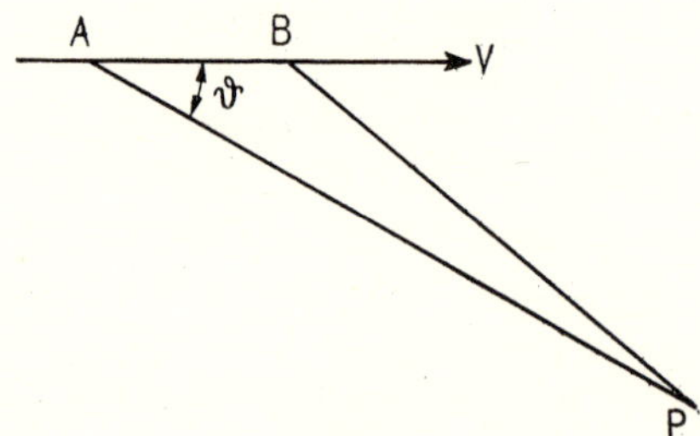

FIG. 72

If P is sufficiently remote we can put $AP - BP = AB \cos\vartheta$. Thus

$$t_2 - t_1 = \frac{AB}{v}\left(\frac{v}{V} - \cos\vartheta\right).$$

If $v/V - \cos\vartheta \neq 0$, we can associate with every point A a corresponding point B such that the waves leaving from A and B arrive at P in opposite phase and extinguish one another. Whereas if

$$\cos\vartheta = \frac{v}{V}, \tag{1}$$

whatever the position of A and B, the waves leaving them arrive at P simultaneously and strengthen one another. Thus, in the direction defined by condition (1), the electron will radiate. Radiation is only possible when $V > v$, i.e. when the electron velocity exceeds the phase velocity of light in the medium.

240. (1) $r_m \approx \sqrt{\dfrac{abm\lambda}{a+b}}$; (2) $r_1 = 0{\cdot}15$ cm.

241. (1) $r_m \approx \sqrt{bm\lambda}$; (2) $r_1 = 0{\cdot}212$ cm.

242. At a distance of 1·2 m.

243. $f = 90$ cm; $r_1 = 0{\cdot}672$ mm. The images, i.e., the maxima, are along the plate axis.

244. $I \approx 4I_0$.

245. $I \approx I_0$.

246. $I \approx I_0$.

247. $y' = by/a = 10{\cdot}5$ mm. The experiment was carried out by Pohl with the figures quoted in the problem. In order for the experiment to succeed, the depth h of the scratches must satisfy the condition $h < \lambda ab/D(a+b) = 180\lambda \approx 0{\cdot}1$ mm. The sphere can be replaced by a disc on condition that $y < (2a/D)\sqrt{ab\lambda/(a+b)} \approx 1$ m.

248. $h = \dfrac{2m + \frac{5}{4}}{2(n-1)}\lambda$; $m = 0, 1, 2, \ldots$

249. The energy is redistributed; at some points of the image plane the light flux density increases, and diminishes at others. The total flux through the image plane is doubled.

250. $r = \sqrt{m\lambda/(1/a + 1/b)}$. The centre of the rings is dark if m is even, and light if m is odd.

Solution. The illumination can be found at the centre of the diffraction pattern by dividing the wave surface ACB (Fig. 73) into Fresnel zones. If it is covered by an even number of Fresnel zones, an illumination minimum is obtained at P; if odd, a maximum is obtained. We draw a sphere of radius PA with centre at P. The number of Fresnel zones on the wave surface ACB is obviously equal to the length CD divided by $\frac{1}{2}\lambda$. This easily leads to the result given in the answer.

251. $$r = \sqrt{\frac{m\lambda}{\frac{1}{f}-\frac{1}{a}}}, \quad \text{if} \quad a > f;$$

$$r = \sqrt{\frac{m\lambda}{\frac{1}{a}-\frac{1}{f}}}, \quad \text{if} \quad a < f.$$

The centre of the rings is dark if m is even, and light if m is odd.

Solution. The method of solution is the same as for the last problem. The only difference is that the spherical wave now converges to the point S (Fig. 74), instead of diverging as previously. The Fresnel zones for the point P are therefore constructed from the

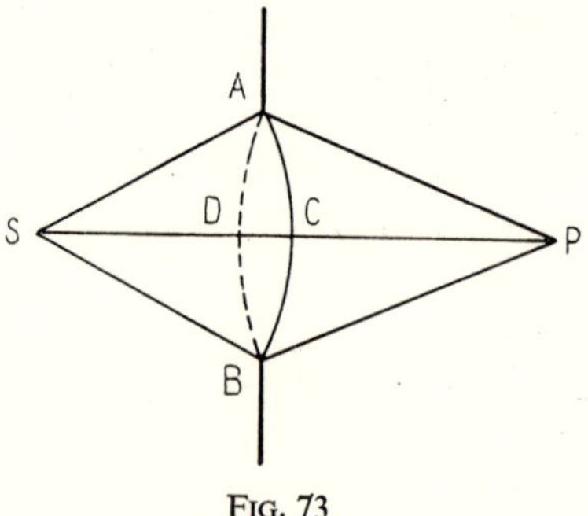

FIG. 73

concave side of the spherical wave surface. The number of zones fitting into the diaphragm aperture will be equal to the length of CD divided by $\frac{1}{2}\lambda$.

252. $$a = \frac{A}{n^2} = 10 \text{ m};$$

$$b = \frac{B}{n^2} = 20 \text{ m}.$$

253. $\varphi \approx \sqrt{\frac{\lambda}{b}} = 3{\cdot}6 \times 10^{-8}$ rad $= 0{\cdot}0075''$, $h \lesssim \sqrt{b\lambda} = 14$ m.

The angle φ is obtained on the assumption that the angular distance between two point stars can be measured when the diffraction

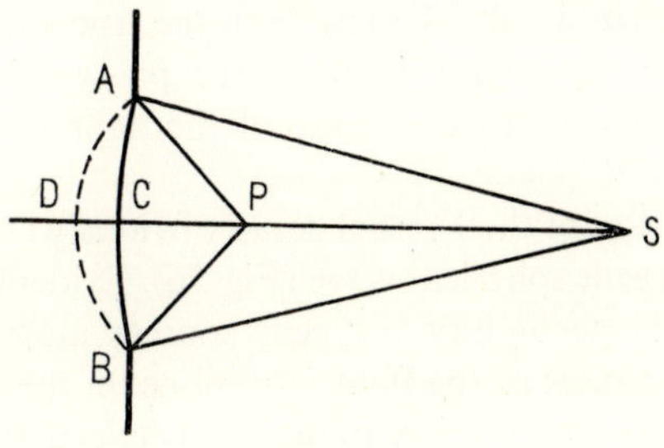

FIG. 74

patterns from them are displaced relative to one another by an amount of the order of the width of a band. The limit in question can be reduced approximately ten times.

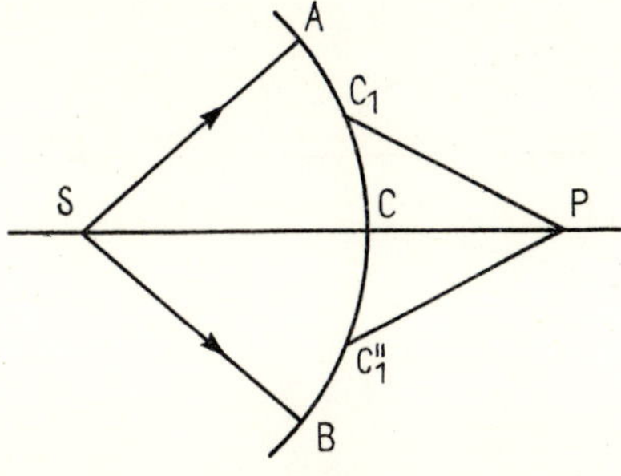

FIG. 75

254. The centre of the rings will be dark.

Solution. Construction of the Fresnel zones for a divergent spherical wave surface (Fig. 75) shows that, when the wave is propagated freely, the action of the wave at the point P is equal to half the action of the central zone and that the secondary Huygens sources must be $\frac{1}{2}\pi$ in phase advance of the light vibrations on the wave surface ACB. If this were not the case, we should obtain an incorrect value for the phase of the vibrations at P. Suppose for instance that the secondary Huygens sources on the wave surface have the same phase as the light vibrations on it. Let C_1CC_1'' be the central Fresnel zone. Since the waves leaving P from the centre of this zone travel a smaller distance than the waves issuing from the edges, a Fresnel zone calculation would give an incorrect value for the phase of the vibrations at P, viz. a value $\frac{1}{2}\pi$ less than the true value. In order to avoid this error, we simply increase the phase of the secondary sources by $\frac{1}{2}\pi$ relative to the phase of the light vibrations on the wave surface ACB.

The construction of the Fresnel zones obviously retains its meaning for a convergent spherical wave (Fig. 76). Evidently, in this case the phases of the secondary Huygens sources must also be $\frac{1}{2}\pi$ in advance of the phases of the light vibrations on the spherical wave surface. Until the observation point lies between the midpoint of the central Fresnel zone and the centre S of the spherical wave surface, we obtain nothing essentially new: the vibrations reach this point earlier from the midpoint of the central zone than from its edges. The situation changes when the observation point P (Fig. 76)

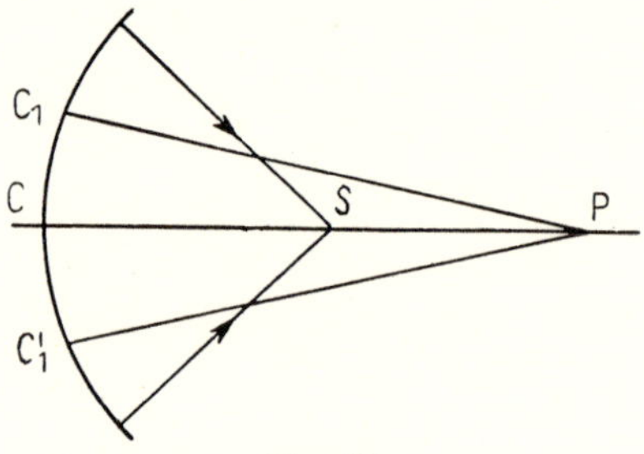

FIG. 76

is further from the midpoint of the central zone than the centre S. The vibrations reaching S from the edges of the central zone will now be π in advance in phase compared with the vibrations arriving from its centre, and the resultant vibrations of the central zone as a whole arrive with the phase advance $\frac{1}{2}\pi$. If account is also taken of the phase advance of the secondary Huygens sources, we reach the conclusion that, when the spherical wave passes through its centre, the phase of the vibrations so to speak changes by a jump of π. By taking account of this jump-type phase change we can avoid physically inadmissible conclusions regarding the propagation of spherical waves. A convergent spherical wave first contracts to the point S, then becomes divergent. We obtain the superposition of two spherical waves, one of which travels to the centre and the other from the centre. These waves have opposite phase at the centre S, as a result of which no infinitely large vibrational amplitudes are obtained there, as would be the case with any other phase relationship.

Strictly speaking, all these arguments refer to the case of free propagation of spherical waves. When the wave is bounded by a diaphragm, they still hold, provided the observation point P is not too close to the focus of geometrical convergence of the rays. In the neighbourhood of the focus a complex distribution of the amplitudes and phases of the light field is observed. But if we exclude this neighbourhood from our consideration, it turns out that the final result is the same as if the phase increased by a jump of π on passing through the focus.

The solution of the problem is now obvious. When the spherical wave travels downwards (Fig. 26), it passes through the focus S'' before it strikes the screen. The wave travelling upwards strikes the screen without passing through its focus S'.

255. $\dfrac{d^2}{\lambda r} \ll 1.$

256. $a(\cos\alpha - \cos\alpha_0) = m\lambda$, where a is the width of the slit, α is the grazing angle corresponding to the minimum, and m is an integer (positive or negative).

257. $L = 3{\cdot}5$ cm.

258. The intensities are not in general equal at the centre; outside the centre the intensities are equal (Babinet's theorem).

259. *Solution.* We consider a slit of the same width as the black screen. If the same plane wave is incident on the slit and the screen, the amount of energy absorbed by the screen will be equal to the amount of energy incident on the slit. By Babinet's principle, the light intensities in all directions except the direction of the incident wave are the same in both cases. Consequently, the energies scattered by the screen and the slit are the same. But in the case of the slit all the energy is scattered. Thus the energy absorbed by the screen is equal to the energy scattered by it.

260. $$I = C\left[\frac{\sin\left(\frac{N\pi d}{\lambda}\sin\vartheta\right)}{\sin\left(\frac{\pi d}{\lambda}\sin\vartheta\right)}\right]^2\left[\frac{\sin\left(\frac{\pi b}{\lambda}\sin\vartheta\right)}{\frac{\pi b}{\lambda}\sin\vartheta}\right]^2,$$

where C is a constant, and ϑ is the angle between the normal to the grating and the given direction to which the intensity I refers.

Solution. Since we require to calculate the intensity distribution in the Fraunhofer diffraction pattern at the grating, it can be assumed that the screen on which the pattern is observed is at a sufficient distance away. The rays travelling from the different slits of the grating to any point of the screen can be regarded as parallel. We choose a point on the screen such that the rays travelling to it

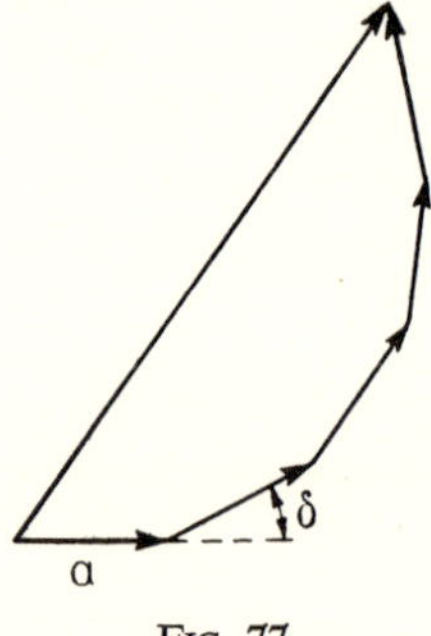

FIG. 77

form an angle ϑ with the normal to the grating. The phase difference between neigbouring interfering rays will be $\delta = (2\pi d/\lambda)\sin\vartheta$. The vibrations reaching the point in question from any slit of the grating can be represented by a vector on a vector diagram. These vectors form a step line with equal steps and equal angles (Fig. 77). The resultant vibration is represented by the geometrical sum of all these vectors. The addition of vectors on a plane is formally the same as addition of complex numbers. If the first vector is represented by the complex number a, the succeeding vectors are represented by the complex numbers $ae^{j\delta}$, $ae^{2j\delta}$, etc. Their sum is

$$A = a[1 + e^{j\delta} + e^{2j\delta} + \cdots + e^{j(N-1)\delta}] = a\frac{1 - e^{jN\delta}}{1 - e^{j\delta}}.$$

The square of the modulus of the complex number A gives the relative intensity at the point of the screen:

$$I = |A|^2 = AA^* = |a|^2 \frac{1 - e^{jN\delta}}{1 - e^{-j\delta}} \cdot \frac{1 - e^{-jN\delta}}{1 - e^{-j\delta}}$$

$$= |a|^2 \frac{2 - (e^{jN\delta} + e^{-jN\delta})}{2 - (e^{j\delta} + e^{-j\delta})} = |a|^2 \frac{1 - \cos(N\delta)}{1 - \cos\delta}.$$

Since $|a|^2$ defines the intensity of the diffracted light from one slit, we have by the familiar formula:

$$|a|^2 = C\left[\frac{\sin\left(\dfrac{\pi b}{\lambda}\sin\vartheta\right)}{\dfrac{\pi b}{\lambda}\sin\vartheta}\right]^2.$$

On substituting this value in the previous expression, the answer is easily obtained.

261. $Nd\sin\vartheta = n\lambda$, but $d\sin\vartheta \neq k\lambda$, $b\sin\vartheta = m\lambda$, where n, m, k are integers. The condition for a minimum is fulfilment of at least one of these equations.

262. $d(\sin\vartheta - \sin\vartheta_0) = n\lambda$.

If $d \gg n\lambda$, the condition for a maximum is

$$d\cos\vartheta_0 \cdot (\vartheta - \vartheta_0) \approx n\lambda,$$

i.e. the grating constant is as it were reduced compared with the case of normal incidence and becomes equal to $d\cos\vartheta_0$ instead of d. The angles $\vartheta - \vartheta_0$ defining the directions at the maxima are measured from the direction of the incident light (or the reflected light in a reflecting grating).

263. $\lambda = 0{\cdot}573$ Å.

264. If the angle of incidence is close to $\frac{1}{2}\pi$, mirror reflection is always observed. At small angles of incidence mirror reflection may be observed if the roughness of the surface is $\ll \lambda$.

Solution. Let the incident rays form an angle with the normal to the plane, represented in Fig. 78 by a dotted line. We consider the interference of the secondary waves issuing from the surface at an angle ϑ' to the normal. The path difference of any two rays travelling in the direction in question is given by

$$\Delta = AD - BC = a(\sin\vartheta' - \sin\vartheta) + h(\cos\vartheta' + \cos\vartheta).$$

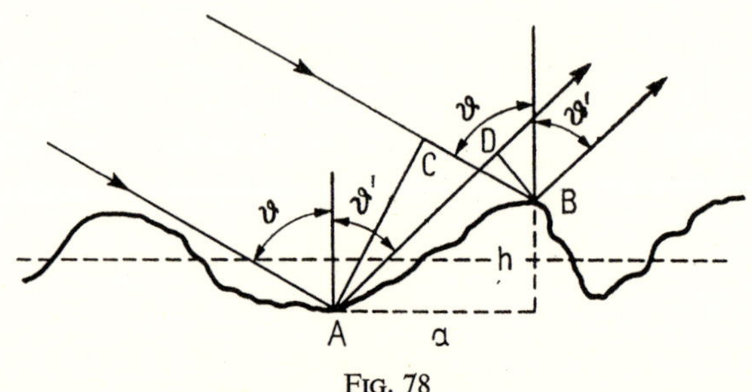

FIG. 78

Here a can take any desired values. Thus if $\vartheta' \neq \vartheta$, the path difference Δ can also take any desired values, and these values will be encountered equally often when the body has an irregular surface. This shows that regular reflection, if such is possible, can only occur at the angle $\vartheta' = \vartheta$. In this case

$$\Delta = 2h\cos\vartheta.$$

It is clear from this that, whatever h, a sufficiently large angle ϑ can be chosen so that $\Delta \ll \lambda$. With this condition, the reflection will be regular. At normal incidence $\Delta = 2h$, regular reflection is only possible provided $h \ll \lambda$.

265. They cannot.

266. $m = \dfrac{nd}{b}; \quad n = 1, 2, \ldots$

267. (1) The spectra of orders 2, 4, 6, etc. disappear; (2) the spectra of orders 3, 6, 9, ..., disappear; (3) the spectra of orders 4, 8, 12, ..., disappear.

268. The maximum order is equal to the greatest integer not exceeding d/λ.

269. $\lambda = 6481$ Å.

270. At normal incidence $\lambda_{max} = d$. The grating period must be not less than 0·01 cm, i.e. the grating must have not more than 10 rulings per mm. At grazing incidence on a transmitting grating, $\lambda_{max} = 2d$.

271. The diffraction angles are unchanged, the intensities tend to zero.

272. The diffraction angles are unchanged, the intensities tend to zero.

273. $h = \dfrac{2m-1}{2(n-1)}\lambda; \quad m = 1, 2, 3, \ldots$

The intensity of the zero principal maximum is zero.

274. The principal maxima of the two-grating system will be in the same positions as for one grating, but the intensity of each maximum will be changed in the proportion $4\cos^2((\pi a/\lambda)\cos\vartheta)$, where ϑ is the angle between the normal to the grating and the direction of the maximum.

276. If the angle between the normal to the series of doublets and the direction of the main lobe is $\vartheta = \Omega t + \delta$, then

$$\Delta\varphi = -\frac{2\pi d}{\lambda}\sin(\Omega t + \delta) + 2\pi m; \quad m = 0, \pm 1, \pm 2, \ldots$$

277. (1) 8·1 sec of arc/Å; (2) 0·0197 mm/Å; (3) 50·7 Å/mm.

278. About 0·12 mm.

279. $D = \dfrac{n}{d\cos\vartheta} = \dfrac{n}{d\sqrt{1-\left(\dfrac{n\lambda}{d}\right)^2}}$

$$= 0{\cdot}63 \times 10^4 \text{ rad/cm} = 13 \text{ sec of arc/Å}.$$

280. 600 rulings/mm.

281. $\Delta\vartheta = \dfrac{\lambda}{Nd\cos\vartheta}$.

282. About 1000.

283. 12,000 and 48,000.

284. No.

285. The resolution is unchanged. The dispersion region is halved.

286. $x \ll \dfrac{f\lambda}{Nd} = 0{\cdot}001$ cm.

287. $m\lambda = 2h\sqrt{n^2 - \cos^2\varepsilon}$, where ε is the angle between the convergent ray and the plate surface.

288. $D = \dfrac{(n^2-1) - \lambda n \dfrac{dn}{d\lambda}}{\lambda\varepsilon}$; $\Delta\lambda = \dfrac{\lambda^2\sqrt{n^2-1}}{2h\left[(n^2-1) - \lambda n \dfrac{dn}{d\lambda}\right]}$.

289. $z = \dfrac{L\sqrt{n^2-1}}{2h} = 17$.

290. The minimum order is $m_1 = (2h/\lambda)\sqrt{n^2-1} \approx 47{,}200$, the maximum order is $m_2 = 2hn/\lambda = 62{,}400$.

291. $\Delta\lambda = 0{\cdot}098$ Å;

$$r = \frac{\lambda}{\delta\lambda} = \frac{L}{\lambda}\left[(n^2-1) - \lambda n \frac{dn}{d\lambda}\right] = 852{,}000.$$

292. $\Delta\varepsilon = \dfrac{\lambda\sqrt{n^2-1}}{2h\varepsilon} \approx 5{\cdot}4'$.

293. The resolution is unchanged, the dispersion region is halved.

294. The resolution is doubled, the dispersion region is unchanged.

295. The plate with the greater refractive index has greater resolution, but a smaller dispersion region.

296. $L = \dfrac{\lambda^2}{(n^2 - 1)\delta\lambda} = 2{\cdot}5$ cm.

297. A system of spots is observed, located at the base-points of the rectangular net.

298. $2h\cos\varphi = m\lambda;\quad \Delta\varphi = -\dfrac{\lambda}{2h\sin\varphi};\quad \dfrac{d\varphi}{d\lambda} = -\dfrac{m}{2h\sin\varphi};$

$$\Delta\lambda = \frac{\lambda}{m} = \frac{\lambda^2}{2h\cos\varphi}.$$

299. $\Delta h = 0{\cdot}125$ Å.

300. $m \approx 36{,}300$.

301. (1) $m = \dfrac{n-1}{\lambda}b = 10{,}000$; (2) $\vartheta = \dfrac{\lambda}{a} = 51{\cdot}5''$.

302. About 1000.

303. About 1 cm.

304. *Solution.* Let $\delta\lambda$ be the minimum difference between the wavelengths of two spectral lines that can be resolved by the prism with an indefinitely narrow collimator slit. By the formula for the theoretical resolution:

$$\frac{\lambda}{\delta\lambda} = a\left|\frac{dn}{d\lambda}\right|,$$

the difference between the refractive indices for these spectral lines is

$$\delta n = \frac{\lambda}{a}.$$

Due to the difference in the refractive indices, an initially parallel beam of rays becomes divergent on leaving the prism. Let us calculate the angular divergence of the departing beam on the assumption that a parallel beam is incident on the prism. We have (Fig. 79):

$$\sin\varphi_1 = n\sin\psi_1.$$

We have from this, with constant φ_1:

$$\delta n\cdot\sin\psi_1 + n\cos\psi_1\delta\psi_1 = 0.$$

Since $\psi_1 + \psi_2 = A = \text{const}$, and hence $\delta\psi_1 + \delta\psi_2 = 0$, we have

$$\delta n \cdot \sin\psi_1 = n\cos\psi_1 \cdot \delta\psi_2.$$

Further, since $\sin\varphi_2 = n\sin\psi_2$, the angular divergence of the departing beam will be

$$\delta\varphi_2 = \frac{\sin\psi_2}{\cos\varphi_2}\delta n + \frac{n\cos\psi_2}{\cos\varphi_2}\delta\psi_2$$

$$= \left(\frac{\sin\psi_2}{\cos\varphi_2} + \frac{n\cos\psi_2}{\cos\varphi_2}\,\frac{\sin\psi_1}{n\cos\psi_1}\right)\delta n,$$

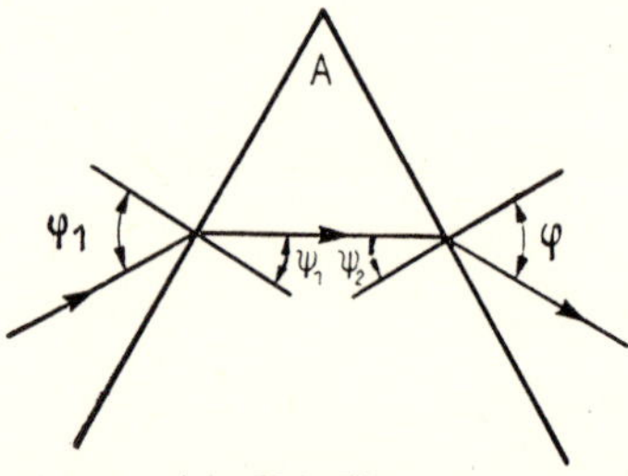

FIG. 79

and on adjusting for the angle of least deviation ($\varphi_1 = \varphi_2 = \varphi$; $\psi_1 = \psi_2 = \psi$):

$$\delta\varphi_2 = 2\frac{\sin\psi}{\cos\varphi}\delta n = 2\frac{\sin\psi}{\cos\varphi}\,\frac{\lambda}{a}.$$

For full use of the theoretical resolution of the prism, the angular width of the collimator slit $\alpha = b/f$ must be small compared with $\delta\varphi_2$. This gives

$$b \ll 2\frac{\sin\psi}{\cos\varphi}\,\frac{f\lambda}{a}.$$

For $\frac{1}{2}A = \psi = 30°$, $n = 1{\cdot}73$, we obtain

$$b \ll \frac{2}{\sqrt{4-n^2}}\,\frac{f\lambda}{a} = \frac{2f\lambda}{a} = 2{\cdot}5 \times 10^{-3}\ \text{mm}.$$

305. The spectrum will be intersected by dark lines, forming segments of the family of parabolas $y^2 = Cmx$ ($m = 0, 1, 2, \ldots$), where C is a constant determined by the data of the arrangement.

(The origin is at the centre of the Newton's rings, the x axis is perpendicular and the y axis parallel to the spectrograph slit.) All the parabolas have the common vertex $x = 0$, $y = 0$, which corresponds to $\lambda = 0$. The pieces of the parabolas from the vertex to the violet end of the spectrum are not reproduced in the experiment. If the slit is shifted a from the centre of the rings, the family of parabolas becomes $y^2 = Cmx - a^2$, where C is the same constant. In this case the parabolas have different vertices for different m, and the pieces on which the vertices are situated can be obtained. On replacing the diffraction by a prismatic spectrograph, the dark lines remain but their shape ceases to be parabolic. (See Problem 564.)

306. *Solution.* Let O be the focus of geometric convergence of rays (Fig. 80); r_0 is the nearest distance from the lens to O. We describe about O as centre a spherical surface S of radius r_0. When

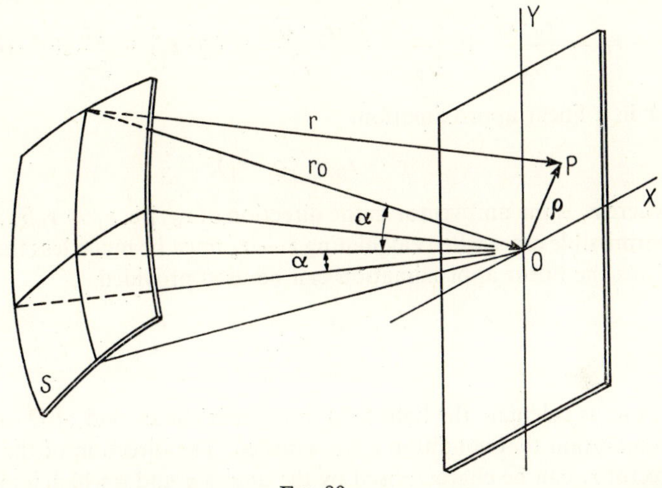

FIG. 80

calculating the light field on S we can confine ourselves to the approximation of geometrical optics. The field on S can be written in the complex form as

$$E_S = \frac{1}{r_0} e^{i(\omega t + kr_0)}.$$

Let P be the observation point, dS the surface element of S, r the distance from dS to P. The light field at P is found from Huygens' principle in accordance with

$$E_P = \int \frac{dS}{r_0 r} e^{i[\omega t - k(r - r_0)]}, \tag{1}$$

where the integration is over the part of S on which the field is non-zero. Obviously,

$$\boldsymbol{r} = \boldsymbol{r}_0 + \boldsymbol{\varrho},$$

where $\boldsymbol{r}$ and $\boldsymbol{r}_0$ are the radius vectors from dS to P and O respectively, and $\boldsymbol{\varrho} = \overrightarrow{OP}$. Hence

$$r = r_0 \sqrt{1 + \frac{2(\boldsymbol{r}_0 \cdot \boldsymbol{\varrho}) + \varrho^2}{r_0^2}}.$$

We use the binomial formula and discount terms higher than ϱ^2:

$$r - r_0 = \frac{(\boldsymbol{r}_0 \cdot \boldsymbol{\varrho})}{r_0} + \frac{\varrho^2}{2r_0} - \frac{1}{2}\frac{(\boldsymbol{r}_0 \cdot \boldsymbol{\varrho})^2}{r_0^3} = (\boldsymbol{\varrho} \cdot \boldsymbol{r}_1) + \frac{\varrho^2}{2r_0} \sin^2 (\boldsymbol{\varrho}, \boldsymbol{r}_1),$$

or in a linear approximation,

$$r - r_0 = (\boldsymbol{\varrho} \cdot \boldsymbol{r}_1),$$

where $\boldsymbol{r}_1$ is the unit vector in the direction of $\boldsymbol{r}_0$, i.e. $\boldsymbol{r}_1 = \boldsymbol{r}_0/r_0$. The permissible error when calculating $r - r_0$ must be much less than λ. Thus the linear approximation can be used provided

$$\frac{\varrho^2}{r_0} \ll \lambda. \tag{2}$$

Let us calculate the light field in the neighbourhood of O on the assumption that condition (2) is satisfied. The direction of the unit vector $\boldsymbol{r}_1$ can be characterised by the angles φ and ψ which it makes with the planes through the optical axis and the parallel sides of the diaphragm. Obviously, $dS = r_0^2 d\varphi d\psi$. We introduce on the plane of observation (screen) a rectangular coordinate system with axes parallel to the sides of the square diaphragm. We denote the coordinates of P by x and y. Now,

$$r - r_0 = (\boldsymbol{r}_1 \cdot \boldsymbol{\varrho}) = x \sin \varphi + y \sin \psi.$$

If the angle α subtended at O by half the side of the diaphragm is small, $\sin \varphi$ and $\sin \psi$ can be replaced by φ and ψ. In addition, r can be replaced approximately by r_0 in the denominator of (1). Finally,

$$E_P = e^{+i\omega t}\int_{-\alpha}^{+\alpha}\int_{-\alpha}^{+\alpha} e^{-ik(x\varphi+y\psi)}\,d\varphi\,d\psi.$$

If the amplitude at O is taken as unity, the amplitude at P is

$$A = \frac{\sin\frac{2\pi x}{\lambda}\alpha}{\frac{2\pi x}{\lambda}\alpha}\cdot\frac{\sin\frac{2\pi y}{\lambda}\alpha}{\frac{2\pi y}{\lambda}\alpha}, \tag{3}$$

whilst the intensity is

$$I = \left(\frac{\sin\frac{2\pi x}{\lambda}\alpha}{\frac{2\pi x}{\lambda}\alpha}\right)^2\left(\frac{\sin\frac{2\pi y}{\lambda}\alpha}{\frac{2\pi y}{\lambda}\alpha}\right)^2. \tag{4}$$

The same diffraction pattern is obtained as in Fraunhofer diffraction from a square aperture. The distance between two neighbouring minima, as also from the centre of the central maximum to the first minimum, is

$$\Delta x = \frac{1}{2}\,\frac{\lambda}{\alpha}. \tag{5}$$

It remains to verify whether condition (2) is satisfied. Since, by (3) a considerable intensity is obtained when ϱ is of the order Δx, on substituting $\varrho \approx \lambda/\alpha$ in (2) we can write (2) as

$$\alpha \gg \sqrt{\frac{\lambda}{r_0}}. \tag{6}$$

This latter condition is satisfied in all optical devices containing lenses or mirrors.

The case of a circular diaphragm is not essentially different from that of a square diaphragm. In the linear approximation the integral (1) for a circular diaphragm can be expressed in terms of a first-order Bessel function. The diffraction pattern in the focal plane consists of light and dark concentric circles with a light centre. The radii of the dark rings are

$$R = 0{\cdot}61\frac{\lambda}{\alpha}; \quad 1{\cdot}12\frac{\lambda}{\alpha}; \quad 1{\cdot}62\frac{\lambda}{\alpha}; \quad \ldots \tag{7}$$

where α is the angle subtended by the diaphragm radius at the point O.

307. *Solution.* In the case of luminous points the waves radiated by them are incoherent. The intensities of the waves issuing from these points are added at the screen. Let the two points be arranged symmetrically with respect to the principal optical axis. We consider the intensity distribution along the x axis (Fig. 81). The position of the observation point on this axis can be characterised by the coordinate $\xi = 2\pi x\alpha/\lambda$. The minimum distance between the diffraction circles must be equal to π in these units, according to Rayleigh (see the solution of Problem 306). The dotted curves on

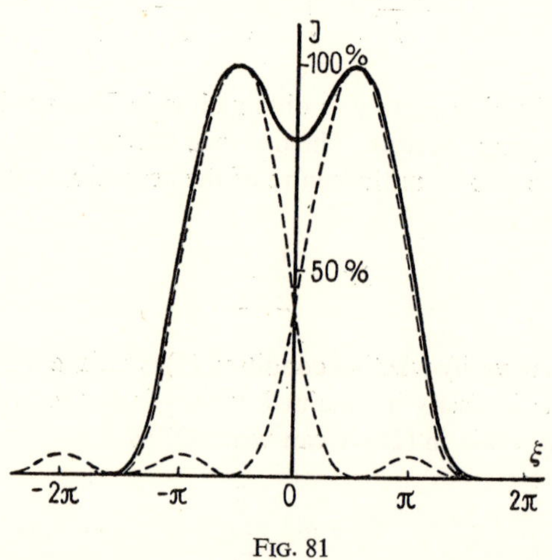

FIG. 81

Fig. 81 give the distribution of the intensities of each of the two luminous points, whilst the continuous curve is the resultant intensity. We see that the intensity at the centre of the pattern is almost 20 per cent less than the maximum intensity, equal to the maximum intensity of a single point. Thus, when Rayleigh's criterion is satisfied, separate images of the luminous points are obtained.

308. *Solution.* If the points are not themselves luminous but are illuminated by the same light source, the waves issuing from them are coherent. Instead of adding the intensities, the amplitudes must be added and account taken of the phases of the vibrations. It follows from the solution of Problem 306 that, in the case of one point, the phase of the vibrations is the same within the limits of each light ring (in the case of a square diaphragm, of each light square) and changes by 180° on passing through the illumination minimum in the adjacent light ring.

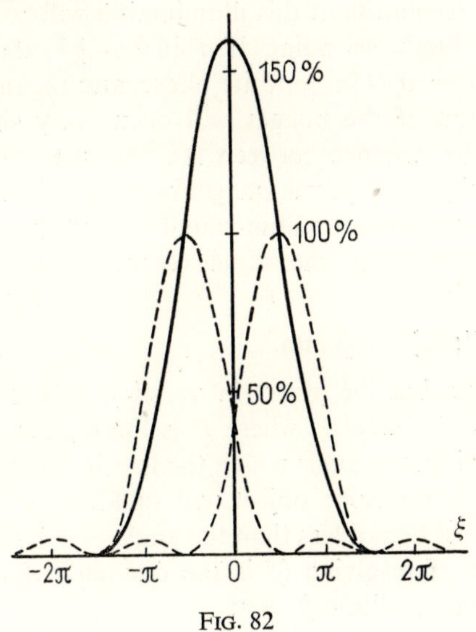

FIG. 82

Case 1. The apertures are illuminated by rays parallel to the principal optical axis. In this case the waves leave them in the same phase. Since the waves travel the same distances to the point O, they are also in phase at O. The amplitude of the resultant vibration at O will be doubled, and the intensity quadrupled, compared with the case of forming the image of a single aperture. The curve of Fig. 82 shows the distribution of the resultant intensity. It has only one maximum, and the image at the eye will be the same as from a single point. Thus, with the method of illumination in question, different images of the points are not obtained if the distance between them is equal to the minimum distance required by Rayleigh's criterion. In order to obtain separate images, this distance has to be increased approximately 1·4 times. Correspondingly, the resolution is reduced the same amount by comparison with the case of points luminous in themselves.

Case 2. The apertures are illuminated by parallel rays inclined at an angle ϑ to the principal optical axis. In this case the waves leave the apertures with a phase difference $\delta = (2\pi d \sin \vartheta)/\lambda$, where d is the distance between the aperture centres. They arrive with the same phase difference at O. If $d \sin \vartheta = \lambda/4$, then $\delta = \frac{1}{2}\pi$, and the intensity at O is twice the intensity when there is only one aperture. The resolution at this illumination will be the same as in the case of a luminous point. If $d \sin \vartheta = \frac{1}{2}\lambda$, then $\delta = \pi$. The waves now arrive at O in opposite phase, and the intensity there is zero. Separation of the images will occur very sharply. At this illumination the distance between the apertures can be less than Rayleigh's limit, and separate images of them will still be obtained.

Case 3. The apertures are illuminated by rays from all directions. In this case practically the same resolution is obtained as for luminous points.

309. (1) 34″; (2) 0·042 mm.

310. *Solution.* Let the object in question subtend at the naked eye an angle $\alpha = 1{\cdot}22\lambda/D$, where D is the diameter of the object lens, i.e. the minimum angle which the lens is capable of resolving. In the telescope the same object will subtend the angle $\beta = N\alpha$. The angle β must be not less than the angle $\gamma = 1{\cdot}22\lambda/d$, which the eye is capable of resolving (d is the diameter of the pupil). We obtain from the condition $\beta \geqslant \gamma$:

$$N \geqslant \frac{D}{d}.$$

The magnification $N_{\text{norm}} = D/d$ is described as normal. At smaller magnifications use is made of only part of the object lens, and the resolution of the telescope-eye system is reduced. Magnifications much greater than normal should not be used, since the resolution of the system is not thereby increased, and the image brightness is diminished (see Problem 184).

311. (1) The angular distance that can be resolved by the telescope is $\vartheta = 1{\cdot}22\lambda/D$, where D is the object lens diameter. In the case of visual observations, we can take $\lambda = 5500$ Å; then $\vartheta = 2{\cdot}76''$. (2) At the magnification $N \geqslant D/d = 10$.

312. The angular diameters of almost all the stars are much less than the angular distances that can be resolved by even the largest telescopes. In these circumstances the size of the star's image on the retina is determined exclusively by the diffraction effects in the optical system (telescope + eye) and is independent of the magnification. But the brightness of the image is proportional to the light flux through the optical system. This light flux is greater, when a telescope is used, than the light flux through the pupil of the naked eye, in the same proportion as the area of the object lens aperture is greater than the area of the pupil of the eye (if the telescope magnification is normal). Thus weaker stars can be seen through the telescope than by the naked eye. At normal magnification the diameter of the exit pupil is equal to the diameter of the pupil of the eye. It is no use employing greater magnifications when looking at stars. At smaller magnifications, only part of the light passing through the telescope reaches the pupil of the eye.

313. See the answer to the previous problem.

314. $\sqrt{\alpha\beta} = 10$ times.

315. $\sqrt{\alpha\beta} = 10$ times.

316. It cannot. The diameter of the pupil of an eagle's eye does not exceed a few millimetres. Even if we take it as 10 mm, the minimum angle subtended at the eagle by two point objects that it can see separately is roughly 3 times the angular dimensions of a mouse.

317. About 40 m on the moon, about 20 km on the sun.

318. About 28 km.

319. *Solution.* At small diffraction angles the required distance x is found from the requirement that the path difference $r_2 - r_1$ between the extreme interfering rays (Fig. 83) is equal to the wavelength λ. On applying Pythagoras' theorem and getting rid of the square roots with the aid of the binomial formula, we easily obtain for this distance:

$$r_2 - r_1 = \frac{xD}{b} - \frac{xD}{2b^3}\left(x^2 + \frac{D^2}{4}\right) + \cdots$$

On confining ourselves to the first term, we find that

$$x = \frac{b\lambda}{D}. \tag{1}$$

The error in evaluating $r_2 - r_1$ must be small compared with λ. This gives us the condition for applicability of the previous formula:

$$\frac{1}{2b^2}\left(\frac{b^2\lambda^2}{D^2} + \frac{D^2}{4}\right) \ll 1. \tag{2}$$

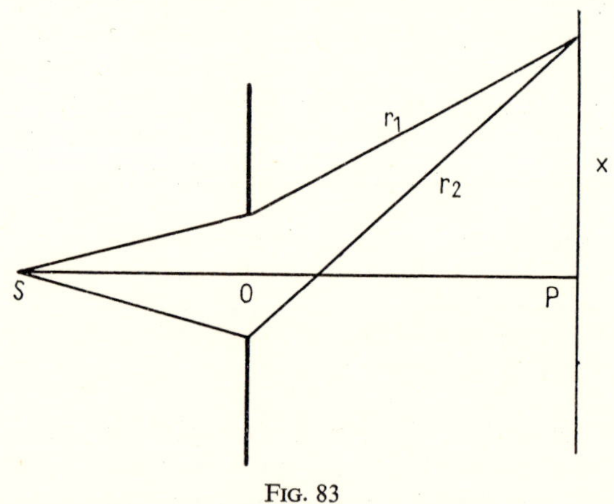

FIG. 83

320. If we use formula (1) for the radius of the first dark diffraction ring (see the solution of the previous problem), we obtain

$$D^2 = \frac{2ab\lambda}{a + b}, \tag{1}$$

i.e. the aperture area must be equal to half the area of the central Fresnel zone constructed for the points S and P (Fig. 83). Condition (2) of the previous problem reduces to

$$\frac{D^2}{4b^2}\left(1 + \frac{b}{a} + \frac{1}{2}\frac{b^2}{a^2}\right) \ll 1$$

and is always satisfied in any camera with a small aperture.

A more exact solution requires the use of the formula

$$x = 1{\cdot}22\frac{b\lambda}{D},$$

for the radius x of the first dark ring, which gives

$$D^2 = \frac{2{\cdot}44ab\lambda}{a+b}. \qquad (2)$$

Rayleigh carried out a more detailed theoretical and experimental investigation of this subject, and found for the best aperture diameter:

$$D = 1{\cdot}8\sqrt{\frac{ab\lambda}{a+b}}, \qquad (3)$$

which is virtually the same as (1) or (2).

321. $D = \sqrt{2{\cdot}44L\lambda} \approx 0{\cdot}35$ mm.

322. $L \approx \dfrac{D^2}{2{\cdot}44\lambda} \approx 1000$ km; $S \approx \left(2{\cdot}44\dfrac{\lambda}{D}\right)^2 \approx 1{\cdot}5 \times 10^{-12}$.

323. The resolution is roughly doubled.

324. $L < Dl/1{\cdot}22\lambda = 3{\cdot}7$ m. It is easily seen that the same condition holds in the case of so-called objective measurement on the scale, i.e. projection of the light spot reflected from the galvanometer mirror on to the scale.

325. (1) About 0·3 micron; (2) about 0·19 micron.

326. (1) It is doubled; (2) 0·095 micron; (3) about 5300.

327. *Solution.* Suppose we view through the microscope an object whose diameter l is equal to the least distance that can be resolved by its objective. In the case of objects which are themselves luminous, or are illuminated by diffusion, $l = 0{\cdot}61\lambda/(n \sin u)$, where $n \sin u$ is the angular aperture of the objective. The angle subtended at the naked eye by this object at the least distance L for distinct vision is $\alpha = l/L$. In the microscope it subtends the angle $\beta = N\alpha$, where N is the magnification. The angle β must be not less than the minimum angular distance $\gamma = 1{\cdot}22\lambda/d$, resolvable by the eye (d is the pupil diameter). The condition $\beta \geqslant \gamma$ gives

$$N \geqslant \frac{2Ln \sin u}{d}.$$

The magnification $N_{\text{norm}} = (2Ln \sin u)/d$ is described as normal. There is no point in using a magnification much greater than normal, since the resolution is not increased, whilst the image brightness is diminished. (See Problem 184.)

328. When the narrow slit is vertical, a system of horizontal bands is obtained on the screen. In the case of a horizontal slit the bands become vertical. When the slit is at 45° to the horizontal, the bands are also at 45° but are perpendicular to the direction of the slit. In the case of a wide slit, a similar image of the wire net is obtained on the screen, independently of the slit direction.

329. The period of variation of the liquid refractive index is equal to the ultrasonic wavelength Λ.

Solution. The refractive index of the liquid depends only on its density. Hence the problem amounts to finding the spatial period of variation of the density. In Fig. 84, the black circles represent the velocity nodes in the sonic standing wave, whilst the arrows indicate the directions of liquid particle motion at a given instant.

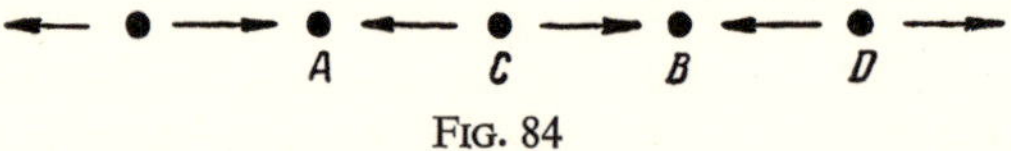

FIG. 84

In the standing wave all the liquid particles between two adjacent velocity nodes move in the same direction. On passing through a node the direction of motion of the particles is reversed. Suppose that the particle displacements have achieved their maximum values at a certain instant. With the velocity directions shown in Fig. 84, there will now be compressions at the nodes $A, B, \ldots$, and rarefactions at the nodes $C, D, \ldots$ After half a period there will be rarefactions at $A, B, \ldots$, and compressions at $C, D, \ldots$ The distance between two adjacent compressions or rarefactions is equal to the spatial period of variation of the density, and hence of the refractive index. As is clear from Fig. 84, it is equal to the ultrasonic wavelength Λ.

330. *Solution.* Since the frequency of the ultrasonic vibrations is very small compared with the frequency of the light vibrations it can be assumed that the light is propagated in a motionless liquid. This liquid is a non-uniform medium whose refractive index changes periodically in a direction parallel to AB. Calculation of the light field in such a non-uniform medium is extremely difficult. But, no matter how the light is propagated in the liquid, we can say that the light field in the plane CD will vary periodically in the direction CD with period A on leaving the vessel. To find the light field behind the vessel, we can use Huygens' principle and replace the real by virtual light sources, distributed over the area CD. The distance between two adjacent identical virtual sources will now be equal to the ultrasonic wavelength Λ (see the solution of Problem 329). The problem thus reduces to the diffraction of light at a two-dimensional plane grating.

331. $v = \dfrac{f\lambda\nu}{\Delta x} = 1200\ \text{m sec}^{-1}$.

332. It is not possible.

Solution. The spatial period of variation of the liquid refractive index is equal in both cases to the ultrasonic wavelength Λ.

The diffraction angles will thus be the same in both cases. Furthermore, the light intensity distribution in the diffraction spectra will be the same, since in both cases the refractive index, as a function of the coordinates (with fixed time), varies in accordance with the same sine law. When the ultrasonic damping is considerable, the laws of variation of the refractive index in space will no longer be the same in the case of standing and travelling waves. In this case, it is possible in principle to distinguish the travelling from the standing wave from the nature of the diffraction pattern.

333. *Solution.* If the eye reacted instantaneously to a light stimulus and did not have the capacity of retaining visual impressions, on looking at the liquid we should see light and dark bands, the distance between which would be equal to the distance between two neighbouring compressions, i.e. Λ. After half a period of the acoustic vibration, a light band would appear in place of the dark one and vice versa. In actual fact the eye retains visual impressions for roughly 0·1 sec, i.e. a time which is very large compared with the period of the ultrasonic vibration. Thus the eye is not in a position to see the interchange of the bands. It registers a mean illumination of the retina, obtained by averaging the instantaneous illumination over a time which is very large compared with the period of the ultrasonic vibration. As a result of the averaging, the light intensity at all the velocity nodes is the same. At all the velocity antinodes the intensity is also the same, but differs from the intensity at the nodes. Hence the period of the visible pattern must be equal to the distance between neighbouring nodes, i.e. $\frac{1}{2}\Lambda$.

Note. In a full investigation of the subject we should have to show why a system of bands is obtained on averaging, and not a uniform illumination of the liquid. This would require a detailed consideration of the complex problem of the propagation of a light wave in a strongly non-uniform medium, such as is presented by a liquid with an ultrasonic field in it. Such an investigation (which agrees with experiment) shows that bands must be observed. The aim of our present problem has been to find the distance between the bands, accepting their existence as an experimental fact.

334. The diffraction spectra contain, in addition to the fundamental frequency ω, the frequencies $\omega \pm m\Omega$, where Ω is the frequency of the ultrasonic vibrations, and m is an integer.

Solution. We take as the xy plane the wall of the vessel on which the light wave is incident, and as the z axis the direction of propagation of the light, whilst the x axis is perpendicular to the ultrasonic wave front. The field of the incident wave has the form

$$E = E_0 \cos(\omega t - kz).$$

On the front wall of the vessel, where $z = 0$, it is equal to $E_1 = E_0 \cos \omega t$. The field E_2 on the rear wall can be written as $E_2 = AE_1$, where A is the transmission of the vessel, which is obviously a periodic function of the x coordinate and time t. On expanding it in a Fourier series and neglecting higher harmonics, we can write

$$A = a + b_1 \cos \Omega t + b_2 \sin \Omega t,$$

where a, b_1, b_2 are independent of time. As a result, the amplitude of the field E_2 is modulated with the modulation frequency Ω. Such a field is equivalent to three harmonic fields with frequencies ω, $\omega - \Omega$, $\omega + \Omega$. For,

$$\begin{aligned} E_2 = AE_1 &= (a + b_1 \cos \Omega t + b_2 \sin \Omega t) \cos \omega t \\ &= a \cos \omega t + \tfrac{1}{2}\{b_1 \cos(\omega - \Omega)t - b_2 \sin(\omega - \Omega)t\} \\ &\quad + \tfrac{1}{2}\{b_1 \cos(\omega + \Omega)t + b_2 \sin(\omega + \Omega)t\}. \end{aligned}$$

Hence it follows that the secondary Huygens waves, propagated from the rear wall of the vessel, will also have the frequencies ω, $\omega - \Omega$, $\omega + \Omega$. The same frequencies appear in the diffraction spectrum. If higher harmonics are taken into account in the expansion of A, the frequencies $\omega \pm 2\Omega$, $\omega \pm 3\Omega$ etc. are added to the diffraction spectrum.

335. $\vartheta = \left(m + \frac{1}{2}\right)\frac{\lambda}{D}$, where m is an integer.

336. $x = f\vartheta = \left(m + \frac{1}{2}\right)\frac{f\lambda}{D}$, where m is an integer.

337. $\vartheta = 2\left(m + \frac{1}{2}\right)\frac{\lambda}{D}$, where m is an integer.

338. *Solution.* In the case of one beam (the mirror M_1 or M_2 is covered) a system of diffraction rings resulting from the diffraction at the circular diphragm of the mirror will be observed in the focal plane. The diameters of the rings are determined by the size of the diaphragm. In the case of two beams (M_1 and M_2 uncovered) two systems of rings, which do not in general coincide with one another, will be observed simultaneously. But, by rotating the mirrors M_2 and M_4, the second system of rings can be made to coincide with the first. In this case they interfere with one another, and the rings are intersected by dark and light bands perpendicular to the line M_1M_2.

339. *Solution.* According to Huygens' principle the real light sources can be replaced by virtual sources located in the planes of the diaphragms in front of the mirrors M_1 and M_2. We can assume for simplicity (without loss of generality) that the diaphragms are so small that they can be regarded as points. The problem now amounts to finding the interference pattern from two point sources S_1 and S_2 (Fig. 85), which are mutually coherent. The light beams from these sources, before arriving at the object lens L, undergo reflections from the mirrors M_1, M_2, M_3, M_4. We can exclude these reflections from our discussion provided we replace the sources S_1 and S_2 by the fictitious sources S_1'' and S_2'', which are their images in the plane mirrors. Given this replacement, the phases of S_1 and S_1'' are the same, and similarly the phases of S_2 and S_2''. The problem now amounts to Problem 335. When the mirrors M_3 and M_4 come closer together, the distance between S_1'' and S_2'' diminishes, and leads to an increase in the width of the interference bands.

Suppose that one of the stars transmits light at right angles to the straight line S_1S_2. The phases of the sources S_1 and S_2 (and hence of S_1'' and S_2'') will be the same. In order for the second star to give a system of bands, displaced relative to the first by half the width of a band, the phases of the secondary sources S_1 and S_2, produced by the second star, must differ by π. This gives

$$D \sin \vartheta \approx D\vartheta = \frac{\lambda}{2},$$

where ϑ is the angular distance between the stars, and D is the distance between the centres of the mirrors M_1 and M_2. Thus

$$\vartheta = \frac{\lambda}{2D}.$$

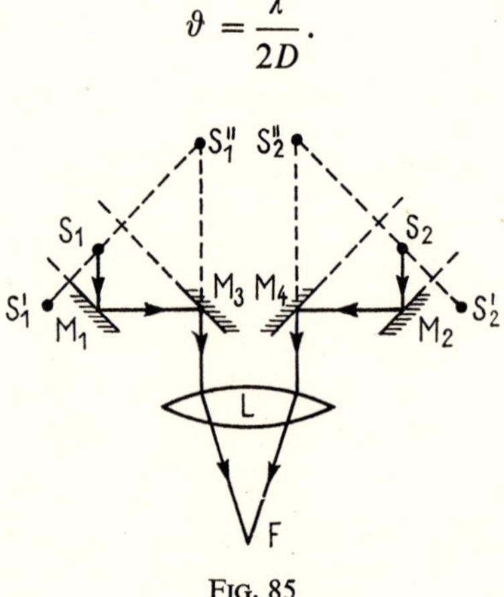

FIG. 85

If both stars are the same, the interference bands vanish when this condition is fulfilled. In general, the interference bands will vanish if

$$\vartheta = \left(m + \frac{1}{2}\right)\frac{\lambda}{D}.$$

If a star is replaced by a square of constant surface brightness, the square can be divided into linear sources, parallel to a side of the square, namely, the side which is perpendicular to S_1S_2. If the angular dimensions of the sides of the square are

$$\vartheta = \frac{\lambda}{D},$$

each linear source of one half of the square annihilates the interference bands given by the corresponding sources of the second half of the square. In general, the interference bands vanish when

$$\vartheta = 2\left(m + \frac{1}{2}\right)\frac{\lambda}{D}.$$

The calculation is rather more difficult for a star with a circular disc of constant surface brightness. It turns out that the first disappearance of the interference bands occurs when

$$\vartheta = 1{\cdot}22\frac{\lambda}{D},$$

where ϑ is the angular diameter of the star.

340. $0{\cdot}047''$.

341. $\delta\varphi \approx \dfrac{\lambda}{D}$.

342. (1) $\delta\varphi \approx \lambda/d$. When $\lambda = 1$ m, $\delta\varphi \approx 1°$; when $\lambda = 10$ cm, $\delta\varphi \approx 7'$.

(2) $\delta\varphi \approx \sqrt{\lambda/b}$. When $\lambda = 1$ m, $\delta\varphi \approx 10''$; when $\lambda = 10$ cm, $\delta\varphi \approx 3''$.

(3) $h \ll \sqrt{b\lambda}$. When $\lambda = 1$ m, $\sqrt{b\lambda} = 19{\cdot}5$ km; when $\lambda = 10$ cm, $\sqrt{b\lambda} = 6{\cdot}2$ km.

343. $\delta\varphi \approx \lambda/D$. When $\lambda = 1$ m, $\delta\varphi \approx 0{\cdot}06''$. When $\lambda = 10$ cm, $\delta\varphi \approx 0{\cdot}006''$.

The method requires that the source of radio radiation be located on the straight line joining the observation point to the centre of the moon. In addition, it imposes very strict requirements on the smoothness of the lunar surface and on the deviations of the shape of the moon from the spherical. The height of a surface irregularity throughout the lunar disc must be small compared with $h = b\lambda/D$. The difference between the greatest and least diameters of the lunar disc must also not exceed this value. When $\lambda = 1$ m, $h \approx 100$ m;

when $\lambda = 10$ cm, $h \approx 10$ m. These rigid demands preclude the possibility of using the method, at least for radio waves with $\lambda < 100$ m.

344. $\vartheta \approx \lambda/2h \approx 3'$.

345. $\vartheta \approx \lambda/2R \approx 0{\cdot}2''$ (R is the radius of the earth).

346. $\vartheta \approx \lambda/2h \approx 20''$, the height of the satellite above the moon's surface $h \approx 500$ km. It is difficult to use an earth satellite operating at the wavelength 100 m, in fact, it is usually quite impossible because of the influence of the ionosphere.

347. The diagram will be a "beavertail" with angular dimensions λ/D in one direction and λ/d in the other.

348. The angular resolving power is of the order λ/D, the area of the order d^2.

§ 4. Polarisation of Light. Fresnel's Formulae

349. The intensity of the transmitted light is the same as in the case of the usual zone plate.

351. It is halved, independently of the polarisation of the incident light.

352. The resolution is unchanged.

353. $r = \left(\dfrac{n-1}{n+1}\right)^2$.

354. 28 per cent.

356. *Solution.* If the reflection is not total, it follows from the law of refraction of light that, for each angle of incidence φ there is a corresponding *real* angle of refraction ψ. Thus both the ratios*

$$\frac{R_s}{\mathscr{E}_s} = -\frac{\sin(\varphi - \psi)}{\sin(\varphi + \psi)}, \quad \frac{R_p}{\mathscr{E}_p} = \frac{\tan(\varphi - \psi)}{\tan(\varphi + \psi)}$$

* $\mathscr{E}_s$ and $\mathscr{E}_p$ are the complex amplitudes of the principal components of the incident wave, the electric vectors of which are respectively perpendicular and parallel to the plane of incidence. R_s and R_p have the same meaning for the reflected wave.

are real. This means physically that, on reflection, there is either no phase change at all, or the phase change is 180°. If the incident wave is linearly polarised, the phase difference between its component having the electric vector perpendicular to the plane of incidence and the component having the electric vector lying in this plane, is equal either to 0° or 180°. In view of what has been said, the components of the reflected wave will have the same phase difference. On addition, these components yield a linearly polarised wave.

357. $\tan \delta = \cos(\varphi - \psi) \tan \alpha$; $\tan \varrho = -\dfrac{\cos(\varphi - \psi)}{\cos(\varphi + \psi)} \tan \alpha$.

358. (1) 56°19′; (2) $\Delta = \dfrac{4n^2 - (1 + n^2)^2}{4n^2 + (1 + n^2)^2} = -0{\cdot}08$.

359. 57°05′.

360. (1) They will. (2) They will not.

361. If the light is polarised at right angles to the plane of incidence, the interference bands vanish for the angles of incidence $\varphi_1 = \arctan n_1$ and $\varphi_2 = \arctan n_2$. If the light is polarised in the plane of incidence, there is no vanishing of the interference bands.

362. The result is obtained directly from Fresnel's formulae.

363. $\varrho = \varrho_1 + \varrho_2\sigma_1^2 + \varrho_2\sigma_1^2\varrho_1\varrho_2 + \cdots = \varrho_1 + \dfrac{\varrho_2\sigma_1^2}{1 - \varrho_1\varrho_2}$;

$$\sigma = \sigma_1\sigma_2 + \sigma_1\sigma_2\varrho_1\varrho_2 + \sigma_1\sigma_2(\varrho_1\varrho_2)^2 + \cdots = \frac{\sigma_1\sigma_2}{1 - \varrho_1\varrho_2}.$$

364. *Solution.* We associate with the system of m planes a similar $(m + 1)$-th plane. The first m planes can be replaced by one plane with reflection and transmission coefficients ϱ_m and σ_m. The problem now reduces to the previous one, and we obtain for the reflection and transmission coefficients of the $(m + 1)$-th plane:

$$\varrho_{m+1} = \varrho_m + \varrho \frac{\sigma_m^2}{1 - \varrho\varrho_m};$$

$$\sigma_{m+1} = \frac{\sigma\sigma_m}{1 - \varrho\varrho_m}.$$

We easily obtain from this, by induction:

$$\varrho_m = \frac{m\varrho}{1 + (m - 1)\varrho};$$

$$\sigma_m = \frac{1 - \varrho}{1 + (m - 1)\varrho}.$$

365. $\varrho_N = \dfrac{2N}{2N + 5{\cdot}76}$; $\sigma_N = \dfrac{5{\cdot}76}{2N + 5{\cdot}76}$ (see Fig. 86).

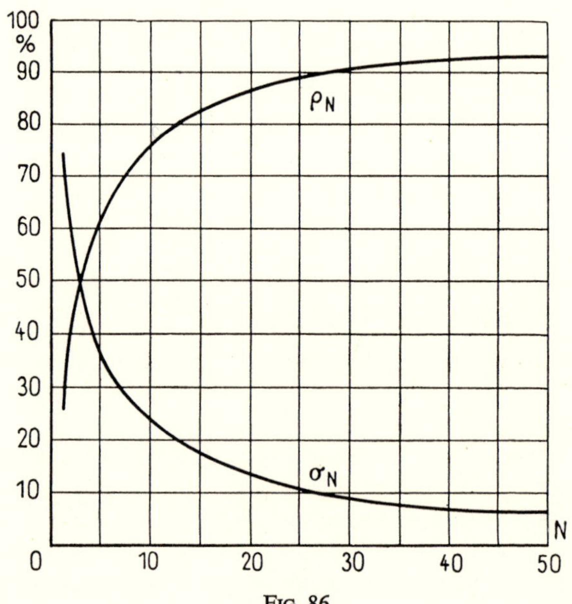

FIG. 86

366. $$\Delta = \frac{N(\varrho_s - \varrho_p)}{(2N - 1)\varrho_s\varrho_p - (N - 1)(\varrho_s + \varrho_p) - 1};$$

$$\Delta' = \frac{\varrho_s - \varrho_p}{2(N - 1)\varrho_s\varrho_p + (\varrho_s + \varrho_p)};$$

$$\frac{I_s}{I_p} = \frac{1 - \varrho_s}{1 - \varrho_p} \cdot \frac{(2N - 1)\varrho_p + 1}{(2N - 1)\varrho_s + 1},$$

where ϱ_s and ϱ_p are the reflection coefficients for waves polarised in the plane of incidence and at right angles to it, for one reflecting surface:

$$\varrho_s = \left(\frac{\cos\varphi - n\cos\psi}{\cos\varphi + n\cos\psi}\right)^2; \quad \varrho_p = \left(\frac{n\cos\varphi - \cos\psi}{n\cos\varphi + \cos\psi}\right)^2.$$

367. $\Delta = \dfrac{\cos^2(\varphi-\psi) - \cos^2(\varphi+\psi)}{\cos^2(\varphi-\psi) + \cos^2(\varphi+\psi)} = 0{\cdot}0;\ 0{\cdot}82;\ 1{\cdot}0;\ 0{\cdot}0.$

368. $-0{\cdot}015$; $-0{\cdot}091$; $-0{\cdot}176$; $-0{\cdot}402$.

369.

N	1	2	3	4	5
$-\Delta = \dfrac{N}{N+5{\cdot}76}$	0·148	0·258	0·342	0·409	0·466

N	6	7	8	9	10
$-\Delta = \dfrac{N}{N+5{\cdot}76}$	0·512	0·548	0·582	0·611	0·635

370. It follows from Fresnel's formula:

$$\frac{R_p}{\mathscr{E}_p} = \frac{\tan(\varphi-\psi)}{\tan(\varphi+\psi)}$$

that R_p changes sign on passing through the Brewster angle. This means physically that R_p here undergoes a jump in phase of π. Given strict validity of Fresnel's formula, this would not lead to a destruction of continuity, since $R_p = 0$ at the Brewster angle. In reality R_p does not vanish for any angle of incidence. Hence there must exist a neighbourhood of the Brewster angle (usually quite narrow), passage through which implies a continuous change of phase of R_p from 0 to π. Such a neighbourhood does not exist for light whose electric vector is at right angles to the plane of incidence. Hence the fact that Brewster's law is not strictly fulfilled implies the elliptic polarisation of the reflected light, as was mentioned in the text of the problem. The converse can be proved if we resolve the incident wave into components with vibrations in the plane of incidence and at right angles to it, and use the fact that these components are reflected independently of one another.

371. $$\frac{R_s}{\mathscr{E}_s} = \frac{\sqrt{\dfrac{\varepsilon_1}{\mu_1}}\cos\varphi - \sqrt{\dfrac{\varepsilon_2}{\mu_2}}\cos\psi}{\sqrt{\dfrac{\varepsilon_1}{\mu_1}}\cos\varphi + \sqrt{\dfrac{\varepsilon_2}{\mu_2}}\cos\psi};$$

$$\frac{R_p}{\mathscr{E}_p} = \frac{\sqrt{\dfrac{\varepsilon_2}{\mu_2}}\cos\varphi - \sqrt{\dfrac{\varepsilon_1}{\mu_1}}\cos\psi}{\sqrt{\dfrac{\varepsilon_2}{\mu_2}}\cos\varphi + \sqrt{\dfrac{\varepsilon_1}{\mu_1}}\cos\psi};$$

$$\frac{D_s}{\mathscr{E}_s} = \frac{2\sqrt{\dfrac{\varepsilon_1}{\mu_1}}\cos\varphi}{\sqrt{\dfrac{\varepsilon_1}{\mu_1}}\cos\varphi + \sqrt{\dfrac{\varepsilon_2}{\mu_2}}\cos\psi};$$

$$\frac{D_p}{\mathscr{E}_p} = \frac{2\sqrt{\dfrac{\varepsilon_1}{\mu_1}}\cos\varphi}{\sqrt{\dfrac{\varepsilon_2}{\mu_2}}\cos\varphi + \sqrt{\dfrac{\varepsilon_1}{\mu_1}}\cos\psi}.$$

372. *Solution.* If Brewster's law holds, the Brewster angle, at which the p-component of the electric field is not reflected, is given by

$$\tan\varphi_B = \sqrt{\frac{\varepsilon_2}{\varepsilon_1}\,\frac{\varepsilon_2\mu_1 - \varepsilon_1\mu_2}{\varepsilon_2\mu_2 - \varepsilon_1\mu_1}}. \qquad (1)$$

It is possible for the s-component not to be reflected. The angle at which this is the case is determined by the equation

$$\tan\varphi_B' = \sqrt{\frac{\mu_2}{\mu_1}\,\frac{\varepsilon_2\mu_1 - \varepsilon_1\mu_2}{\varepsilon_1\mu_1 - \varepsilon_2\mu_2}}. \qquad (2)$$

These two cases are mutually exclusive, since the signs of the expressions under the square roots in (1) and (2) are opposite. It is assumed that ε and μ are essentially positive. Thus there is always an angle at which either the p-, or the s-component of the incident wave is not reflected.

374. The optical thickness of the film must be equal to a quarter the wavelength of the light *in vacuo*. The film refractive index $n' = \sqrt{n}$, where n is the refractive index of the glass. There will also be no reflection in the case when the optical thickness of the film is $ln' = l\sqrt{n} = \lambda/4 + N\lambda/2$, where N is an integer. But thick films cannot be employed when using white light.

The problem is easily solved if we consider the interference of the waves reflected from the upper and lower surfaces of the film and neglect multiple reflections (an accurate calculation shows that the result is unchanged if these are taken into account).

375. There is no loss of generality if we choose the positive directions of the deflections in the two waves so that the phase difference between them lies between 0 and π. The terminus of the resultant of the two added vectors will now describe an ellipse in the direction from the vector which is advanced in phase to the vector lagging in phase.

376. The required angle φ is given by the equation

$$\sin^4\varphi - \frac{n^2+1}{n^2}\cos^2\frac{\pi}{8}\sin^2\varphi + \frac{1}{n^2}\cos^2\frac{\pi}{8} = 0,$$

which gives $\varphi_1 = 60°32'$; $\varphi_2 = 38°42'$.

377. To the left.

378. $\varphi = \arcsin\sqrt{\dfrac{2n^2}{1+n^2}}$; $\quad \delta = 2\arctan\dfrac{1-n^2}{2n}$,

where n is the refractive index of the second (optically less dense) medium relative to the first ($n < 1$).

379. $n \geqslant \dfrac{1}{\sqrt{2}-1} \approx 2{\cdot}41.$

380. It is not possible.

381. $n = \dfrac{1 + \sin\dfrac{3\pi}{8}}{\cos\dfrac{3\pi}{8}} = 5{\cdot}028.$

Since there is no substance with a refractive index of 5, it is not possible to realise this case in optics. It could be realised for the longer electromagnetic waves.

382. $6°29'$ or $44°38'$. Right-handed.

383. $69°21'$ or $42°46'$. Right-handed.

384. $n = \dfrac{1}{\sqrt{2} - 1} = 2{\cdot}4143; \quad A = 35°34'$.

385. *Solution.* Suppose that the electric vector oscillates at right angles to the plane of incidence. We consider the electric field in the first medium at a point on the boundary. The electric field of the incident wave at this point has a harmonic variation in time. It can be represented by a vector $\overrightarrow{OA}$, rotating uniformly about the point O with angular velocity ω (Fig. 87). The projection of the terminus of this vector on to the plane of the boundary gives the value of the electric field of the incident wave at the point in question at the given instant. The electric field of the reflected wave can be represented by a vector $\overrightarrow{AB}$ of the same length and rotating with

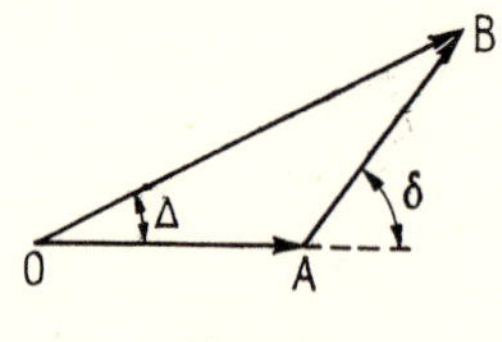

FIG. 87

the same angular velocity about the point A. The angle δ between the vectors $\overrightarrow{OA}$ and $\overrightarrow{AB}$ is the phase jump on reflection. The resultant field at the point of the first medium is given by the vector $\overrightarrow{OB} = \overrightarrow{OA} + \overrightarrow{AB}$, rotating about the point O. In view of the continuity of the tangential components of the electric field the same vector $\overrightarrow{OB}$ will represent the electric field along the other side of the boundary, i.e. the field of the refracted wave. Thus the angle Δ (Fig. 87) is the phase jump of the wave when it penetrates the second medium. Since triangle OAB is isosceles, $\delta = 2\Delta$. The proof is easily extended to the case when the electric vector oscillates in the plane of incidence.

386. $n > 3{\cdot}732$.

387. *Solution.* We locate the origin on the upper boundary of the layer and introduce the notation $\zeta = z + a$. We can now write:

$$k_0 n = \frac{p}{\zeta}, \tag{1}$$

where p is a constant, and k_0 is the wave number *in vacuo*. On the upper boundary $z = 0$, and hence $\zeta = a$. Let b denote the value of ζ on the lower boundary. Obviously,

$$l = b - a, \quad k_0 n_1 = \frac{p}{a}, \quad k_0 n_2 = \frac{p}{b},$$

whence

$$a = \frac{n_2}{n_1 - n_2} l,$$

$$b = \frac{n_1}{n_1 - n_2} l,$$

$$p = \frac{n_1 n_2}{n_1 - n_2} k_0 l = 2\pi \frac{n_1 n_2}{n_1 - n_2} \frac{l}{\lambda}, \tag{2}$$

$$n = \frac{n_1 n_2}{n_2\left(1 - \frac{z}{l}\right) + n_1 \frac{z}{l}}. \tag{3}$$

If the incident wave is linearly polarised, the reflected and transmitted waves, as also the field inside the layer, will also be linearly polarised (in the same plane). Let the electric field $\boldsymbol{E}$ be parallel to the y axis, and the magnetic field $\boldsymbol{H}$ parallel to the x axis. Inside the layer

$$\left.\begin{aligned} \frac{\partial E}{\partial \zeta} &= -ik_0 H, \\ \frac{\partial H}{\partial \zeta} &= -ik_0 n^2 E. \end{aligned}\right\} \tag{4}$$

On eliminating H, we get

$$\frac{\partial^2 E}{\partial \zeta^2} + \frac{p^2}{\zeta^2} E = 0. \tag{5}$$

The general solution of this equation is

$$E = \sqrt{\zeta}\,(A\zeta^q + B\zeta^{-q}), \tag{6}$$

where A and B are arbitrary constants, and q is given by

$$q^2 = \frac{1}{4} - p^2. \tag{7}$$

We obtain from (4) and (6):

$$H = \frac{i}{k_0\sqrt{\zeta}}\left\{\left(q + \frac{1}{2}\right)A\zeta^q - \left(q - \frac{1}{2}\right)B\zeta^{-q}\right\}. \tag{8}$$

On the upper boundary of the layer $E = \mathscr{E} + R, H = n_1(R - \mathscr{E})$. On the lower boundary,

$$E = D\exp(-ik_0n_2l), \quad H = -n_2D\exp(-ik_0n_2l).$$

On equating these with the values of E and H on the boundary obtained from (6) and (8), we find that

$$\sqrt{a}\,(Aa^q + Ba^{-q}) = \mathscr{E} + R,$$

$$\frac{i\sqrt{a}}{p}\left[\left(q + \frac{1}{2}\right)Aa^q - \left(q - \frac{1}{2}\right)Ba^{-q}\right] = R - \mathscr{E},$$

$$\sqrt{b}\,(Ab^q + Bb^{-q}) = De^{-ik_0n_2l},$$

$$\frac{i\sqrt{b}}{p}\left[\left(q + \frac{1}{2}\right)Ab^q - \left(q - \frac{1}{2}\right)Bb^{-q}\right] = -De^{-ik_0n_2l}.$$

On solving these equations, we obtain after a few transformations:

$$\left.\begin{aligned} \frac{R}{\mathscr{E}} &= -\frac{1}{2}\,\frac{\sinh\alpha}{q\cosh\alpha + ip\sinh\alpha}, \\ \frac{D}{\mathscr{E}} &= \frac{q\sqrt{\dfrac{n_1}{n_2}}}{\cosh\alpha + ip\sinh\alpha}\,e^{ik_0n_2l}, \end{aligned}\right\} \tag{9}$$

where

$$\alpha = q \ln \frac{n_2}{n_1}. \tag{10}$$

The solution is most conveniently written in this form if $p^2 < \frac{1}{4}$, i.e. when q is real. If $p^2 > \frac{1}{4}$, then $q^2 < 0$. In this case q and α are purely imaginary. We put

$$\alpha = i\alpha'; \quad q = iq', \tag{11}$$

where α' and q' are real. Now,

$$\left.\begin{aligned} \frac{R}{\mathscr{E}} &= -\frac{1}{2}\,\frac{\sin \alpha'}{q' \cos \alpha' + ip \sin \alpha'}, \\ \frac{D}{\mathscr{E}} &= \frac{q' \sqrt{\dfrac{n_1}{n_2}}}{q' \cos \alpha' + ip \sin \alpha'}\, e^{ik_0 n_2 l}. \end{aligned}\right\} \tag{12}$$

The intermediate case $p^2 = \frac{1}{4}$ corresponds to $q = q' = 0$. In this case (9) and (12) both lead to the indeterminate form $\frac{0}{0}$, which can be treated by the usual methods. We obtain

$$\left.\begin{aligned} \frac{R}{\mathscr{E}} &= \frac{\ln \dfrac{n_2}{n_1}}{2 + i \ln \dfrac{n_2}{n_1}}, \\ \frac{D}{\mathscr{E}} &= \frac{2\sqrt{\dfrac{n_1}{n_2}}}{2 + i \ln \dfrac{n_2}{n_1}}\, e^{ik_0 n_2 l}. \end{aligned}\right\} \tag{13}$$

If $l = 0$, then $p = 0$, $q = \frac{1}{2}$, and (9) gives

$$\frac{R}{\mathscr{E}} = -\tanh \alpha = -\tanh\left(\ln \sqrt{\frac{n_2}{n_1}}\right) = -\frac{n_2 - n_1}{n_2 + n_1},$$

$$\frac{D}{\mathscr{E}} = \frac{1}{\cosh \alpha}\sqrt{\frac{n_1}{n_2}} = \frac{\sqrt{\dfrac{n_1}{n_2}}}{\cosh\left(\ln \sqrt{\dfrac{n_2}{n_1}}\right)} = \frac{2n_1}{n_2 + n_1}.$$

The same results are obtained as a first approximation if $l \ll \lambda$. Hence, if the thickness of the intermediate layer is very small compared with the wavelength, as would be expected, the reflection and refraction become practically the same as in the case of a sharp boundary.

Let us take the other extreme case, when $l \gg \lambda$. Inthis case $p^2 \gg 1$, and the term $\frac{1}{4}$ in (7) can be neglected, i.e. we put $q' = p$. We now obtain from (12), for the reflection coefficient:

$$\varrho = \left| \frac{R}{\mathscr{E}} \right|^2 = \frac{\sin^2\left(p \ln \frac{n_2}{n_1}\right)}{4p^2}. \tag{14}$$

It is clear from this that the reflection coefficient ϱ is a damped oscillatory function of the layer thickness l. The amplitudes of the oscillations are

$$\varrho_{\max} = \frac{1}{4p^2} = \left(\frac{n_1 - n_2}{4\pi n_1 n_2}\right)^2 \left(\frac{\lambda}{l}\right)^2 \tag{15}$$

and decrease inversely proportional to the square of the intermediate layer thickness. Hence, for layers whose thickness is large compared with the wavelength, reflection is virtually absent. This conclusion is not connected with the special law of variation of the refractive index (3), but refers to any thick intermediate layer with smoothly varying refractive index.

388. *Solution.* The transversality of the wave, and equation (1), follow directly from Maxwell's equations.

To obtain the approximate solutions of (1), we shall seek a particular solution in the form

$$E = A(z)\, e^{i\frac{\omega}{c}\Phi(z)},$$

where $A(z)$ and $\Phi(z)$ are real functions. After substituting in (1) and separating real and imaginary parts, we obtain the two equations:

$$\frac{d^2A}{dz^2} + \frac{\omega^2}{c^2} A \left\{ n^2 - \left(\frac{d\Phi}{dz}\right)^2 \right\} = 0, \tag{1}$$

$$2\frac{dA}{dz}\frac{d\Phi}{dz} + A\frac{d^2\Phi}{dz^2} = 0. \tag{2}$$

If

$$\left|\frac{d^2A}{dz^2}\right| \ll \frac{\omega^2}{c^2}|A|, \tag{3}$$

the first term in (1) can be discarded, and we get

$$\left(\frac{d\Phi}{dz}\right)^2 = n^2, \tag{4}$$

whence

$$\Phi = \pm\int_{z_0}^{z} n(z)\,dz. \tag{5}$$

Equation (2) now gives

$$\frac{d}{dz}(A^2n) = 0, \quad A = \frac{\text{const}}{\sqrt{n}}. \tag{6}$$

The general solution is

$$\boldsymbol{E} = \frac{\boldsymbol{C}_1}{\sqrt{n}}e^{+\frac{i\omega}{c}\int_{z_{01}}^{z} n(z)dz} + \frac{\boldsymbol{C}_2}{\sqrt{n}}e^{-\frac{i\omega}{c}\int_{z_{02}}^{z} n(z)dz}, \tag{7}$$

where $\boldsymbol{C}_1$, $\boldsymbol{C}_2$ are arbitrary, in general complex, constants. Notice that there are only two arbitrary constants in this solution, since any previously assigned values can be given to the constants z_{01} and z_{02} by a suitable choice of $\boldsymbol{C}_1$, $\boldsymbol{C}_2$.

On using (6) it can easily be shown that (3) is satisfied on satisfying the two conditions

$$\frac{\lambda}{2\pi}\left|\frac{dn}{dz}\right| \ll n, \quad \frac{\lambda}{2\pi}\left|\frac{d^2n}{dz^2}\right| \ll \left|\frac{dn}{dz}\right|, \tag{8}$$

where $\lambda = 2\pi c/\omega n$ is the wavelength in the medium. Since $\lambda n = \text{const}$, the first of these conditions can also be written as

$$\left|\frac{d\lambda}{dz}\right| \ll 2\pi. \tag{9}$$

389. *Solution.* Evaluation of the time average of the energy flux density:

$$\bar{\boldsymbol{S}} = \frac{c}{4\pi}[\boldsymbol{E} \wedge \boldsymbol{H}]$$

for each of the waves mentioned in the problem, shows that $\bar{S}$ = const, i.e. $\bar{S}$ is independent of z. It follows from this that the wave is propagated without reflection.

390. The assertion may be verified by direct substitution. The proof of the absence of reflection follows the same lines as in the previous problem.

391. *Solution.* If we locate the origin on the boundary between the media and write $\mathscr{E}$, R, D for the amplitudes of the incident, reflected and transmitted waves, we can write for the electric fields in the first and second media:

$$\left.\begin{aligned} E_1 &= \frac{\mathscr{E}}{\sqrt{n}} e^{-i\frac{\omega}{c}\int_0^z n\,dz} + \frac{R}{\sqrt{n}} e^{+i\frac{\omega}{c}\int_0^z n\,dz}, \\ E_2 &= \frac{D}{\sqrt{n}} e^{-i\frac{\omega}{c}\int_0^z n\,dz}. \end{aligned}\right\} \tag{1}$$

In view of the continuity of the tangential components of the electric vector:

$$\mathscr{E} + R = D. \tag{2}$$

It may easily be seen by using Maxwell's equations that the continuity of the tangential components of the magnetic vector is expressible as

$$\frac{dE_1}{dz} = \frac{dE_2}{dz}, \tag{3}$$

which must be satisfied on the boundary between the media. On substituting expression (1) in this, we easily find from the resulting relationship and (2) that

$$\frac{R}{\mathscr{E}} = ic\frac{\left(\frac{dn}{dz}\right)_2 - \left(\frac{dn}{dz}\right)_1}{4\omega n^2(0)} = \frac{i\lambda_0}{8\pi n^2(0)}\left[\left(\frac{dn}{dz}\right)_2 - \left(\frac{dn}{dz}\right)_1\right]. \tag{4}$$

In the denominator, we have neglected the small quantity $(dn/dz)_2 - (dn/dz)_1$ by comparison with $2n\omega/c$. The reflection coefficient is obtained by squaring the modulus of expression (4).

§ 5. Crystal Optics

392. See Fig. 88 (*o* is the ordinary ray, *e* the extraordinary ray).

393. Rays issuing from a point A of the remote object and incident on the observer's eye are virtually parallel. Each ray splits into two when it enters the plane-parallel crystal plate. On leaving the plate the two rays remain parallel, even though they have undergone different lateral displacements. The eye collects the two rays at the same point of the retina, since it is accommodated to viewing remote objects (to infinity). This point of convergence of the rays is in fact the (unique) image of the point A.

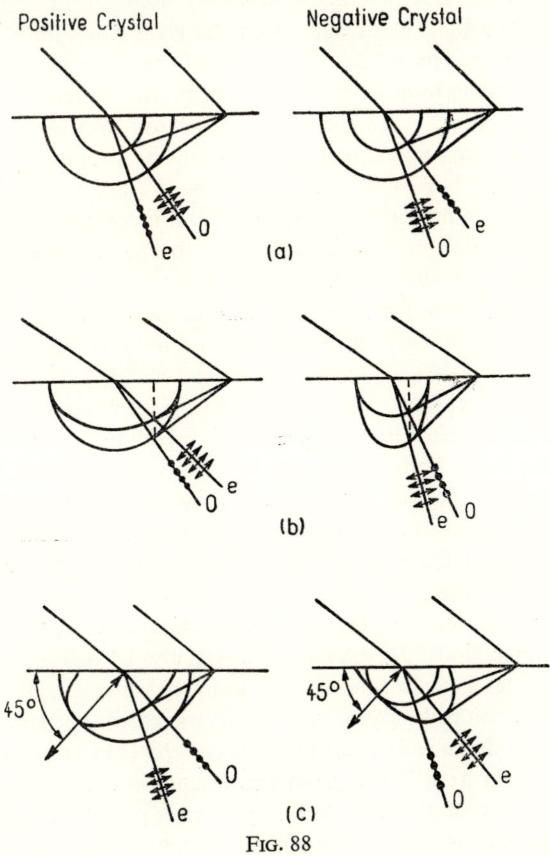

Fig. 88

394. $f = 5$ cm.

395. The refractive indices yield the ratios of the normal velocities.

396. Any orientation of the plate can be used to find the refractive index of the ordinary ray. To obtain the principal refractive index of the extraordinary ray, it must be orientated so that the plane through the optical axis of the crystal and the normal to the boundary between the plate and the glass of the crystal refractometer is at right angles to the plane of incidence.

Solution. The crystal refractometer is based on the phenomenon of total internal reflection. A plate of the investigated crystal is stuck to the surface of glass with a very high (up to 2) refractive index N. The light is incident from the glass side and is reflected from the plate. The refractive index n of the plate material is calculated from the limiting angle of total internal reflection from the formula $n = N \sin \varphi$. In the case of reflection from a crystal there are two limiting angles, corresponding to the ordinary and extraordinary rays. The limiting angle for the ordinary ray is independent of the plate orientation, and can therefore be measured with any orientation. The limiting angle for the extraordinary ray is measured by varying the plate orientation.

We shall assume for simplicity that the incident light is always polarised so that only the extraordinary wave is obtained in the crystal.

Generally speaking, in the case of total internal reflection the light field penetrates into the "second" medium as a non-uniform wave. But if the light is incident at exactly the limiting angle for total internal reflection, the wave in the second medium is uniform. It travels parallel to the boundary surface. To be more precise, the wave normal of the wave in the second medium is parallel to the line of intersection of the plane of incidence with the boundary plane. We rotate the crystal so that its optical axis is at right angles to this line of intersection. The wave in the crystal now travels at right angles to the optical axis. In this case the uniform wave is well known to split up into an ordinary wave with electric vector perpendicular to the optical axis, and an extraordinary wave with electric vector parallel to the optical axis. Thus, given this orientation of the crystal, the electric vector of the extraordinary wave is parallel to the optical axis. This means that the principal refractive index of the extraordinary wave is measured in this case on the crystal refractometer.

397. The optical axis must be parallel to the refracting edge of the prism.

398. The plate must be cut parallel to the optical axis. $d_1 = 0{\cdot}603$ mm; $d_2 = 0{\cdot}673$ mm.

399. 4 spots are formed on the screen. The intensities are in the ratios 1:3:1:3.

400. It is diminished in the ratio 3:2.

401. The principal planes of the polaroids in the glass and lamps of the automobile must be parallel to one another and at 45° to the horizontal. They must be turned in the same direction on all cars (reckoned with respect to the direction of travel).

402. $\varphi = 5°17'$.

403. $R = 5160$ mμ.

404. *Solution.* After passing through the polariser the light becomes linearly polarised. It splits up in the crystal plate into two waves, polarised in perpendicular planes and propagated with different velocities. Thus, if the light is monochromatic, a phase difference arises between these waves after passing through the plate, and on addition they in general yield an elliptically polarised wave. The orientation and shape of the ellipse will depend on the phase difference. Given the same plate thickness, they will vary with variation of the wavelength. In particular, the ellipse may degenerate into a straight line. The fraction of the light passing through the analyser depends on the shape of the ellipse and its orientation relative to the principal plane of the analyser. Thus, if the incident light is white, the different monochromatic components will in general be transmitted by the system in different degrees, which leads to the colouration observed.

405. When the principal plane of the analyser is parallel to the principal direction in the plate.

406. The brightness ratio is (1) proportional to the square of the cosine of the angle of rotation and (2) proportional to the square of the cotangent of the angle of rotation.

407. *Solution.* The plane wave in the crystal has the form

$$E = E_0 e^{i[\omega t - (k \cdot r)]},$$
$$D = D_0 e^{i[\omega t - (k \cdot r)]}, \qquad (1)$$
$$H = H_0 e^{i[\omega t - (k \cdot r)]},$$

where F_0, D_0, H_0 are constant vectors, and k is the wave vector, connected with the normal wave velocity v by

$$k = \frac{\omega}{v} N.$$

We substitute expressions (1) in Maxwell's equations

$$\text{curl } H = \frac{1}{c} \frac{\partial D}{\partial t}, \quad \text{curl } E = -\frac{1}{c} \frac{\partial H}{\partial t}. \qquad (2)$$

Differentiation of vectors (1) with respect to time amounts to multiplication by $i\omega$, and differentiation with respect to the coordinates x, y, z to multiplication by $-ik_x$, $-ik_y$, $-ik_z$. Hence

$$\text{curl } H = \begin{vmatrix} e_x & e_y & e_z \\ \frac{\partial}{\partial x} & \frac{\partial}{\partial y} & \frac{\partial}{\partial z} \\ H_x & H_y & H_z \end{vmatrix} = -i \begin{vmatrix} e_x & e_y & e_z \\ k_x & k_y & k_z \\ H_x & H_y & H_z \end{vmatrix} = -i[k \wedge H)$$

and similarly for curl E. Substitution in (2) gives

$$D = -\frac{c}{v}[N \wedge H], \quad H = \frac{c}{v}[N \wedge E]. \qquad (3)$$

408. *Solution.* On eliminating H from formulae (3) (see the solution of the previous problem), we get

$$v^2 D - c^2 E = -c^2 (N \cdot E) N, \qquad (1)$$

whence

$$v^2 = c^2 \frac{(D \cdot E)}{D^2}. \qquad (2)$$

409. *Solution.* The first two statements follow at once from (2) of the previous solution, as also from the connection between the vectors $\boldsymbol{D}$ and $\boldsymbol{E}$:

$$D_\alpha = \sum_\beta \varepsilon_{\alpha\beta} E_\beta \quad (\alpha, \beta = x, y, z).$$

The vectors $\boldsymbol{E}$ and $\boldsymbol{D}$ define a plane to which the vector $\boldsymbol{H}$ is perpendicular. After this, the vector $\boldsymbol{N}$ is defined as perpendicular to the plane $(\boldsymbol{D}, \boldsymbol{H})$ or to the plane $(\boldsymbol{E}, \boldsymbol{H})$.

410. $a_\alpha = \dfrac{c}{\sqrt{\varepsilon_\alpha}} \quad (\alpha = x, y, z),$

where a_α is the normal velocity of the wave when the electric vector is along the dielectric axis α. The three quantities a_α are called the principal light velocities in the crystal.

411. *Solution.* On expressing the vector $\boldsymbol{E}$ in terms of $\boldsymbol{D}$ in the left-hand side of (1) (solution of Problem 408), we get

$$D_\alpha = -\frac{c^2}{v^2 - a_\alpha^2}(\boldsymbol{N} \cdot \boldsymbol{E}) N_\alpha \quad (\alpha = x, y, z). \tag{1}$$

On multiplying both sides of this equation by N_α, summing over α and noting that $(\boldsymbol{N} \cdot \boldsymbol{D}) = 0$, we find that

$$\sum_\alpha \frac{N_\alpha^2}{v^2 - a_\alpha^2} = 0, \tag{2}$$

or more fully:

$$\frac{N_x^2}{v^2 - a_x^2} + \frac{N_y^2}{v^2 - a_y^2} + \frac{N_z^2}{v^2 - a_z^2} = 0. \tag{3}$$

This formula is called Fresnel's law for the normal velocities in the crystal.

412. *Solution.* We write down Fresnel's law (3) (see the solution of the previous problem) as

$$F(v^2) \equiv (v^2 - a_y^2)(v^2 - a_z^2)N_x^2 + (v^2 - a_z^2)(v^2 - a_x^2)N_y^2$$
$$+ (v^2 - a_x^2)(v^2 - a_y^2)N_z^2 = 0. \tag{1}$$

This quadratic equation in v^2 has two real positive roots. To prove this, we choose the coordinates axes so that

$$a_x \geqslant a_y \geqslant a_z. \tag{2}$$

We now have:

$$F(a_x^2) = (a_x^2 - a_y^2)(a_x^2 - a_z^2) \geqslant 0,$$
$$F(a_y^2) = (a_y^2 - a_z^2)(a_y^2 - a_x^2) \leqslant 0,$$
$$F(a_z^2) = (a_z^2 - a_x^2)(a_z^2 - a_y^2) \geqslant 0.$$

It is clear from this that (1) has two real positive roots, one of which v'^2 lies between a_x^2 and a_y^2, and the other v''^2 between a_y^2 and a_z^2. These roots correspond to two waves travelling with normal velocities v' and v'':

$$a_x \geqslant v' \geqslant a_y \geqslant v'' \geqslant a_z. \qquad (3)$$

The linear polarisation of each of the waves follows from

$$\left.\begin{aligned} D'_x : D'_y : D'_z &= \frac{N_x}{v'^2 - a_x^2} : \frac{N_y}{v'^2 - a_y^2} : \frac{N_z}{v'^2 - a_z^2}, \\ D''_x : D''_y : D''_z &= \frac{N_x}{v''^2 - a_x^2} : \frac{N_y}{v''^2 - a_y^2} : \frac{N_z}{v''^2 - a_z^2}, \end{aligned}\right\} \qquad (4)$$

which are obtained from (1) (see the solution of Problem 411). The primes refer to one wave, and the double primes to the other. Formulae (4) show that the ratios $D_x : D_y : D_z$ are real for both waves. This means physically that there is no phase shift between the oscillations D_x, D_y, D_z, whence follows the linear polarisation of the two waves.

On now multiplying the first of the equations

$$v'^2\boldsymbol{D}' - c^2\boldsymbol{E}' = -c^2(\boldsymbol{N}\cdot\boldsymbol{E}')\boldsymbol{N},$$
$$v''^2\boldsymbol{D}'' - c^2\boldsymbol{E}'' = -c^2(\boldsymbol{N}\cdot\boldsymbol{E}'')\boldsymbol{N}$$

by $\boldsymbol{D}''$, and the second by $\boldsymbol{D}'$, subtracting one from the other and recalling that $(\boldsymbol{E}'\cdot\boldsymbol{D}'') = (\boldsymbol{E}''\cdot\boldsymbol{D}')$, $(\boldsymbol{D}'\cdot\boldsymbol{N}) = (\boldsymbol{D}''\cdot\boldsymbol{N}) = 0$, we get

$$(v'^2 - v''^2)(\boldsymbol{D}'\cdot\boldsymbol{D}'') = 0. \qquad (5)$$

Hence we obtain $(\boldsymbol{D}'\cdot\boldsymbol{D}'') = 0$ for $v' \neq v''$, which is what we wished to prove.

413. *Solution.* We conclude from (3) (of the solution of the previous problem) that the equality $v' = v''$ is only possible on condition that $v' = v'' = a_y$. On substituting $v = a_y$ in (1) of the same solution, we find that

$$(a_y^2 - a_z^2)(a_y^2 - a_x^2)N_y^2 = 0.$$

If all three principal velocities are distinct, it follows from this that $N_y = 0$, i.e. the optical axes, if they exist, lie in the coordinate plane zx. The angle β between the optical axis and the z axis is found from (3) (solution of Problem 411), if we set $v = a_y$, $N_y = 0$ in it. This gives

$$\tan\beta = \frac{N_x}{N_z} = \pm\sqrt{\frac{a_x^2 - a_y^2}{a_y^2 - a_z^2}} = \pm\frac{n_z}{n_x}\sqrt{\frac{n_x^2 - n_y^2}{n_y^2 - n_z^2}}, \tag{1}$$

where n_x, n_y, n_z are the principal refractive indices of the crystal. Hence the optical axes of the first kind lie in the zx plane and are symmetrical relative to the z axis.

414. *Case* 1. The optical axis coincides with the z axis (positive crystal):

$$v' = a_x; \quad v''^2 = a_x^2 \cos^2\alpha + \alpha_z^2 \sin^2\alpha,$$

where α is the angle between the optical axis (z axis) and the normal to the wave front.

Case 2. The optical axis coincides with the x axis (negative crystal):

$$v'' = a_z; \quad v'^2 = a_x^2 \sin^2\alpha + a_z^2 \cos^2\alpha,$$

where α is the angle between the optical axis (x axis) and the normal to the wave front.

417. *Solution.* All the formulae of crystal optics, in which we are dealing with wave propagation along the wave normals, are obtained from the formulae

$$\boldsymbol{D} = -\frac{c}{v}[\boldsymbol{N} \wedge \boldsymbol{H}], \quad \boldsymbol{H} = \frac{c}{v}[\boldsymbol{N} \wedge \boldsymbol{E}], \quad D_\alpha = \varepsilon_\alpha E_\alpha.$$

If we carry out vector multiplication of the first two equations by $\boldsymbol{s}$, we can easily write the system as

$$\boldsymbol{E} = -\frac{u}{c}[\boldsymbol{s} \wedge \boldsymbol{H}], \quad \boldsymbol{H} = \frac{u}{c}[\boldsymbol{s} \wedge \boldsymbol{D}], \quad E_\alpha = \frac{1}{\varepsilon_\alpha} D_\alpha,$$

whence the theorem stated in the problem follows.

418. The result is easily obtained with the aid of the conversion theorem.

419. The optical axes of the second kind lie in the zx plane and are symmetrical with respect to the z axis, with which they form the angle γ, given by

$$\tan \gamma = \pm \frac{a_z}{a_x} \sqrt{\frac{a_x^2 - a_y^2}{a_y^2 - a_z^2}} = \pm \sqrt{\frac{n_x^2 - n_y^2}{n_y^2 - n_z^2}} = \frac{a_z}{a_x} \tan \beta .$$

Hence it follows that the optical axes of the second kind are closer to the z axis than the optical axes of the first kind.

420. The crystal is positive if $n_z - n_y > n_y - n_x$, and negative if $n_z - n_y < n_y - n_x$.

421. The crystal is positive.

423. *Case* 1. The optical axis is along the z axis (positive crystal):

$$u' = a_x; \quad \frac{1}{u''^2} = \frac{1}{a_x^2} \cos^2 \alpha + \frac{1}{a_z^2} \sin^2 \alpha ,$$

where α is the angle between the optical axis (z axis) and the direction of the ray.

Case 2. The optical axis is along the x axis (negative crystal):

$$u'' = a_z; \quad \frac{1}{u'^2} = \frac{1}{a_x^2} \sin^2 \alpha + \frac{1}{a_z^2} \cos^2 \alpha .$$

425. *Solution.* The components of the induction vector $\boldsymbol{D}$ are connected with the components of the electric field-strength vector $\boldsymbol{E}$ in the crystal by the relationships:

$$\left.\begin{aligned} D_x &= \varepsilon_{xx} E_x + \varepsilon_{xy} E_y + \varepsilon_{xz} E_z , \\ D_y &= \varepsilon_{yx} E_x + \varepsilon_{yy} E_y + \varepsilon_{yz} E_z , \\ D_z &= \varepsilon_{zx} E_x + \varepsilon_{zy} E_y + \varepsilon_{zz} E_z . \end{aligned}\right\} \tag{1}$$

Crystals of the tri-, tetra- and hexagonal systems have axes of symmetry of the third, fourth and sixth order respectively. We take this axis as the z axis in a Cartesian system, and choose the x and y axes arbitrarily. For the sake of clarity we shall consider a crystal of the tetragonal system. We connect the coordinate system rigidly with the crystal. Keeping the direction of the electric field fixed in space, we rotate the crystal 90° about the z axis (Fig. 89, positions *I* and *II*). We shall use primes to denote the components of the vectors $\boldsymbol{D}$ and $\boldsymbol{E}$ relative to the new (rotated) coordinate system. Since the properties of the crystal in any direction are unchanged on rotating this direction in the crystal 90° about the z axis, the following relationships hold in the new coordinate system:

$$\left.\begin{aligned} D'_x &= \varepsilon_{xx}E'_x + \varepsilon_{xy}E'_y + \varepsilon_{xz}E'_z\,, \\ D'_y &= \varepsilon_{y\alpha}E'_x + \varepsilon_{yy}E'_y + \varepsilon_{yz}E'_z\,, \\ D'_z &= \varepsilon_{zx}E'_x + \varepsilon_{zy}E'_y + \varepsilon_{zz}E'_z\,. \end{aligned}\right\} \qquad (2)$$

But the components of the vectors $\boldsymbol{E}$ and $\boldsymbol{D}$ in the initial and the new coordinate systems are connected by (see Fig. 89, positions *I* and *II*)

$$E'_x = E_y; \quad E'_y = -E_x; \quad E'_z = E_z;$$
$$D'_x = D_y; \quad D'_y = -D_x; \quad D'_z = D_z.$$

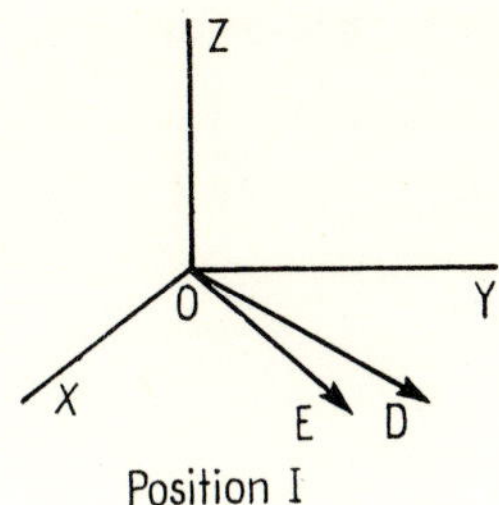

FIG. 89

In view of this, equations (2) can be written as

$$\begin{aligned} D_y &= \varepsilon_{xx}E_y - \varepsilon_{xy}E_x + \varepsilon_{xz}E_z\,, \\ -D_x &= \varepsilon_{yx}E_y - \varepsilon_{yy}E_x + \varepsilon_{yz}E_z\,, \\ D_z &= \varepsilon_{zx}E_y - \varepsilon_{zy}E_x + \varepsilon_{zz}E_z\,. \end{aligned}$$

Like equations (1), these equations hold whatever the vector $\boldsymbol{E}$, and this is only possible if

$$\varepsilon_{xx} = \varepsilon_{yy}; \qquad \varepsilon_{xy} = -\varepsilon_{yx};$$
$$\varepsilon_{xz} = -\varepsilon_{yz}; \quad \varepsilon_{xz} = \varepsilon_{yz}.$$

It follows from these relationships and the symmetry of the tensor ε that the non-diagonal elements of the tensor vanish. Furthermore, since $\varepsilon_{xx} = \varepsilon_{yy}$, we have for any $\boldsymbol{E}$ perpendicular to the z axis: $\boldsymbol{D} = \varepsilon_{xx}\boldsymbol{E}$. With this direction of $\boldsymbol{E}$ the crystal behaves like an isotropic medium. All the directions at right angles to the z axis are characterised by the same properties from the optical point of view. Hence it follows that the crystal is uniaxial, its optical axis being parallel to the z axis.

Crystals of the tri- and hexagonal systems may be considered along the same lines.

427. $\delta = 6°15'$.

Solution. Iceland spar is a negative crystal, and the x axis is the optical axis. Any straight line perpendicular to the optical axis can be taken as the y or z axis. The vectors $\boldsymbol{E}$ and $\boldsymbol{D}$ of the extraordinary wave lie in the plane through the optical axis. We take this plane as the xy plane. Now, in the extraordinary wave, $E_z = D_z = 0$. The angle δ between the vectors $\boldsymbol{s}$ and $\boldsymbol{N}$ is equal to the angle between the vectors $\boldsymbol{E}$ and $\boldsymbol{D}$, since the sides of these angles are mutually perpendicular. Let φ and ψ be the angles formed by the vectors $\boldsymbol{E}$ and $\boldsymbol{D}$ with the x axis. Now,

$$D_x = D\cos\psi = \varepsilon_x E_x = \varepsilon_x E\cos\varphi,$$

$$D_y = D\sin\psi = \varepsilon_y E_y = \varepsilon_y E\sin\varphi,$$

whence

$$\tan\psi = \frac{\varepsilon_y}{\varepsilon_x}\tan\varphi = \frac{n_0^2}{n_e^2}\tan\varphi,$$

$$\tan\delta = \tan(\psi - \varphi) = \frac{(n_0^2 - n_e^2)\tan\psi}{n_0^2 + n_e^2\tan^2\psi}.$$

This easily leads to the following expression for the maximum of the angle δ:

$$\tan\delta = \frac{n_0^2 - n_e^2}{2n_0 n_e}.$$

428. The crystal is negative, the plate is cut parallel to the optical axis.

429. Both indices will have constant values, corresponding to the minimum and maximum values quoted in the previous problem.

430. *Solution.* When the plates have the same orientation the path difference introduced by them is large, i.e. corresponds to a high order of interference. In white light high order interference cannot be observed, as is well known. If one of the plates is turned through 90° relative to the other, the path difference introduced by the plates will be the same as that introduced by a thin plate, whose thickness is equal to the difference between the thicknesses of the plates in question. If this difference in thicknesses is small, so small a path difference can be obtained that interference in white light is possible.

431. 5·97 and 28·57.

432. 14·91 and 19·50.

433. $d = \dfrac{\lambda}{4(n_1 - n_2)} = 0{\cdot}027$ mm

434. $d = \dfrac{\lambda}{4(n_e - n_0)} = 0{\cdot}014$ mm.

435. $\dfrac{2l}{\lambda}\left(\sqrt{\varepsilon_y} - \sqrt{\varepsilon_z}\right) = 2m + \dfrac{1}{2}$,

where m is an integer.

436. When the half-wave plates are introduced the interference bands are shifted half the width of a band; when the polaroid is turned through 90°, they are shifted half the width of a band in the opposite direction relative to the initial position; if the polaroid is removed, the position of the bands is unchanged, but their intensity is doubled. When quarter-wave plates are introduced the bands are shifted a quarter the width of a band; if the polaroid is removed in this case, the interference bands disappear.

437. $d \sin\vartheta = \dfrac{\lambda}{2}\left(m + \dfrac{1}{2}\right); \quad m = 0, \pm 1, \pm 2, \ldots,$

ϑ is the angle between the normal to the segment d in the horizontal plane and the direction of the radiation.

438. $A^2 = a^2\left\{\cos^2(\alpha - \beta) - \sin 2\alpha \sin 2\beta \sin^2\dfrac{\delta}{2}\right\}.$

When

(1) the Nicol prisms are crossed:

$$A^2 = a^2 \sin^2 2\alpha \sin^2 \frac{\delta}{2};$$

(2) the Nicol prisms are parallel:

$$A^2 = a^2 \left(1 - \sin^2 2\alpha \sin^2 \frac{\delta}{2}\right).$$

Here δ is the phase difference, between the two principal components of the transmitted wave, which is introduced by the plate.

440. Blue (complementary to orange).

441. (1) When the principal directions of the plate are the same as the principal planes of the Nicol prisms; (2) when the plate is cut at right angles to the optical axis; (3) when the path difference produced by the plate is equal to an even number of half-waves.

442. $d = 0{\cdot}07$ mm.

443. (1) The Nicol prisms are crossed and the plates are parallel: the path difference $\Delta R = d_1 \Delta n_1 + d_2 \Delta n_2 \approx 3\lambda_1$, where $\lambda_1 \approx 6000$ Å. The field of vision has a reddish colouration (third order).

(2) The Nicol prisms are parallel, whilst the plates are crossed: $\Delta R = d_1 \Delta n_1 - d_2 \Delta n_2 \approx \lambda_2 \approx 5000$ Å. The field of vision has a greenish tinge (first order).

444. $l = \dfrac{n_e - n_0}{n'_e - n'_0} \cdot \dfrac{d}{\alpha}.$

445. To the frequency 2ω.

446. 12 bands.

Solution. The path difference between the extraordinary and ordinary rays produced by the quartz plate is equal to $\Delta = d(n_e - n_0)$. On substituting in this the numerical values of d, n_e, n_0, it is easily seen that Δ is virtually the same for λ_D and λ_F. The number of wavelengths λ_D contained in the interval Δ will be $k_1 = \Delta/\lambda_D$. Similarly, $k_2 = \Delta/\lambda_F$. The number of dark bands is $k_2 - k_1 = 12$, since the dark bands are obtained at the places in the spectrum corresponding to those wavelengths for which the polarisation is unchanged as a result of passing through the quartz plate, i.e. for which the path difference Δ contains an integral number of wavelengths.

447. In the case of Iceland spar, there is a very great difference between the refractive indices of the ordinary and extraordinary rays, so that, even with thin plates, large path differences are obtained, for which interference in white light is impossible.

448. The analyser and polariser between which the plate is inserted must be turned through the same angle.

449. The following colours are obtained on rotation through 360°: twice blue-green of the second order, twice yellow of the first order, twice a sensitive tint of the first order.

450. Because of pleochroism.

451. *Solution.* By putting a quarter-wave plate and a Nicol prism in the path of the light. After passing through the plate the light becomes linearly polarised, the direction of oscillation of the electric vector being at $\pm 45°$ to the crystal axis. Figure 90a shows this direction for right-hand and left-hand polarised light in the case

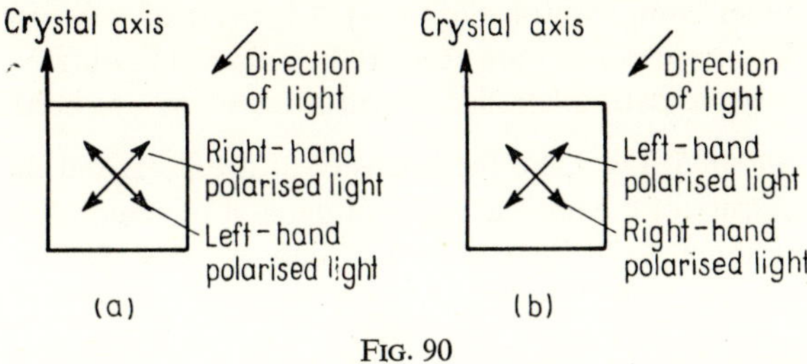

FIG. 90

when the plate is made of positive uniaxial crystal. The direction may be determined with the aid of an analyser. Figure 90b refers to the case when the plate is made of negative crystal.

452. *Solution.* By putting a quarter-wave plate and a Nicol prism in the path of the light. If the Nicol prism is turned whilst the position of the plate is arbitrary, the fact that the intensity remains unchanged implies natural light; if the intensity varies and falls to zero, the light is circularly polarised; if the intensity varies but does not fall to zero, the light is partially circularly polarised.

Instead of a plate, a Babinet compensator can be used; this is set up so as to introduce a path difference of $\lambda/4$.

453. A quarter-wave plate with a Nicol prism behind it must be placed in the path of the light propagation. If, when the plate is turned about the direction of the ray, a position can be found at which the light passing through it can be extinguished by subsequent rotation of the Nicol prism, the incident light must be elliptically polarised. If it is not possible to do this, we are dealing either with a mixture of natural and linearly polarised light, or with a mixture of natural and elliptically polarised light. In order to differentiate between these last two cases, we first mount only one Nicol prism in the path of the light and adjust it for minimum intensity of the transmitted light. A quarter-wave plate is then placed in front of the Nicol prism. The plate and prism are again adjusted for minimum intensity. If this minimum is obtained at the previous position of the prism (or with the prism turned through 180°), we have a mixture of natural and linearly polarised light. If, on the other hand, the prism has to be turned through a certain angle in order to obtain the minimum, we have a mixture of natural and elliptically polarised light.

A Babinet compensator can be used instead of a quarter-wave plate. The compensator only needs to be adjusted to obtain roughly a quarter-wave path difference. Great accuracy is not needed.

454. *Solution.* Let I_p be the intensity of the polarised light, and I_n the intensity of the natural light. In the first position of the Nicol prism the intensity of the transmitted light is

$$I_p + \tfrac{1}{2}I_n,$$

and in the second:

$$I_p \cos^2 60° + \tfrac{1}{2}I_n = \tfrac{1}{4}I_p + \tfrac{1}{2}I_n.$$

By hypothesis,

$$I_p + \tfrac{1}{2}I_n = 2\left(\tfrac{1}{4}I_p + \tfrac{1}{2}I_n\right)$$

whence $I_n = I_p$. The maximum intensity $I_s = 3I_p/2$, the minimum is

$$I_m = \frac{1}{2}I_p, \quad \Delta = \frac{1}{2}, \quad \frac{I_s}{I_m} = 3.$$

455. (1) $\sin 2I = \sin 2i \sin \delta$; (2) $\tan 2\vartheta = \tan 2i \cos \delta$, where ϑ is the angle between one of the principal directions of the plate and one of the semiaxes of the ellipse, whilst the required ratio of the semiaxes is tan I.

Solution. On leaving the plate, a linearly polarised ray is transformed to an elliptically polarised ray, the characteristic ellipse of the vibrations being

$$x = a \cos \omega t; \quad y = b \cos (\omega t + \delta).$$

To find the semiaxes of the elliptic vibration, we find the components x' and y' of the light vector along the coordinate axes, turned through the angle ϑ relative to the initial system of axes, which coincide with the principal directions of the plate:

$$x' = a \cos \vartheta \cos \omega t + b \sin \vartheta \cos (\omega t + \delta) = A \cos (\omega t + \alpha),$$

$$y' = -a \sin \vartheta \cos \omega t + b \cos (\omega t + \delta) = B \cos (\omega t + \beta),$$

where A and B are given by

$$\left.\begin{aligned} A \cos \alpha &= a \cos \vartheta + b \sin \vartheta \cos \delta, \\ A \sin \alpha &= b \sin \vartheta \sin \delta, \\ B \cos \beta &= -a \sin \vartheta + b \cos \vartheta \cos \delta, \\ B \sin \beta &= b \cos \vartheta \sin \delta. \end{aligned}\right\} \tag{1}$$

Hence

$$\left.\begin{aligned} A^2 &= a^2 \cos^2 \vartheta + b^2 \sin^2 \vartheta + ab \sin 2\vartheta \cos \delta, \\ B^2 &= a^2 \sin^2 \vartheta + b^2 \cos^2 \vartheta - ab \sin 2\vartheta \cos \delta. \end{aligned}\right\} \tag{2}$$

On adding and subtracting, we get

$$A^2 - B^2 = a^2 + b^2 = R^2, \tag{3}$$

$$A^2 - B^2 = (a^2 - b^2) \cos 2\vartheta + 2ab \sin 2\vartheta \cos \delta, \tag{4}$$

where R is the amplitude of the wave passing through the polariser.

In order for the amplitudes A and B to correspond to the oscillations along the axes of the ellipse, the angle ϑ must be chosen so that the difference $A^2 - B^2$ is a maximum or minimum.

On equating the first derivative to zero, we get

$$\tan 2\vartheta = \frac{2ab}{a^2 - b^2} \cos \delta. \tag{5}$$

We find from (1) that

$$\left.\begin{aligned} AB \sin(\alpha - \beta) &= -ab \sin \delta, \\ AB \cos(\alpha - \beta) &= ab \cos 2\vartheta \cos \delta - \frac{a^2 - b^2}{2} \sin 2\vartheta \end{aligned}\right\} \quad (6)$$

or

$$\frac{AB \cos(\alpha - \beta)}{ab \cos 2\vartheta \cos \delta} = 1 - \frac{a^2 - b^2}{2ab \cos \delta} \tan 2\vartheta .$$

On substituting the value of $\tan 2\vartheta$ from (5), we obtain

$$\frac{AB \cos(\alpha - \beta)}{ab \cos 2\vartheta \cos \delta} = 0,$$

whence $\cos(\alpha - \beta) = 0$, $(\alpha - \beta) = \pm\frac{1}{2}\pi$. Consequently, we have from the first of equations (6):

$$AB = \pm ab \sin \delta .$$

Since $b/a = \tan i$, we have

$$\sin 2i = \frac{2ab}{a^2 + b^2},$$

$$\cos 2i = \frac{a^2 - b^2}{a^2 + b^2},$$

$$\tan 2i = \frac{2ab}{a^2 - b^2}.$$

Hence equation (5) takes the form

$$\tan 2\vartheta = \tan 2i \cos \delta .$$

On putting $\tan I = B/A$, we find that

$$\sin 2I = \frac{2AB}{A^2 + B^2} = \frac{2ab \sin \delta}{a^2 + b^2} = \sin 2i \sin \delta .$$

456. *Solution.* When the angle between the principal plane of the polariser and one of the principal directions of the plate is equal to i and $90° - i$, the light passing through the plate has the same ratio of semi-axes B/A (see the solution of Problem 455).

Let 2α denote the angle between the corresponding semiaxes of the similar ellipses corresponding to these cases. Now, $2\alpha = 90° - 2(i - \vartheta)$ or $2\vartheta = 2(\alpha + 1) - 90°$, where ϑ is the angle between one of the principal directions of the plate and the axis of the ellipse. We obtain from $\tan 2\vartheta = \tan 2i \cos \delta$:

$$\cos \delta = \frac{\cot 2(i + \alpha)}{\tan 2i}.$$

The quantities i and α can be measured in two ways:

(1) By mounting the plate between crossed Nicol prisms, and determining its principal directions. The plate is then turned through

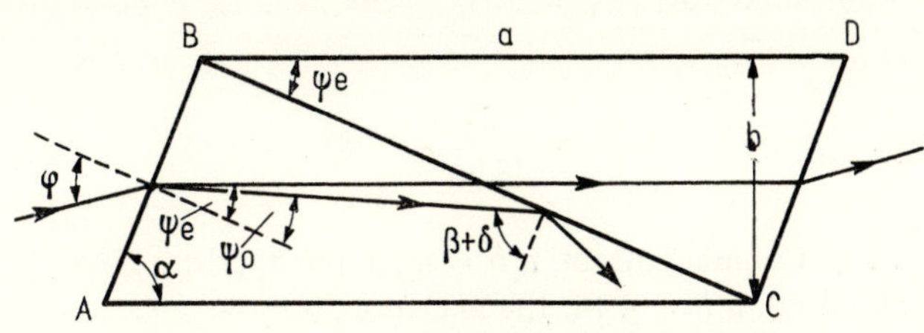

FIG. 91

an angle i and a second plate mounted behind it, by means of which the elliptic oscillations are transformed into rectilinear oscillations. The resulting oscillations are extinguished by an analyser. The plate being studied is turned through $90° - i$, the analyser clamped to the compensating plate and turned so as to obtain a new position of complete extinction. The angle of rotation of the analyser is 2α.

(2) The compensating plate is clamped to the analyser U, then the analyser and plate under study rotated so as to obtain two positions of complete darkening. The angle of rotation of the plate under study is now $90° - 2i$ or $90° + 2i$, whilst the angle of rotation of the analyser is 2α.

457. *Solution.* It follows from the law of refraction (Fig. 91) that

$$\frac{\sin \psi_e}{\sin \psi_0} = \frac{n_0}{n_e}.$$

The section BC in the Nicol prism is perpendicular to its bases AB and CD, whilst the wave normal of the extraordinary wave must be parallel, by hypothesis, to the given edge of the prism. Hence

$$\alpha = \frac{\pi}{2} - \psi_e.$$

Furthermore, by hypothesis,

$$\psi_0 = \frac{\pi}{2} - (\beta + \delta),$$

where β is the limiting angle of total internal reflection at the boundary BC for the ordinary ray. It is given by $\sin \beta = n/n_0$. On substituting the figures for n, n_o and n_e, we find that

$$\beta = 68°15'; \quad \psi_0 = 20°; \quad \psi_e = 22°; \quad \alpha = 68°.$$

Finally,

$$\frac{a}{b} = \frac{2}{\sin 2\alpha} = 2{\cdot}88.$$

458. For Canada balsam, $a/b = 4{\cdot}93$, the aperture $2\varphi = 34°20'$. For linseed oil, $a/b = 4{\cdot}14$, the aperture $2\varphi = 40°50'$.

Solution. Since the electric vector is here either perpendicular to the optical axis (ordinary wave), or parallel to it (extraordinary wave),

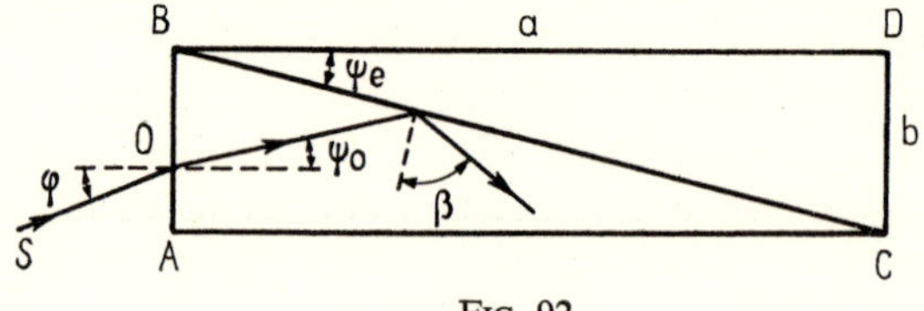

FIG. 92

the directions of the wave normals and the light rays are the same. The extraordinary ray, incident on the boundary plane BC (Fig. 92), always passes through it, without reflection. In particular, extraordinary rays directed along the diagonal of the prism can pass through it. This ray corresponds to the maximum possible angle of incidence φ for which there is an extraordinary ray passing through the prism. If the angle of incidence exceeds φ, there is no extraordinary ray that can pass through the prism: in this case the extraordinary ray is incident on the lateral face of the prism and is absorbed in it. The angle φ corresponds to the extraordinary ray refraction angle ψ_e, given by

$$\tan \psi_e = \frac{b}{a}.$$

We choose the ratio a/b so that, at angles of incidence not exceeding the limiting angle φ, no ordinary ray can pass through the cut BC, at which it undergoes total internal reflection. It is sufficient for this that the ordinary ray SO, incident on AB at the angle φ from below, encounters the plane BC of the cut at the limiting angle of total internal reflection β: $\sin \beta = n/n_0$. As is clear from Fig. 92,

$$\beta = \frac{\pi}{2} - (\psi_e + \psi_0),$$

and consequently we must have

$$\cos (\psi_e + \psi_0) = \frac{n}{n_0}.$$

On adding to this the law of refraction:

$$\sin \varphi = n_0 \sin \psi_0 = n_e \sin \psi_e,$$

we obtain a complete system of equations for the required quantities: the ratio a/b and the aperture 2φ. We obtain the following convenient computational formulae:

$$(n_0^2 - n^2)\left(\frac{a^2}{b^2}\right)^2 + [n_0^2 - n_e^2 - 2n(n + n_e)]\frac{a^2}{b^2} - (n + n_e)^2 = 0,$$

$$\sin \varphi = \frac{n_e}{\sqrt{1 + \left(\frac{a}{b}\right)^2}}.$$

459. *Solution.* In order for the ordinary ray, incident on the boundary AB from below at the angle φ (Fig. 93), to undergo total internal reflection from the plane BC of the cut, the angle of incidence at this plane must exceed the limiting angle of total internal reflection:

$$\alpha - \psi_0 \geqslant \beta_0, \quad \sin \beta_0 = \frac{1}{n_0}. \tag{1}$$

The ordinary ray, incident on AB from above, will all the more undergo total internal reflection.

In order for the extraordinary ray, incident on the face AB from above at the angle φ', to pass through the plane BC, it must be incident on BC at an angle not exceeding the limiting angle of total internal reflection:

$$\alpha + \psi_e' \leqslant \beta_e, \quad \sin \beta_e = \frac{1}{n_e}. \tag{2}$$

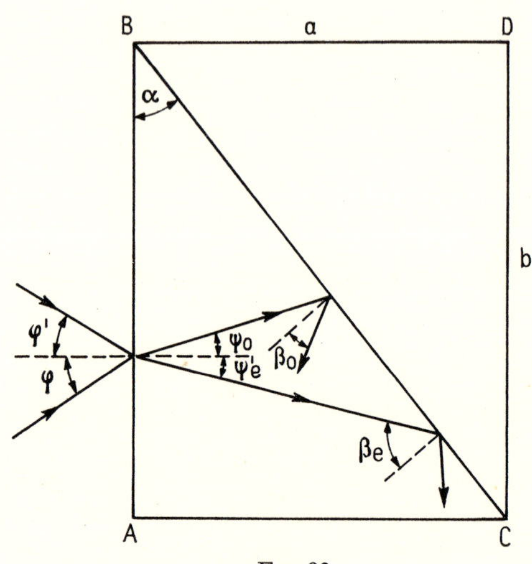

FIG. 93

The extraordinary ray, incident on AB from below, now passes through BC. The greatest aperture of the prism corresponds to the signs of equality in (1) and (2). In this case the angle $\varphi + \varphi'$ is equal to the aperture. On requiring in addition that $\varphi = \varphi'$, we have

$$\alpha - \psi_0 = \beta_0, \quad \alpha + \psi_e = \beta_e, \tag{3}$$

where

$$\sin \varphi = n_0 \sin \psi_0 = n_e \sin \psi_e. \tag{4}$$

$$\tan \alpha = \frac{a}{b}. \tag{5}$$

All the quantities of interest can be found from this. We obtain from (3):

$$\psi_0 + \psi_e = \beta_e - \beta_0 = 5°12'. \tag{6}$$

The angles ψ_o, ψ_e, φ are therefore small, and their sines can be replaced by the angles themselves. This gives for the aperture:

$$2\varphi = \frac{2n_0 n_e}{n_0 + n_e}(\beta_e - \beta_0) = 8°10' \tag{7}$$

and for the ratio of the sides:

$$\frac{a}{b} = \tan(\beta_0 + \psi_0) = \tan\left(\beta_0 + \frac{\varphi}{n_0}\right) = 0{\cdot}826. \tag{8}$$

This prism is thus the shortest of all polarisation prisms. In practice the prism is cut as shown in Fig. 94, instead of along the diagonal; this makes it easier to mount and prevents the surface of the cut from getting dusty. Nevertheless, in practice the ratio of the length to the width of the prism remains less than unity.

460. The crystal is positive, the axis of the maximum dielectric constant is perpendicular to the plate.

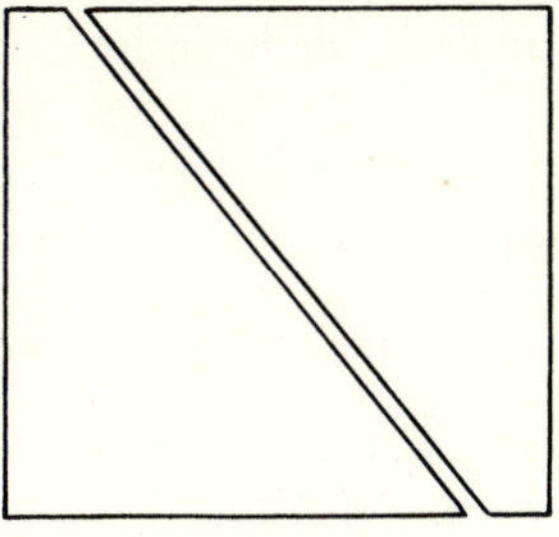

FIG. 94

461. Perpendicularly to any of the dielectric axes of the crystal.

462. *Solution.* (1) If the light is circularly polarised, the component vibrations along the coordinate axes can be written as

$$x = a\cos\omega t; \quad y = a\sin\omega t.$$

After passing through a crystal plate, which produces a certain path difference, the equations of the vibrations can be written as

$$x = a\cos\omega t; \quad y = a\sin(\omega t + \delta).$$

If α is the angle between the principal plane of the analyser and one of the principal directions of the plate, the resultant vibration on leaving the analyser will be

$$a \cos \alpha \cos \omega t + a \sin \alpha \sin (\omega t + \delta)$$
$$= a (\cos \alpha + \sin \alpha \sin \delta) \cos \omega t + a \sin \alpha \cos \delta \sin \omega t;$$

whence we obtain for the intensity:

$$I = a^2\{(\cos \alpha + \sin \alpha \sin \delta)^2 + (\sin \alpha \cos \delta)^2\} = a^2(1 + \sin 2\alpha \sin \delta).$$

(2) Given constant δ, the intensity is a maximum or minimum when $\cos 2\alpha = 0$, i.e. when $\alpha = \pi/4;\ 3\pi/4$. If $\sin \delta > 0$, the first value of α corresponds to a maximum, and the second to a minimum; when $\sin \delta < 0$, vice versa.

463. *Solution.* In accordance with the previous problem, the intensity of the light passing through the analyser is

$$I = a^2(1 + \sin 2\alpha \sin \delta).$$

Given a constant angle α, the intensity is a minimum when

$$\sin \delta = -1, \quad \text{i.e. when} \quad \delta = 3\pi/2, 7\pi/2, \ldots,$$

and a maximum when

$$\sin \delta = 1, \quad \text{i.e. when} \quad \delta = \pi/2, 5\pi/2, 9\pi/2, \ldots,$$

if $\sin 2\alpha > 0$. If $\sin 2\alpha < 0$, there is a minimum in the first case and a maximum in the second. Consequently, alternating light and dark bands will be seen in the field of vision. On turning the wedge the angle α varies, so that the intensity will vary at each point of the wedge.

At angles $\alpha = 90°$, $180°$ and $270°$ the whole of the wedge will be uniformly illuminated, whilst at angles $\alpha = 45°$, $135°$, $225°$, $315°$, the sharpest difference will be observed in the intensities of the dark and light bands; on passing through the angles $\alpha = 90°$, $180°$, $270°$ the dark bands become light and the light dark.

464. Because rotation of the plane of polarisation occurs in quartz. The angle of rotation of the plane of polarisation is less than 180° for visible light of any colour in the case of a quartz plate 1 mm thick.

465. If a quartz plate cut at right angles to the optical axis (quartz being a material which rotates the plane of polarisation) is placed between two crossed Nicol prisms, the resulting system will pass light (see the solution of the previous problem), and the pattern will not be affected on turning the plate about the direction of propagation of the light. If the plate is cut parallel to the axis, the behaviour is much more complicated. A linearly polarised wave, on striking the plate, splits up into the linearly polarised waves, travelling with difference velocities. The phase difference between them consequently varies, and the polarisation changes from linear to elliptic. This system also passes light, but the intensity varies on turning the plate about the direction of propagation.

466. Because of the dispersion of the rotatory power of the quartz.

467. Because of the difference in the direction of rotation of the plane of polarisation (laevo- and dextro-rotatory quartz).

468. If a quartz plate cut at right angles to the optical axis is placed between the crossed Nicol prisms and the system illuminated by monochromatic light, the system will pass the light; on turning the analyser through an angle less than 90°, we can again extinguish the light. If it is a question of turning the analyser in a clockwise direction (viewed from the observer), the quartz will be dextro-rotatory, if counter-clockwise the quartz is laevo-rotatory.

If the system is illuminated by white light, the plate will appear coloured to the eye. If the analyser is turned clockwise, in the case of dextro-rotatory quartz the colouration changes towards the shorter wavelengths of the visible spectrum. In the case of laevo-rotatory quartz the colouration changes in the reverse order.

469. $d = 4\cdot5$ mm.

470. (1) 7·5 mm; (2) 3·75 mm.

471. $d = \pi\lambda^3/8B\delta\lambda \approx 1900$ mm (it is assumed in the formula that the angle of rotation of the plane of polarisation is measured in radians).

472. $$d = \frac{\lambda^2}{2\delta\lambda}\cdot\frac{1}{(n_0 - n_e) - \lambda\left(\dfrac{dn_0}{d\lambda} - \dfrac{dn_e}{d\lambda}\right)} \approx 1\cdot5 \text{ mm}.$$

473. $\Delta n = \dfrac{\varphi \cdot \lambda}{\pi \cdot l} \approx 1{\cdot}1 \times 10^{-8}$.

474. $\Delta n = 7{\cdot}1 \times 10^{-5}$.

475. *Solution.* The device is placed between parallel Nicol prisms so that the line of contact of the right-hand and left-hand quartzes coincides with the principal section of the polariser. Uniform illumination of the field of vision will only be observed in the case when one of the principal directions in the plate coincides with the principal section of the polariser. When monochromatic light is used, we can arrange for the best conditions for operation of the device by varying the thickness of the wedges in such a way that the angle of rotation of the plane of polarisation is close to 90° for the given light. In these conditions the device has maximum sensitivity to the deviation of one of the principal directions of the plate away from the principal section of the polariser.

476. The angle Θ between the direction of motion of the particle and the wave vector $\boldsymbol{k}$ (or what amounts to the same thing, the wave normal $\boldsymbol{N}$) of the Cherenkov radiation is given by

$$\cos \Theta = \frac{v(\omega, \boldsymbol{N})}{V}, \tag{1}$$

where v is the normal wave velocity (i.e. the velocity of propagation of the phase in the direction $\boldsymbol{N}$), which depends on the frequency ω and the direction of the normal $\boldsymbol{N}$, whilst V is the velocity of the particle in the medium. The velocity v in the given direction $\boldsymbol{N}$ can have two values v_1 and v_2. Correspondingly, equation (1) splits into two:

$$\cos \Theta_1 = \frac{v_1(\omega, \boldsymbol{N})}{V}, \quad \cos \Theta_2 = \frac{v_2(\omega, \boldsymbol{N})}{V}.$$

Generally speaking, Cherenkov radiation in a crystal forms two composite conical surfaces, the generators of which (the wave normals) are given by equations (2). Radiation is only possible when one of the two conditions: $v_1 < V$ or $v_2 < V$ is fulfilled. For certain values of V, only one conical surface, or none at all, may be obtained. Finally, the case is possible when only part of one of the conical surfaces (2) is obtained (since v_1 and v_2 depend on the direction of $\boldsymbol{N}$). Cones of rays correspond to the cones of normals (2), and may be found by the general formulae of crystal optics.

§ 6. Velocity of Light. Optics of Moving Media and Sources. Some Problems of the Theory of Relativity

478. The aberration is the change in the direction of propagation of a light wave on passing from one frame of reference to another which moves relative to the first. If one frame of reference is connected with a star, and the other with the earth, the angle of aberration will be given by $\tan \vartheta = v/c$. It is in fact different for different stars. But we are not thinking of this angle when we speak of the aberration of light. If the velocity v of the earth relative to the star remained fixed, the motion of the earth would only affect the apparent position of the star on the vault of the sky, and aberration would not be observed. The aberration results from the variation of v caused by the rotation of the earth about the sun. The angle of aberration $\Delta\vartheta$ is defined by the difference between the relative velocities of the earth Δv at diametrically opposed points of the earth's orbit: $\tan \Delta\vartheta = \frac{1}{2}\Delta v/c$. This difference between the relative velocities, and hence the angle $\Delta\vartheta$, is the same for all stars and is independent on the actual motion of the latter.

479. (1) 0·32″; (2) 1/64.

480. $c = \dfrac{4DZN}{2n-1} = 2{\cdot}99 \times 10^5 \text{ km sec}^{-1}$.

481. $u = \dfrac{\omega' - \omega}{k' - k} = \dfrac{d\omega}{dk}$.

482. $u = v - \lambda dv/d\lambda$, where λ is the wavelength in the medium (Rayleigh's formula);

$$u = v\left(1 + \frac{\lambda}{n}\frac{dn}{d\lambda}\right).$$

485. (1) $u = a = v$; (2) $u = \dfrac{a\sqrt{\lambda}}{2} = \dfrac{v}{2}$;

(3) $u = \dfrac{3}{2}\dfrac{a}{\sqrt{\lambda}} = \dfrac{3}{2}v$; (4) $u = \dfrac{2a}{\lambda} = 2v$;

$$(5)\ u = \frac{c^2}{\sqrt{c^2 + b^2\lambda^2}} = \frac{c^2}{v};$$

$$(6)\ u = \frac{1}{\varepsilon\mu}\,\frac{c^2}{v\left\{1 + \dfrac{\omega}{2\varepsilon\mu}\dfrac{d(\varepsilon\mu)}{d\omega}\right\}}.$$

486. $\varepsilon = 1 + A/\omega^2$, where A is a constant.

488. *Solution.* Let the free oscillations in the circuit at $t < 0$ be

$$I = I_0 e^{i\omega t}, \quad V = V_0 e^{i\omega t},$$

where I is the current in the circuit and V is the voltage across the condenser terminals; these latter are connected by the relationship

$$L\frac{dI}{dt} + V = 0 \quad \text{or} \quad i\omega LI + V = 0.$$

If a resistance R is introduced into the circuit at the instant $t = 0$, the oscillations will be described as from this instant by

$$L(\tilde{\omega})\frac{d^2I}{dt^2} + R\frac{dI}{dt} + \frac{I}{C(\tilde{\omega})} = 0,$$

whence

$$I = I_0 e^{i\tilde{\omega} t}, \quad t > 0,$$

where $\tilde{\omega}$ is the complex frequency defined by the equation

$$\tilde{\omega}L(\tilde{\omega}) - \frac{1}{\tilde{\omega}C(\tilde{\omega})} = iR.$$

If R is vanishingly small, the difference between $\tilde{\omega}$ and ω must also be infinitesimal. But ω satisfies

$$\omega L(\omega) - \frac{1}{\omega C(\omega)} = 0.$$

On subtracting this from the previous relationship and replacing all the differences by their differentials, we get

$$\left[\frac{d}{d\omega}(\omega L) + \frac{1}{\omega^2 C^2}\frac{d}{d\omega}(\omega C)\right](\tilde{\omega} - \omega) = iR,$$

whence $\tilde{\omega} = \omega + i\delta$, where

$$\frac{R}{\delta} = \frac{d(\omega L)}{d\omega} + \frac{1}{\omega^2 C^2}\frac{d(\omega C)}{d\omega} = \frac{d(\omega L)}{d\omega} + \frac{L}{C}\frac{d(\omega C)}{d\omega}.$$

To determine the Joule heat we have to integrate the expression RI^2 over time. Since squaring is a non-linear operation, it is necessary to pass to the real form, i.e. to make the substitution

$$I \to \operatorname{Re}(I) = \tfrac{1}{2}(I + I^*).$$

The energy initially stored in the circuit is

$$W = \int_0^\infty R\left(\frac{I + I^*}{2}\right)^2 dt = \frac{R\,|I_0|^2}{4}\left\{\frac{\delta}{\omega^2 + \delta^2} + \frac{1}{\delta}\right\}$$

or in the limit, as $\delta \to 0$:

$$W = \frac{|I_0|^2}{4}\frac{R}{\delta}.$$

On substituting in this the value for R/δ and using the relationship $\omega L\,|I_0| = |V_0|$, we get

$$W = \frac{L_0\,|I_0|^2}{4}\frac{d(\omega\mu)}{d\omega} + \frac{C_0\,|V_0|^2}{4}\frac{d(\omega\varepsilon)}{d\omega}.$$

If there were a vacuum between the condenser plates and inside the solenoid, we should be able to write for the time-averaged values of the magnetic and electric energies:

$$\frac{L_0\,|I_0|^2}{4} = \frac{1}{8\pi}\overline{\boldsymbol{H}^2}\tau_m, \qquad \frac{C_0\,|V_0|^2}{4} = \frac{1}{8\pi}\overline{\boldsymbol{E}^2}\tau_e,$$

where τ_m and τ_e are the volumes of the coil and the condenser, whilst $\boldsymbol{E}$ and $\boldsymbol{H}$ are the electric and magnetic field-strengths when the amplitudes of the voltage across the condenser and the current in the coil are V_0 and I_0. But, given V_0 and I_0, the fields $\boldsymbol{E}$ and $\boldsymbol{H}$ are independent of the medium filling the condenser and coil. Hence the above relationships still hold when the condenser and coil are filled with the material. Using these relationships, we obtain the following expressions for the time-averages of the electric and magnetic energy densities:

$$\overline{w_e} = \frac{\overline{W_e}}{\tau_e} = \frac{1}{8\pi}\frac{d(\omega\varepsilon)}{d\omega}\overline{E^2}, \quad \overline{w_m} = \frac{\overline{W_m}}{\tau_m} = \frac{1}{8\pi}\frac{d(\omega\mu)}{d\omega}\overline{H^2}.$$

489. We easily obtain for the mean densities of the energy and its flux:

$$\overline{w} = \frac{c}{8\pi}\sqrt{\frac{\varepsilon}{\mu}}\,\frac{dk}{d\omega}(E \cdot E^*), \quad \overline{S} = \frac{c}{8\pi}\sqrt{\frac{\varepsilon}{\mu}}(E \cdot E^*),$$

whence the required result follows.

490. The group velocity.

491. *Solution.* The electromagnetic energy density

$$\overline{w} = \frac{1}{8\pi}\frac{d(\omega\varepsilon)}{d\omega}(E \cdot E^*) + \frac{1}{8\pi}\frac{d(\omega\mu)}{d\omega}(H \cdot H^*)$$

is essentially positive. In a plane wave $\varepsilon(E \cdot E^*) = \mu(H \cdot H^*)$. Hence

$$\frac{d(\omega\varepsilon)}{d\omega} + \frac{\mu}{\varepsilon}\frac{d(\omega\mu)}{d\omega} > 0.$$

This inequality must hold for any media in which the signs of ε and μ are the same, since it is derived on the assumption that a uniform monochromatic wave for which $k^2 = \omega^2\varepsilon\mu/c^2 > 0$ can be propagated in the medium. On the same assumption it is meaningful to speak of the group velocity. On transforming the above inequality to

$$\mu\frac{\omega}{k}\frac{d\omega}{dk} = \mu v u > 0,$$

the required result is easily obtained.

493. *Solution.* On writing Fresnel's law $\sum_\alpha N^2/(v_\alpha^2 - a_\alpha^2) = 0$ for the normal wave velocity in the form $\sum_\alpha k_\alpha^2/(\omega^2 - k^2 a_\alpha^2) = 0$ and differentiating with respect to k_i, we easily obtain

$$v\frac{\partial\omega}{\partial k_i}\sum_\alpha \frac{N_\alpha^2}{(v^2 - a_\alpha^2)^2} = N_i\left\{\frac{1}{v^2 - a_i^2} + \sum_\alpha \frac{N_\alpha^2 a_\alpha^2}{(v^2 - a_\alpha^2)^2}\right\}.$$

We find from (1) of the solution of Problem 411:

$$\sum_{\alpha} \frac{N_{\alpha}^2}{(v^2 - a_{\alpha}^2)^2} = \frac{1}{c^4} \frac{D^2}{(N \cdot E)^2}, \qquad \frac{1}{v^2 - a_i^2} = -\frac{D_i}{c^2(N \cdot E)N_i},$$

$$\sum_{\alpha} \frac{N_{\alpha}^2 a_{\alpha}^2}{(v^2 - a_{\alpha}^2)^2} = \frac{1}{c^4} \frac{\Sigma(a_{\alpha} D_{\alpha})^2}{(N \cdot E)^2} = \frac{1}{c^2} \frac{(E \cdot D)}{(N \cdot E)^2}.$$

Substitution of these values in the previous relationship gives

$$\frac{\partial \omega}{\partial k} \equiv \frac{\partial \omega}{\partial k_x} e_x + \frac{\partial \omega}{\partial k_y} e_y + \frac{\partial \omega}{\partial k_y} e_z = \frac{c^2}{vD^2} [E \wedge [N \wedge D]].$$

From (3) of the solution of Problem 407:

$$[N \wedge D] = -\frac{c}{v} [N \wedge [N \wedge H]] = \frac{c}{v} H.$$

Hence

$$\frac{\partial \omega}{\partial k} = \frac{c^3}{v^2 D^2} [E \wedge H].$$

By (2) (solution of Problem 408) $v^2 D^2 = c^2(E \cdot D) = c^2 H^2$, so that

$$\frac{\partial \omega}{\partial k} = \frac{c}{H^2} [E \wedge H] = \frac{cE}{H} s.$$

Finally, on applying the conversion theorem to (2) (solution of Problem 408), we get

$$u^2 = c^2 \frac{E^2}{(D \cdot E)} = c^2 \frac{E^2}{H^2}.$$

Finally,

$$\frac{\partial \omega}{\partial k} = us,$$

which is what we wished to prove.

494. It is possible. There is no contradiction, because a spot velocity v does not correspond to a signal transmission with velocity v (photons emitted at difference instants reach the screen simultaneously and this does not constitute the transmission of a signal along the screen).

495. If a ring were a continuous solid formation its periphery would have to have a higher linear velocity than its inner edge. Conversely, if the ring consisted of separate small satellites of the planet, the opposite situation would apply to the linear velocities of satellites remote from and close to the planet. By observing the Doppler effect from the edges of the rings, we can determine the edge whose velocity is the greater, and hence decide between the two propositions.

A. A. Belopol'skii found in 1896 that the velocity of the inner edge of the Saturn's ring was 21 km/sec, and of the outer edge 16 km/sec. Hence it follows that the ring cannot be a solid formation, but must consist of a large number of small satellites.

496. *Solution.* We first take the medium as the frame of reference. Let a plane acoustic wave

$$\psi = a \cos [\omega t - (\boldsymbol{k} \cdot \boldsymbol{r})], \quad \boldsymbol{k} = \frac{\omega}{c} \boldsymbol{N},$$

be propagated in it, where $\boldsymbol{N}$ is the normal to the wave front. We find the frequency of the wave in a system relative to which the source is fixed. On substituting in the above expression the source radius vector $\boldsymbol{r} = \boldsymbol{v}_{so} t + \text{const}$, we find for the phase: $[\omega - (\boldsymbol{k} \cdot \boldsymbol{v}_{so})]t + \text{const}$. Hence

$$\omega_{so} = \omega - (\boldsymbol{k} \cdot \boldsymbol{v}_{so}).$$

Similarly, for the frequency perceived by the observer,

$$\omega_{obs} = \omega - (\boldsymbol{k} \cdot \boldsymbol{v}_{obs}).$$

On eliminating ω and passing from angular to ordinary frequencies, we obtain

$$\frac{\nu_{obs}}{\nu_{so}} = \frac{1 - \dfrac{1}{c}(\boldsymbol{N} \cdot \boldsymbol{v}_{obs})}{1 - \dfrac{1}{c}(\boldsymbol{N} \cdot \boldsymbol{v}_{so})} = \frac{1 - \dfrac{v_{obs}}{c} \cos \Theta_{obs}}{1 - \dfrac{v_{so}}{c} \cos \Theta_{so}} = \frac{1 + \dfrac{v_{obs}}{c} \cos \vartheta_{obs}}{1 + \dfrac{v_{so}}{c} \cos \vartheta_{so}}$$

where Θ_{obs} and Θ_{so} are the angles between the direction of wave propagation and the directions of the velocities of the observer and source; $\vartheta_{obs} = \pi - \Theta_{obs}$, $\vartheta_{so} = \pi - \Theta_{so}$ are the complements of these angles, i.e. the angles between the same velocities and the line joining observer and source. In the case of high observer or source velocities the ratio ν_{obs}/ν_{so} may be negative; the sign then has to be changed in the above formula.

497. $\frac{\nu_{obs}}{\nu_{so}} = \frac{c + v_{obs}}{c + v_{so}}$,

where the velocities v_{obs} and v_{so} are regarded as positive if they are directed from the observer to the source.

498. *Solution.* We agree to regard as fixed the frame of reference in which the observer is at rest, and as moving the system in which the source is at rest. Putting (see the solution of Problem 496) $\nu \equiv \nu_{obs}$, $v_{obs} = 0$, $v_{so} = v$, $\vartheta_{so} = \vartheta$, we get

$$\frac{\nu}{\nu_1} = \frac{c}{c + v \cos \vartheta},$$

where ν_1 is the frequency of the light wave at the position of the source, measured by a fixed clock. If it is measured by a moving clock (i.e. a clock fixed in the source system), as a result of the slowing of the latter we obtain instead of ν_1 the frequency

$$\nu_0 \equiv \nu_{so} = \nu_1 \sqrt{1 - \beta^2}, \quad \beta = \frac{v}{c},$$

and hence

$$\frac{\nu}{\nu_0} = \frac{\sqrt{1 - \beta^2}}{1 + \beta \cos \vartheta} = \frac{\sqrt{1 - \beta^2}}{1 - \beta \cos \Theta}.$$

When $\vartheta = 0$,

$$\frac{\nu}{\nu_0} = \sqrt{\frac{1 - \beta}{1 + \beta}}.$$

When $\vartheta = \frac{1}{2}\pi$ (transverse Doppler effect),

$$\nu = \nu_0 \sqrt{1 - \beta^2}.$$

499. $\frac{\nu}{\nu_0} = \frac{1}{1 + \frac{v}{c} \cos \vartheta} \approx 1 - \frac{v}{c} \cos \vartheta$.

500. Putting $v_{so} = 0$, $v_{obs} = v$, $\vartheta_{obs} = \vartheta_0$, we get

$$\frac{\nu}{\nu_0} = \frac{1 + \beta \cos \vartheta_0}{\sqrt{1 - \beta^2}}.$$

501. The required formula is found from the requirement that the frequency ratio ν/ν_0 be independent of the method of computation. Let the same plane light wave be observed in two reference systems K_0 and K, the second of which moves with a velocity $\boldsymbol{v}$ relative to the first. The source is at rest in the system K_0. Let ϑ_0 and ϑ be the angles between the direction of the vector $\boldsymbol{v}$ and the reverse directions of the ray in these systems. Then

$$\cos\vartheta - \cos\vartheta_0 = \beta(\cos\vartheta\cos\vartheta_0 - 1).$$

502. $$\frac{\nu}{\nu_0} = \begin{cases} \dfrac{\sqrt{1-\beta^2}}{1-\beta n(\nu)\cos\Theta}, & \text{if } \beta n(\nu)\cos\Theta < 1; \\[2ex] \dfrac{\sqrt{1-\beta^2}}{\beta n(\nu)\cos\Theta - 1}, & \text{if } \beta n(\nu)\cos\Theta > 1, \end{cases}$$

where Θ is the angle between the vector $\boldsymbol{v}$ and the ray direction, and $n(\nu)$ is the refractive index of the medium.

503. *Solution.* Let the plane of the mirror be perpendicular to the x axis, whilst the mirror itself moves along this axis with velocity v. Given a suitable choice of the time origin the mirror abscissa will now be $x_3 = vt$. We write the incident and reflected waves as

$$ae^{i\omega\left(t-\frac{x}{c}\right)} \quad \text{and} \quad a'e^{i\omega'\left(t+\frac{x}{c}\right)}.$$

In view of the boundary conditions, the fields of the incident, reflected and transmitted waves at the mirror surface are connected by a homogeneous linear equation with coefficients independent of time. This can be the case when and only when the phases of these waves are equal at the mirror surface at any instant: $\omega t - \omega x_3/c = \omega' t + \omega' x_3/c$, whence

$$\frac{\omega'}{\omega} = \frac{\nu'}{\nu} = \frac{1-\dfrac{v}{c}}{1+\dfrac{v}{c}} = 1 - 2\frac{v}{c}.$$

504. $\nu' = \nu\left(1 \mp \dfrac{2Nv}{c}\right)$. The minus sign corresponds to reflection from a retreating mirror, the plus sign to reflection from an approaching mirror.

505. *Solution.* The rays from the source S (Fig. 95), after passing through the glass plate M and the lens L, are reflected from the plane mirror R, which can turn about an axis perpendicular to the plane of the figure. The lens L gives an image of the source S on the surface of the concave mirror C, the centre of curvature of which lies on the axis of rotation of the mirror R. The vessel P is filled with the substance in which the velocity of light is to be measured. If the mirror R is fixed, the rays reflected from C and R converge again

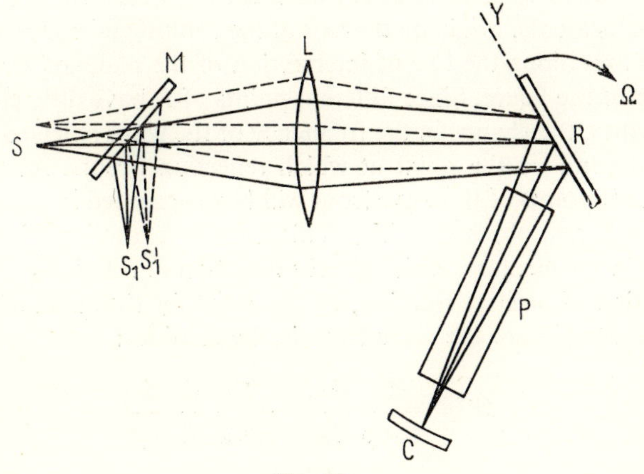

FIG. 95

at the point S. The mirror M deflects part of the rays to one side and gives a real image of the source at S_1. When the mirror R rotates the image S_1 is displaced to S_1'. The velocity of light in the substance under investigation can be calculated from the displacement S_1S_1'. Since the aim of the problem is to answer the essential question as to what velocity is given by Foucault's method, the air gaps between R and P, as also between P and C, can be regarded as indefinitely narrow, and the thickness of these gaps will be neglected throughout the working. The usual calculation is carried out as follows. The time required by the wave front, which travels with the phase velocity, to travel the distance from R to C and back is $T = 2D/v$, where D is the distance between R and C. During this time the mirror R turns through the angle $\varphi = T\Omega$, where Ω is the angular velocity of the mirror. The ray reflected from R rotates with twice the angular velocity. In the same time it turns through the angle $\alpha = 2\varphi = 2T\Omega = 4D\Omega/v$. The angle α is easily calculated from the displacement S_1S_1'. Hence,

$$v = \frac{4D\Omega}{\alpha}. \tag{1}$$

In this discussion no account has been taken of the change in frequency which must occur by Doppler's principle when the light is reflected from the moving mirror R. Thus it does not provide an answer as to what velocity is calculated from formula (1).

We locate the origin on the axis of the rotating mirror R and take the y axis along the line of intersection of the plane of R with the plane of the figure. Since different points of R have different linear velocities, the change in the frequency of the wave reflected from R will depend on the point at which reflection occurs. As a result, different points of the wave front will be propagated in the medium with different phase velocities. This leads to a rotation of the wave front in the medium. If we take the direction of rotation of R as the direction of positive rotation, we can write for the angular velocity of the rotation of the wave front in the medium:

$$\Omega' = \frac{1}{\cos\varphi}\frac{dv}{dy} = \frac{1}{\cos\varphi}\frac{dv}{d\omega}\frac{d\omega}{dy},$$

where φ is the angle of incidence of the light ray on the mirror R. Since $v = \omega/k$, we have

$$\frac{dv}{d\omega} = \frac{1}{k} - \frac{\omega}{k^2}\frac{dk}{d\omega} = \frac{v}{\omega} - \frac{v^2}{\omega u},$$

where u is the group velocity. It remains to find $d\omega/dy$. If ω is the frequency of the wave reflected from the mirror at the point with the coordinate y, and $\omega + d\omega$ at the point with coordinate $y + dy$, by Doppler's principle $d\omega/\omega = -(2\Omega/c)\cos\varphi\, dy$, whence

$$\frac{1}{\cos\varphi}\frac{d\omega}{dy} = -2\Omega\frac{\omega}{c} = -2\Omega\frac{\omega}{nv},$$

where n is the refractive index. Therefore,

$$\Omega' = \left(\frac{v^2}{\omega u} - \frac{v}{u}\right)2\Omega\frac{\omega}{nv} = \frac{2\Omega}{n}\left(\frac{v}{u} - 1\right).$$

The wave front reflected from the mirror C will also be rotated when travelling in the medium with the angular velocity Ω', in the same direction as the incident wave front, as may easily be seen. On the other hand, the wave front take the time $T = 2D/v$ to pass through a layer of the medium of thickness $2D$. During this time it rotates in the medium through the angle

$$\Omega' T = (4D\Omega/nv)(v/u - 1).$$

The wave front is refracted on passing from the vessel P into the vacuum, as a result of which the angle of rotation is magnified n times and becomes

$$n\Omega' T = \frac{4D\Omega}{v}\left(\frac{v}{u} - 1\right) = \frac{4D\Omega}{u} - \frac{4D\Omega}{v}.$$

This rotation has to be added to the rotation $4D\Omega/v$, obtained previously without taking account of the Doppler effect. Thus the measured angle of rotation α is actually

$$\alpha = \frac{4D\Omega}{v} + \left(\frac{4D\Omega}{u} - \frac{4D\Omega}{v}\right) = \frac{4D\Omega}{u},$$

so that we obtain instead of (1):

$$u = \frac{4D\Omega}{\alpha}. \tag{2}$$

Hence Foucault's rotating mirror method gives the group velocity.

506. The rotating mirror method gives the group velocity:

$$u = v\left(1 + \frac{\lambda}{n}\frac{dn}{d\lambda}\right).$$

Since

$$n = \frac{c}{v},$$

we have

$$\frac{c}{u} = \frac{n}{1 + \dfrac{\lambda}{n}\dfrac{dn}{d\lambda}} = 1{\cdot}76.$$

Michelson found by experiment that $c/u = 1{\cdot}75$.

507. Let the light wave travel in the ether at an angle α to the z axis. Let us take as the xz plane the plane through the wave normal and the z axis. If the coordinate system is at rest relative to the ether, the wave motion can be written as

$$E = E_0 \cos [\omega t - k(x \sin \alpha + z \cos \alpha)],$$

where the velocity of light $c = \omega/k$ is independent of the direction of propagation. Let us write the same wave in the coordinate system moving with velocity v relative to the ether in the direction of the z axis. If the two systems are the same at the initial instant, the coordinates in the new system can be expressed in terms of those in the old by the formulae

$$x' = x, \quad y' = y, \quad z' = z - vt.$$

Thus the wave motion relative to the new system is

$$E = E_0 \cos [\omega' t - k(x' \sin \alpha + z' \cos \alpha)],$$

where

$$\omega' = \omega - kv \cos \alpha.$$

Hence the wave frequency changes when observed in the new system. Conversely, the wavelength $\lambda = 2\pi/k$ remains unchanged. The phase velocity c' of the light in the moving system also changes. It is obviously equal to

$$c' = \frac{\omega'}{k} = c - v \cos \alpha. \tag{1}$$

We must differentiate the velocity of the light signal from the phase velocity. The former is obviously found from the classical theorem on the addition of velocities. The components of the light signal velocity in the fixed system are $c \sin \alpha$ and $c \cos \alpha$. In the moving system the x component remains the same, whilst the z component is lowered by v. Thus the components of the light signal velocity u relative to the moving system are

$$u_x = c_x = c \sin \alpha,$$

$$u_z = c_z - v = c \cos \alpha - v.$$

It is clear from this that the light signal travels in the moving system at an angle to the z axis different from that in the fixed system (aberration of light!). We obtain for the light signal velocity u:

$$u^2 = u_x^2 + u_z^2 = c^2 - 2cv\cos\alpha + v^2.$$

We shall neglect v^2 compared with c^2 in further working. In this approximation,

$$u = c - v\cos\alpha, \tag{2}$$

i.e. the signal velocity is equal to the phase velocity of the light. The velocity of light relative to the moving coordinate system depends on the direction of propagation. Relative to this system the ether behaves like an anisotropic medium at rest.

Having established this, let us suppose that an observer with a diffraction grating moves with velocity v relative to the ether in the direction of the z axis; the plane of the grating is parallel to the xz plane, whilst the rulings are parallel to the y axis. The secondary Huygens waves issuing from two adjacent points A and B of the grating, spaced the grating period d apart (Fig. 96), meet at the

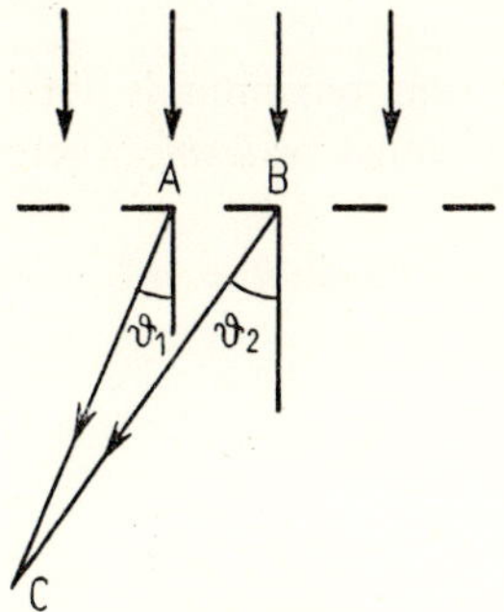

FIG. 96

point C and interfere. The time taken by the first wave to travel from the grating to the point C is

$$t_1 = \frac{AC}{u(\vartheta_1)} = \frac{AC}{c - v\cos\vartheta_1} \approx \frac{AC}{c}\left(1 + \frac{v}{c}\cos\vartheta_1\right),$$

and by the second wave:

$$t_2 = \frac{BC}{u(\vartheta_2)} = \frac{BC}{c - v\cos\vartheta_2} \approx \frac{BC}{c}\left(1 + \frac{v}{c}\cos\vartheta_2\right).$$

Since $AC \cos \vartheta_1 = BC \cos \vartheta_2$, the time difference is

$$t_2 - t_1 = \frac{BC - AC}{c}.$$

To observe the Fraunhofer diffraction, the point C must be moved to infinity. In the limit $\vartheta_1 = \vartheta_2 = \vartheta$, $BC - AC = d \sin \vartheta$, and we get

$$t_2 - t_1 = \frac{d \sin \vartheta}{c}.$$

Let us assume for simplicity that the incident wave travels along the z axis (i.e. perpendicular to the plane of the grating). Then $\alpha = 0$, $\omega' = \omega - kv$. The secondary Huygens waves issue from the grating points A and B in phase. They arrive at C with the phase difference

$$\Delta = \omega'(t_2 - t_1) = (\omega - kv)\frac{d \sin \vartheta}{c} = \frac{2\pi}{\lambda}\left(1 - \frac{v}{c}\right) d \sin \vartheta.$$

If the principal diffraction maximum is obtained in the direction ϑ, the phase difference Δ must be $2\pi m$, where m is an integer. This gives

$$d \sin \vartheta = m\lambda', \qquad (3)$$

where

$$\lambda' = \frac{\lambda}{1 - \frac{v}{c}}. \qquad (4)$$

The phenomenon therefore occurs as though the ether were at rest, and the wavelength were displaced towards red in accordance with (4).

The case of oblique incidence on the grating is easily considered by the same method. We leave this to the reader.

508. $\Delta\lambda = 21$ Å.

509. $\delta\lambda = 0{\cdot}046$ Å.

510. $\Delta\lambda \approx 450$ Å.

511. $\delta\lambda = 21$ Å.

512. If α is the angle between the direction of the beam of canal rays and the perpendicular to the line of observation, we must have

$$\alpha \ll \frac{v}{2c} = 0{\cdot}22 \times 10^{-2} \text{ rad} = 7'.$$

The difficulty mentioned in the problem was overcome as follows by Ives. The light reflected from the mirror as well as the direct radiation from the canal particles was directed into the spectrograph. The plane of the mirror was at right angles to the spectrograph axis. If the beam of canal rays now forms an angle α with the perpendicular to the line of observation, its image in the mirror will form the angle $-\alpha$ with this direction. The longitudinal Doppler effects, corresponding to the longitudinal velocities $+v \sin\alpha$ and $-v \sin\alpha$, were thus observed simultaneously. In both cases the transverse Doppler effect must give a displacement in the same direction (towards red). Experiment showed that the displaced lines were arranged asymmetrically to the undisplaced lines in this case: in fact, an extra shift towards red was added to the longitudinal Doppler shift. This extra shift can be calculated from the position of the displaced lines relative to the undisplaced line. Ives found that, within the limits of measurement error, it agreed with the relativistic formula for the transverse Doppler effect.

513. It moves away with the velocity $v = 1380 \text{ km sec}^{-1}$.

514. $v = 2 \text{ km sec}^{-1}$.

515. $\Delta\lambda = 1{\cdot}1$ Å.

516. $V = 3600\, v$.

517. $I(\nu) = I_0 e^{-\left(\frac{\nu - \nu_0}{\frac{\delta}{2}}\right)^2}$, where $\frac{\delta}{2} = \frac{\nu_0}{c}\sqrt{\frac{2RT}{\mu}}$.

(R is the gas constant, μ the molecular weight of the gas).

Solution. The probability of the gas molecule velocity in the direction of the observer lying in the interval $(v, v + dv)$ is

$$dw(v) = \sqrt{\frac{\mu}{2\pi RT}}\, e^{-\frac{\mu v^2}{2RT}}\, dv.$$

From the point of view of a fixed observer, a molecule with velocity v radiates light of the frequency $\nu = \nu_0(1 + v/c)$. Hence the probability of the molecule radiating light of frequency between ν and $\nu + d\nu$ is

$$dw(\nu) = \sqrt{\frac{\mu}{2\pi RT}}\, e^{-\frac{\mu}{2RT}\frac{c^2}{\nu_0^2}(\nu-\nu_0)^2}\, \frac{c}{\nu_0}\, d\nu .$$

Since the radiations of the different molecules are incoherent, $I(\nu)\, d\nu$ (the intensity of the light with frequency between ν and $\nu + d\nu$) is proportional to $dw(\nu)$, whence the expression given in the answer easily follows.

518. $\Delta\lambda = \dfrac{\lambda_0}{c}\sqrt{\dfrac{2RT}{A}}\sqrt{\ln 2} \approx 0{\cdot}042$ Å,

where A is the atomic weight of hydrogen.

519. $\dfrac{\Delta\lambda}{\lambda} = \dfrac{vn}{c}\cos\vartheta$,

where ϑ is the angle between the direction of observation and the direction of motion.

520. $\lambda = 2\dfrac{v}{\Delta\nu} = 50$ cm.

521. $\Delta t = \dfrac{2L}{v}(1 - \sqrt{1-\beta^2}) \approx \dfrac{L}{c}\left(\dfrac{v}{c}\right)$

$= 0{\cdot}0143$ year $= 5{\cdot}24$ days.

522. $E = mc^2 = 9 \times 10^{27}$ erg $= 9 \times 10^{20}$ Joules;

$M = 13{,}000$ tons, $v = c\sqrt{3}/2 = 2{\cdot}6 \times 10^5$ km sec^{-1}.

523. $M \approx me^{v/v_0} \approx 2 \times e^{26{,}000} \approx 10^{11{,}300}$ ton. This figure is enormous even from the point of view of the galactic and metagalactic scales (Mass of the earth is 6×10^{21} ton, of the sun 2×10^{27} ton, of our galaxy 2×10^{38} ton). At the same time, it is clear that the problem of interstellar rockets will remain unsolved until a "fuel" has been found, with which the exhaust velocity v_0 is of roughly the same order as the velocity c of light.

524. $\tau = \dfrac{\tau_0}{\sqrt{1-\beta^2}} = \dfrac{E}{mc^2}\tau_0 \approx 9{\cdot}5\tau_0 \approx 2{\cdot}1 \times 10^{-5}$ sec.

525. *Solution.* We consider a frame of reference moving with constant acceleration $\boldsymbol{a}$ relative to the inertial system. Let a light wave be radiated at an instant t_1 at the point 1 (Fig. 97) in the direction towards the observer 2, at a distance L from 1. We introduce an inertial reference system relative to which the velocity

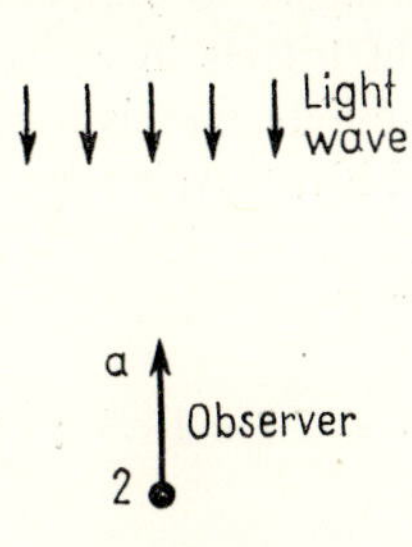

FIG. 97

of the observer is zero at the instant t_1. Let the frequency of the wave in this reference system be ν_1. The wave reaches the observer at the instant $t_2 = t_1 + L/c$. (We have neglected the small correction connected with the motion of the observer.) At this instant the observer 2 has acquired the velocity $a(t_2 - t_1) = aL/c$, and hence measures the frequency

$$\nu_2 = \nu_1\left(1 + \frac{aL}{c^2}\right)$$

in accordance with Doppler's principle. From the point of view of Einstein's equivalence principle the present case is no different physically from the case when the observer is at rest relative to the inertial system, but is in a gravitational field of intensity $\boldsymbol{g} = -\boldsymbol{a}$. In the latter case $aL = gL$ is the gravitational potential difference $\varphi_1 - \varphi_2$ between the points 1 and 2. (By definition of the gravitational potential, $\boldsymbol{g} = -\operatorname{grad}\varphi$.) Consequently the previous formula becomes

$$\nu_2 - \nu_1 = \nu \frac{\varphi_1 - \varphi_2}{c^2}, \qquad (1)$$

where, up to the accuracy of the calculation, ν is taken either as ν_1, or as ν_2. (An accurate formula can only be obtained in the general theory of relativity.)

Formula (1) remains valid when light travels in a non-uniform gravitational field, since the space over the path of the light ray can be split into sufficiently small regions, in each of which the gravitational field can be regarded as uniform. It is sufficient to apply to these regions formula (1) and to eliminate the intermediate frequencies by addition, in order to verify our assertion. It follows from (1) that, when light travels in a gravitational field, the frequency is increased if the light travels towards lower gravitational potential, and is lowered if it travels towards higher potential.

526. Towards the red.

527. $\dfrac{\Delta\nu}{\nu} = \dfrac{gRh}{c^2(R+h)} = 7{\cdot}8 \times 10^{-11}$; towards the violet.

528. $\dfrac{\Delta\nu}{\nu} = \dfrac{gh}{c^2} = 5{\cdot}45 \times 10^{-13}$.

529. With circular motion of the satellite $\Delta\nu/\nu = hv^2/Rc^2$. With elliptic motion, a coefficient of the order of unity appears on the right-hand side.

530. $\dfrac{\Delta\nu}{\nu} = \dfrac{v}{c}\cos\Theta - \dfrac{v^2}{2c^2}(1 - 2\cos^2\Theta) + \dfrac{\varphi_1 - \varphi_2}{c^2}$.

In case (a) $\Theta = \dfrac{\pi}{2}$,

$$\frac{\Delta\nu}{\nu} = -\frac{v^2}{2c^2} + \frac{gRh}{c^2(R+h)} = -2{\cdot}3 \times 10^{-10}.$$

In case (b) $\Theta = 89°$, $\dfrac{\Delta\nu}{\nu} = +4{\cdot}38 \times 10^{-7}$.

§ 7. Radiation Pressure

531. $P = u(1+r)\cos^2\varphi$, where u is the incident wave energy density; $T = \frac{1}{2}u(1-r)\sin 2\varphi$.

Solution. If N is the number of photons of the incident wave per unit volume, the momentum of the photons striking the mirror per sec is $(Nh\nu/c).\ cS\cos\varphi$, where S is the area of the mirror. Since $Nh\nu = u$, this momentum is equal to $\boldsymbol{p}_1 = uS\cos\varphi\cdot\boldsymbol{i}$, where $\boldsymbol{i}$ is the unit vector in the direction of the incident ray. The momentum of the photons reflected per sec is $\boldsymbol{p}_2 = ruS\cos\varphi\cdot\boldsymbol{i}'$, where $\boldsymbol{i}'$ is the unit vector in the direction of the reflected ray. Hence the change in momentum of the wave per sec due to reflection from the mirror is

$$\boldsymbol{p}_2 - \boldsymbol{p}_1 = -uS(\boldsymbol{i} - r\boldsymbol{i}')\cos\varphi.$$

By the law of conservation of momentum, the change in momentum of the mirror will have the same magnitude but in the opposite direction. Thus the force $\boldsymbol{F}$ acting on the mirror from the radiation is

$$\boldsymbol{F} = \boldsymbol{p}_1 - \boldsymbol{p}_2 = uS(\boldsymbol{i} - \boldsymbol{i}r')\cos\varphi,$$

and the force f acting per unit area of the mirror is

$$f = u(\boldsymbol{i} - r\boldsymbol{i}')\cos\varphi.$$

On projecting this expression on to the normal to the mirror and on to the plane of the mirror, we obtain the results quoted in the answer.

532. $P = u(\cos^2\varphi + \frac{1}{2}\cos\varphi)$, $\quad T = \frac{1}{2}u\sin 2\varphi$.

Solution. If the reflecting surface is ideally mat, it completely reflects the light incident on it, and rays are obtained in all directions after reflection, all these directions being equiprobable. The probability of the direction of travel of a reflected photon being at an angle between ϑ and $\vartheta + d\vartheta$ to the normal to the mirror is $(1/2\pi)\,d\Omega = \sin\vartheta\,d\vartheta$, since the corresponding element of solid angle is $d\Omega = 2\pi\sin\vartheta\,d\vartheta$. The resultant momentum of all the reflected photons will be perpendicular to the plane of the mirror. The mean value of the projection of the momentum of one reflected photon onto the normal to the mirror is

$$\int_0^{\pi/2}\frac{h\nu}{c}\cos\vartheta\sin\vartheta\,d\vartheta = \frac{1}{2}\frac{h\nu}{c}.$$

Consequently, we obtain for the resultant momentum of all the reflected photons:

$$p_2 = NcS\cos\varphi\cdot\frac{1}{2}\frac{h\nu}{c}\boldsymbol{n} = \frac{1}{2}uS\cos\varphi\,\boldsymbol{n},$$

where $\boldsymbol{n}$ is the unit vector along the normal to the mirror. The force f acting per unit area of the mirror is

$$f = \frac{p_1 - p_2}{S} = u\left(\boldsymbol{i} - \frac{1}{2}\boldsymbol{n}\right)\cos\varphi.$$

On projecting this expression on to the normal $\boldsymbol{n}$ to the plane of the mirror, we obtain the results quoted in the answer.

534. $P = u/3$, where u is the radiation density.

535. (1) $P = 0{\cdot}46$ dyne m^{-2} or approximately half a milligram weight per square metre; (2) $P_2 = 2P_1 = 0{\cdot}92$ dyne m^{-2}; (3) $P_3 = 3P_1/2 = 0{\cdot}69$ dyne m^{-2}.

536. $F = Q/c \approx 3{\cdot}5 \times 10^{-5}$ dynes.

537. (1) $F = Su$, where S is the area of the diametral section of the sphere; (2) $F = Su$; (3) $F = 4Su/3$, where u is the energy density of the incident wave.

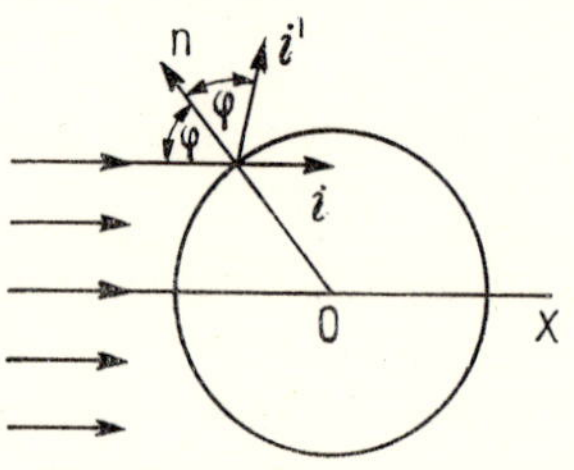

FIG. 98

Solution. Since the sphere is large compared with the light wavelength, we can confine ourselves to the approximation of geometrical optics when solving the problem, and neglect diffraction. In order to combine the first two cases, we suppose that the reflection coefficient of the spherical surface is equal to r and is independent of the angle of incidence φ. The force f acting per unit area of the sphere is $f = u\cos\varphi(\boldsymbol{i} - r\boldsymbol{i}')$ (see the solution of Problem 531). We direct the x axis parallel to the incident ray (Fig. 98). In view of the symmetry, the resultant force of the light pressure on the sphere must be directed along the x axis and be equal to $F = \int f_x dS$, where dS is the element of the spherical surface, whilst the integration is over the illuminated half of this surface. We have

$$f_x = u \cos\varphi - ru \cos\varphi \cos(\pi - 2\varphi) = (1 - r)\, u \cos\varphi + 2ru \cos^3\varphi.$$

Further,

$$dS = 2\pi a^2 \sin\varphi\, d\varphi,$$

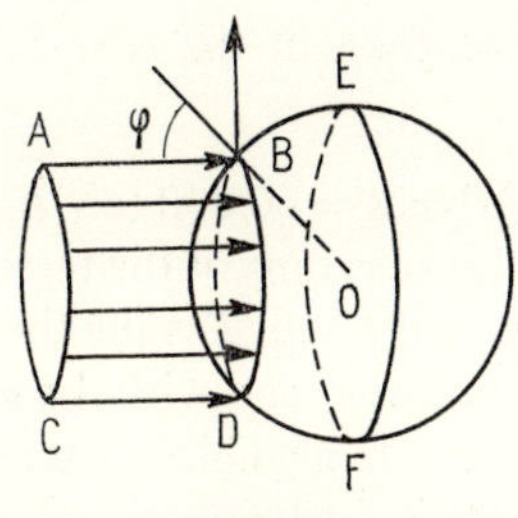

FIG. 99

where a is the radius of the sphere. Integration gives

$$F = \pi a^2 u.$$

The force F is therefore independent of the reflection coefficient and is the same for absolutely reflecting (mirror-type) and absolutely black spheres. The case of an ideally mat spherical surface is solved in the same way and gives $F = 4\pi a^2 u/3$.

538. The light pressure is greater on an ideally reflecting sphere.

Solution. If the reflection coefficient r were independent of the angle of incidence, the force of the light pressure would be the same in both cases (see the solution of the previous problem). But in fact r depends on the angle of incidence and the forces are therefore different in the two cases. Let the ray AB (Fig. 99) strike the sphere at the angle of incidence $\varphi = 45°$. The reflected photons will now travel at right angles to the incident ray, and each of them will transmit momentum $h\nu/c$ to the sphere. If the photon were incident on the sphere within the limits of the surface bounded by the circle BD, on reflection it would have a component of momentum in the opposite direction to the incident light; in this case it transmits a momentum greater than $h\nu/c$ to the sphere. Conversely, if the photon is incident on the sphere within the limits of the ring $BEFD$, the momentum transmitted by it will be less than $h\nu/c$. If r is independent of the angle of incidence, the excess of the transmitted momenta by comparison with $h\nu/c$ on the circle BD will be fully compensated by the lack on the ring $BEFD$. In reality r depends on the angle of incidence. In the case of unpolarised light r increases with the angle of incidence. Thus the lack of the transmitted momenta on the ring $BEFD$ will exceed the excess on the circle BD. It follows from this that the force of the light pressure on the sphere that partially reflects light will be less than in the case of an ideally reflecting sphere.

539. $F_1 = 5{\cdot}9 \times 10^{13}$ dynes $= 60\,000$ ton. $F_1/F_2 = 3uT^2/16\pi^2 aR\delta = 1{\cdot}6 \times 10^{-14}$. Here a is the radius of the terrestrial sphere, R is the distance from the earth to the sun, T is the time of revolution of the earth about the sun. By comparison with the gravitational force the force of the light pressure is negligibly small and its influence on the motion of the planets is far below the limits of the accuracy of astronomical measurements.

540. $a < \dfrac{3}{16}\dfrac{uT^2}{\pi^2 R\delta} = 5{\cdot}8 \times 10^{-5}$ cm.

The result is obtained on the assumption that geometrical optics is applicable to the present case. In actual fact, since the calculated value of a is of the same order as the light wavelength, the effect of diffraction is important. When this is taken into account, a smaller value of a is evidently obtained, since the light exerts a pressure on the rear as well as the front of the particle. Thus geometrical optics can only yield an upper limit for a.

541. $u' = u\left(1 \pm \dfrac{4v}{c}\right)$, where u is the incident wave energy density, u' the reflected wave energy density, and v the velocity of the mirror. The plus sign corresponds to the mirror moving in the opposite direction to the light, and the minus to the opposite case.

Solution. We imagine an infinitely long cylinder, in which a mirror piston moves slowly without friction with velocity v ($v \ll c$). A wave train of length $l = c$ moves in the cylinder in the same direction as the piston. Let the head of the train have reached the piston at time $t = 0$. Then it is easily seen that the end of the train reaches the piston at $t = c/(c - v)$. During this time the piston has travelled

$$x = vt = \frac{vc}{c - v},$$

whilst the forward front of the reflected wave has travelled ct. Thus the length of the reflected train will be

$$l' = ct + x = c\,\frac{c + v}{c - v}.$$

If the piston area is unity, the light wave energy change in this process is $u'l' - ul$. The light pressure p has done the work px. Consequently,

$$ul = u'l' + px.$$

When the piston moves slowly the light pressure can be taken equal to $p = 2u$, if we neglect the additional terms of the order $u(v/c)$. On substituting the values of p, x, l, l' in the previous expression, we obtain the result quoted in the answer for a retreating piston. This result is correct if we neglect magnitudes of the order $(v/c)^2$.

542. If the beam intensity is so great that it causes energy vapourisation on the surface of the body, the momentum communicated to the body can substantially exceed $2uSt$. This is explained by the fact that the particles evaporating into the vacuum carry away momentum, as a result of which the body acquires a recoil.

§ 8. Molecular Optics

543. $\alpha = \dfrac{n - 1}{2\pi N} = 2{\cdot}66 \times 10^{-24}\ \text{cm}^3.$

545. $v_{\max} = \dfrac{eE_0}{m\omega} = \dfrac{eE_0\lambda}{2\pi mc} \approx 5{\cdot}3\ \text{cm}\,\text{sec}^{-1};$

$$\frac{F_m}{F_e} = \frac{v_{\max}}{2c} \approx 0{\cdot}9 \times 10^{-10}.$$

In spite of its smallness, the force F_m plays an important part, since it is responsible for the light pressure. (See the solution of Problem 546.)

546. $$\overline{F} = \frac{1}{2}\,\frac{\dfrac{e^2}{mc}E_0^2\omega^2\gamma}{(\omega^2-\omega_0^2)^2+(\gamma\omega)^2} = \frac{\varepsilon}{c},$$

$$\varepsilon = \frac{1}{2}\,\frac{\dfrac{e^2}{m}E_0^2\omega^2\gamma}{(\omega^2-\omega_0^2)^2+(\gamma\omega)^2},$$

where E_0 is the amplitude of the electric field of the light wave.

Solution. If the wave is propagated along the z axis, the vector $\boldsymbol{E}$ is along the x axis, and $\boldsymbol{H}$ along the y axis, then

$$E = E_x = E_0 \cos\omega t, \quad H = H_y = H_0 \cos\omega t.$$

If the action of the magnetic field is neglected, the equation of motion of the electron can be written as

$$\ddot{x} + \gamma\dot{x} + \omega_0^2 x = \frac{e}{m}E_0 \cos\omega t.$$

Integration of this gives the velocity $\dot{x}$ of the electron in a steady-state forced oscillation:

$$\dot{x} = \frac{\dfrac{e}{m}E_0\omega}{(\omega^2-\omega_0^2)^2+(\gamma\omega)^2}\{\gamma\omega\cos\omega t + (\omega^2-\omega_0^2)\sin\omega t\}.$$

As a result of the magnetic field of the light wave, the force $\boldsymbol{F} = (e/c)\,[\boldsymbol{v} \wedge \boldsymbol{H}]$ will act on the oscillating electron. As is easily seen, this force is directed along the z axis. It is equal to

$$F = \frac{e}{c}H_y\dot{x}$$

$$= \frac{\dfrac{e^2}{mc}E_0^2\omega}{(\omega^2-\omega_0^2)^2+(\gamma\omega)^2}\{\gamma\omega\cos\omega t + (\omega^2-\omega_0^2)\sin\omega t\}\cos\omega t.$$

On averaging this expression over time, we obtain the result given in the answer.

The energy absorbed by the electron per sec is equal to the work done by the friction force $m\gamma\dot{x}$ during this time, i.e.

$$\int_0^1 m\gamma\dot{x}^2 dt.$$

Integration and averaging over time gives ε.

547. (1) p/p_0 is of the order 10^{-8}, where p is the induced moment. (2) p/p_0 is of the order 10^{-5}.

548. The law $v = c/\sqrt{\varepsilon}$ is not fulfilled because water molecules have a large constant dipole moment ($1{\cdot}8 \times 10^{-18}$ e.s.u.) which plays no part in optical phenomena for frequencies of the visible spectrum. At lower frequencies (radio waves) the dipole molecules have time during the period of oscillation of the electromagnetic field to orientate mainly in the direction of the electric field. The polarisability of the medium and its refractive index therefore depend at such frequencies on the molecules possessing constant dipole moments. The refractive index for radio waves is equal to the square root of the static dielectric constant (for water $n = \sqrt{\varepsilon} = \sqrt{81} = 9$). But even in the centimetre wave region the constant dipole moments of the molecules do not ensure their orientation in the direction of the electric field. In this region the refractive index falls sharply with increase of frequency. In the optical region the dipole molecules virtually cease to rotate under the action of the electric field of the light wave, and their constant moments have no effect on the refractive index.

549. $n = 1{\cdot}107$.

550. $$\varepsilon = 1 - \frac{4\pi e_e^2 N_e}{m_e\omega^2} - \sum \frac{4\pi e_i^2 N_i}{m_i\omega^2},$$

where N_e and N_i are the electron and ion concentrations (i.e. the number of particles per cm^3); e_e, e_i, m_e, m_i are their charges and masses. The summation is over all the ions. In view of the quasi-neutrality of the ionosphere, the concentration of positive ions is equal, to a high order of accuracy, to the sum of the concentrations of the electrons and negative ions. The last term in the expression for ε can therefore be neglected, since the mass of an ion is large compared with the mass of an electron. On proceeding thus and omitting the subscript "e", we get

$$\varepsilon = 1 - \frac{\omega_0^2}{\omega^2},$$

where

$$\omega_0 = \frac{4\pi e^2 N}{m}.$$

551. It is possible: $n < 1$ for radio waves in the ionosphere; $n < 1$ for X-rays.

552. There is strong absorption in the region of anomalous dispersion, and $u = v - \lambda\, dv/d\lambda$ becomes meaningless, as the speed of propagation of the signal or of the energy. (The formula for the group velocity is derived on the assumption that absorption is absent or small.)

553. Putting $\sqrt{\varepsilon} = \pm i\varkappa$, we can transform $\boldsymbol{E} = \boldsymbol{E}_0 \exp i(\omega t - kz)$ to the form

$$\boldsymbol{E} = \boldsymbol{E}_0 e^{\varkappa z} e^{i\omega t},$$

or

$$\boldsymbol{E} = \boldsymbol{E}_0 e^{-\varkappa z} e^{i\omega t}.$$

In the real form:

$$\boldsymbol{E} = \boldsymbol{E}_0 e^{\varkappa z} \cos \omega t,$$

or

$$\boldsymbol{E} = \boldsymbol{E}_0 e^{-\varkappa z} \cos \omega t.$$

These are standing waves. The amplitude of the first wave increases exponentially, whilst the second is damped exponentially along the z axis. The choice of the sign in front of $\varkappa$ has to be determined by the physical conditions. There is damping in both cases, but no absorption.

554. If $\omega > \omega_0$, the wave passes through the ionosphere; if $\omega < \omega_0$, the wave is completely reflected. Here $\omega_0 = \sqrt{4\pi N_{\max} e^2/m} = 5{\cdot}64 \times 10^4 \sqrt{N_{\max}}\ \mathrm{sec}^{-1}$, where $N_{\max}$ is the electron concentration at the height where this is a maximum.

555. $N = \dfrac{\pi m}{e^2}\nu^2 = 1{\cdot}24 \times 10^{-8}\nu^2.$

556. In order for a radio wave to be able to reach the earth, its wavelength must be $\lambda < (3{\cdot}34/N) \times 10^6$ cm $= 2{\cdot}3 \times 10^2$ cm $= 2{\cdot}3$ m.

557. $v = \sqrt{c^2 + \dfrac{Ne^2}{\pi m}\lambda^2}$.

558. When $\varepsilon(\omega) = 0$, which gives in the case of a plasma $\omega = \sqrt{4\pi Ne^2/m}$. The wave vector $\boldsymbol{k}$, and with this the phase velocity, can have any value.* The group velocity $u = d\omega/dk = 0$. It is therefore better to speak simply of vibrations of the electric field, and of the vibrations of the electrons of the plasma relative to the ions, rather than of a "wave".

559. Radiation is absent in a vacuum, since in this case the electromagnetic waves are transverse. The only preferred direction for a body with spherical symmetry is radial. For this last reason, in the case of vibrations with spherical symmetry, only purely longitudinal waves can be radiated, propagated along the radius. Examples exist of such waves in a medium, e.g. longitudinal acoustic waves and plasma waves (the dielectric constant $\varepsilon(\omega_0) = 0$ in plasma waves).

560. When there is a centre of symmetry the effects of spatial dispersion are of the order $(a/\lambda)^2 \approx 10^{-7} - 10^{-8}$. Taking account of spatial dispersion leads to optical anisotropy of the cubic crystals E.g. if the light wave vector $\boldsymbol{k}$ is directed along the z axis of the cube, the tensor ε_{ij} has the form

$$\varepsilon_{zz} = \varepsilon + \alpha_1 k^2, \quad \varepsilon_{xx} = \varepsilon_{yy} = \varepsilon, \quad \varepsilon_{xy} = \varepsilon_{xz} = \varepsilon_{yz} = 0$$

(when $k = 0$ the tensor ε_{ij} for cubic crystals with a centre of symmetry degenerates to the scalar $\varepsilon\delta_{ij}$).

561. $n^2 \simeq \dfrac{1 - \dfrac{\omega_0^2}{\omega^2}}{3\dfrac{k_B T}{mc^2}}, \quad v_{ph} \simeq \dfrac{\sqrt{\dfrac{3k_B T}{m}}}{\sqrt{1 - \dfrac{\omega_0^2}{\omega^2}}},$

$$v_{gr} \simeq \frac{3k_B T}{m\omega_0} k = v_{ph}\left(1 - \frac{\omega_0^2}{\omega^2}\right).$$

* This statement holds if the thermal motion of the electrons can be neglected (the mean velocity of the thermal motion of an electron is small compared with the velocity c of light). When account is taken of the thermal motion of the electrons, ω is found to depend on k.

562. *Solution.* If the electron moves uniformly and its velocity component v_n along the wave normal coincides with the phase velocity ω/k of the wave itself, its motion takes place "in phase with the wave", like the motion of the electrons in a linear accelerator entering the acceleration state. In this case the electron is subject to the action of a force (from the electric field of the wave), which is always directed either forwards (in the direction of propagation of the wave), or backwards. As a result a strong interaction must be observed between the electron and the wave, accompanied either by absorption or by the radiation of plasma waves. Since $v_n = (\boldsymbol{v} \cdot \boldsymbol{k})/k$, the condition for strong interaction of the electron and wave can be written as

$$(\boldsymbol{v} \cdot \boldsymbol{k}) = \omega. \tag{1}$$

This is the condition for Cherenkov absorption or radiation of plasma waves.

Since the frequency ω of the plasma waves is weakly dependent on the wave number k (see the previous problem), we can replace ω in condition (1) by the plasma frequency $\omega_0 = \sqrt{4\pi Ne^2/m}$. Let $v_T \simeq \sqrt{k_B T/m}$ be the mean thermal velocity of the electrons in the plasma. If $kv_T \ll \omega_0$, there are very few (fast) electrons satisfying condition (1) and the absorption is weak. It will be strong when $kv_T \gtrsim \omega_0$.

563. *Solution.* The equation $\ddot{\boldsymbol{r}} + \omega_0^2 \boldsymbol{r} = e\boldsymbol{E}/m$ for the oscillations of a harmonic oscillator in an electric field $\boldsymbol{E} = \boldsymbol{E}_0 e^{i\omega t}$ gives for the steady-state oscillations $\boldsymbol{r} = (e/m)\boldsymbol{E}/(\omega_0^2 - \omega^2)$.

The electric field energy density is

$$w_1 = \frac{1}{8\pi}\left(\frac{\boldsymbol{E} + \boldsymbol{E}^*}{2}\right)^2 = \frac{\boldsymbol{E}^2}{32\pi} + \frac{(\boldsymbol{E} \cdot \boldsymbol{E}^*)}{32\pi} + \text{conj. compl.}$$

The potential energy density is

$$w_2 = \frac{Nm\omega_0^2}{2}\left(\frac{\boldsymbol{r} + \boldsymbol{r}^*}{2}\right)^2 = \frac{Nm\omega_0^2}{8}[\boldsymbol{r}^2 + (\boldsymbol{r} \cdot \boldsymbol{r}^*)] + \text{conj. compl.}$$

The kinetic energy density is

$$w_3 = \frac{Nm}{2}\left(\frac{\dot{\boldsymbol{r}} + \dot{\boldsymbol{r}}^*}{2}\right)^2 = -\frac{Nm\omega^2}{8}[\boldsymbol{r}^2 - (\boldsymbol{r} \cdot \boldsymbol{r}^*)] + \text{conj. compl.}$$

On substituting in this the expression for $\boldsymbol{r}$ and remarking that, by the dispersion formula, $\varepsilon = 1 + 4\pi Ne^2/m(\omega_0^2 - \omega^2)$, it follows that $d(\varepsilon\omega)/d\omega = 1 + (\varepsilon - 1)(\omega_0^2 + \omega^2)/(\omega_0^2 - \omega^2)$, we obtain for the electric energy density:

$$w_e = \frac{\varepsilon \boldsymbol{E}^2}{32\pi} + \frac{1}{32\pi}\frac{d(\varepsilon\omega)}{d\omega}(\boldsymbol{E}\cdot\boldsymbol{E}^*) + \text{conj. compl.}$$

We have the usual expression for the magnetic energy density, as in the case of a non-dispersive medium.

564. The spectrum is intersected by dark bands, narrowing from the red to the violet end. The zero band (i.e. the band which corresponds to zero path difference) is horizontal. The bands become oblique on introducing the glass plate.

565. The slope of the bands is the greater, the greater the thickness of the plate, and it is virtually independent of the dispersion of the refractive index. On transferring the plate from one arm of the interferometer to the other the slope changes sign.

566. Let y_k denote the distance of the kth order interference band from the position which the zero order band occupied prior to introducing into the interferometer arms the glass plate and the layer of sodium vapour. Prior to the introduction $y_k = ak\lambda$, where a is a constant of the apparatus. After introducing the plate and sodium vapour the band in question is displaced, and we obtain $y_k = a[k\lambda - (n_g - 1)l_g + (n_{\text{Na}} - 1)l_{\text{Na}}]$. At the vertex of the hook $dy_k/d\lambda = 0$, which gives

$$\left(\frac{dn}{d\lambda}\right)_{\text{Na}} = -\frac{k}{l_{\text{Na}}} + \frac{l_g}{l_{\text{Na}}}\left(\frac{dn}{d\lambda}\right)_g . \qquad (1)$$

The order of the interference $k = l_g(n_g - 1)/\lambda$ is large (several thousands), so that the last term in (1) can be neglected.

567. $f_0 = \dfrac{4\pi mc^2}{N_0 e^2 \lambda_0^4}\dfrac{l_g}{l}(n_g - 1)(\Delta\lambda)^2.$

568. No, light of frequency ω_0 will be radiated.

569. No. The dipole moment of all particles of charge e and mass m is equal to $\boldsymbol{p} = e\sum \boldsymbol{r}_i$ and its time derivative is constant since $m \sum \dot{\boldsymbol{r}}_i$ is the momentum of the system which in the present case is conserved and the dipole radiation is determined by the derivative $\ddot{\boldsymbol{p}}$.

570. *Solution.* At the Brewster angle the refracted ray is perpendicular to the reflected ray, the vibrations of the electrons in the molecules of the medium are perpendicular to the direction of the refracted ray and hence coincide with the direction in which the reflected ray must lie (it is assumed that the molecules are isotropic). Thus light polarised in the plane of incidence cannot radiate in the direction of the reflected ray.

571. If light polarised at right angles to the plane of incidence is incident at the Brewster angle, even though the induced dipole moments of the molecules of the medium are parallel to the direction of the reflected ray, the dipole moments of the molecules of the layer are not parallel to this direction. Hence the molecules of the layer radiate in this direction, which leads to the appearance of reflected light.

572. For reflection to be possible, it is not sufficient that the molecules of the medium radiate in the direction of reflection. It is also necessary that their radiation be coherent or, at any rate, partially coherent. This is not the case for isotropic media made up of anisotropic molecules, because the condition for such media to be isotropic is that the orientation of the anisotropic molecules be completely random. Unless this condition is fulfilled, the medium behaves as though its molecules were isotropic. The fluctuations of anisotropy, which always occur, lead to an additional scattering of the light in all directions, but no regular reflection is obtained. It would be obtained if the condition that the orientation of the molecules be random no longer held exactly. In all probability, this is the case for the monomolecular layer of boundary anisotropic molecules of the medium. This type of orientation is possibly one of the reasons for the deviation from Fresnel's formulae when light is reflected from completely pure liquid surfaces.

573. *Solution.* The field radiated by the medium as a whole is

$$\boldsymbol{E} = \boldsymbol{E}_1 - \boldsymbol{E}_2 + \boldsymbol{E}_3 - \cdots, \tag{1}$$

where the individual terms are the radiation fields of the individual layers. When the polarisation wave $\boldsymbol{P} = \boldsymbol{P}_0 \exp i[\omega t - (\boldsymbol{k} \cdot \boldsymbol{r})]$ is strictly uniform, the terms of the series (1) have the same absolute value, and the sum does not have a definite value. In reality, the polarisation wave has a forward front, in front of which the wave disturbance is zero. In reality, therefore, series (1) contains a finite number of terms, and the indeterminacy disappears. In order to compute the sum, we imagine that the first layer, together with the field radiated by it, is removed, whilst the rest of the medium is moved upwards a distance equal to the layer thickness l. We imagine further that the phases of all the dipole moments of the media are changed by the same amount, in such a way that the dipoles coming on to the boundary after the displacement have the same phase as the removed dipoles of the first layer would have had at the same instant. In view of the slowness of the variation of the terms of series (1) and the fact that the layers are identical, it is clear that the radiation field outside the medium is unchanged as a result of these fictitious operations. But the field can now be written as $\boldsymbol{E} = \boldsymbol{E}_2 - \boldsymbol{E}_3 + \cdots$. In conjunction with (1), this gives $\boldsymbol{E} = \frac{1}{2}\boldsymbol{E}_1$. We easily obtain for the layer thickness $l = \pi/(k_z + f_z)$. (The z axis is at right angles to the boundary towards the medium.) The wave vector $\boldsymbol{f}$ in the vacuum is defined by the components:

$$f_x = k_x, \quad f_y = k_y, \quad f_z = +\sqrt{\frac{\omega^2}{c^2} - k_x^2 - k_y^2}\,.$$

574. *Solution.* We split the fictitious medium filling the upper half-space into layers of thickness $L = \pi/(k_z - f_z)$. The plane waves radiated in the lower half-space by adjacent layers will now have opposite phases. On arguing as in the previous problem, we find that the radiation field of the entire fictitious medium is equivalent to half the radiation field of its first layer. If the electric vector (and hence also the vector $\boldsymbol{P}$) is perpendicular to the plane of incidence, we obtain for the ratio of the complex amplitudes of the reflected and incident waves:

$$\frac{R_s}{\mathscr{E}_s} = -\frac{l}{L} = \frac{f_z - k_z}{f_z + k_z} = \frac{\cos\varphi - n\cos\psi}{\cos\varphi + n\cos\psi}.$$

Fresnel's second formula is similarly obtained. It is only necessary to take account of the dependence of the radiation on its direction. The only component of $\boldsymbol{P}$ that plays a part is that perpendicular to the direction of the radiated wave; the parallel component gives no radiation.

575. *Solution.* We first take case (a). Let the dipole $\boldsymbol{p}$ be at the point 0 inside the slit (Fig. 100). Let $\boldsymbol{E}'$ denote the field of the dipole. We take a second dipole $\boldsymbol{p}_1$ at the point 1 outside the slit, at a distance from it which is large compared with λ. Let the field of this dipole be $\boldsymbol{E}_1$. Then by the reciprocity theorem:

$$(\boldsymbol{p} \cdot \boldsymbol{E}_1(0)) = (\boldsymbol{p}_1 \cdot \boldsymbol{E}'(1)). \qquad (1)$$

If there were no slit, we should have instead of (1):

$$(\boldsymbol{p} \cdot \boldsymbol{E}_1^0(0)) = (\boldsymbol{p}_1 \cdot \boldsymbol{E}(1)), \qquad (2)$$

where $\boldsymbol{E}_1^0$ is the field of dipole 1 in the absence of the slit. The field $\boldsymbol{E}_1^0$ in the neighbourhood of the point 0 can be regarded as uniform. Hence, in view of the continuity of the tangential components of the electric field, the left-hand sides of (1) and (2) are equal. Consequently $(\boldsymbol{p}_1 \cdot \boldsymbol{E}'(1)) = (\boldsymbol{p}_1 \cdot \boldsymbol{E}(1))$, whence, in view of the arbitrariness of the vector $\boldsymbol{p}_1$ and of the position of the point 1, we obtain $\boldsymbol{E}' = \boldsymbol{E}$ outside the slit.

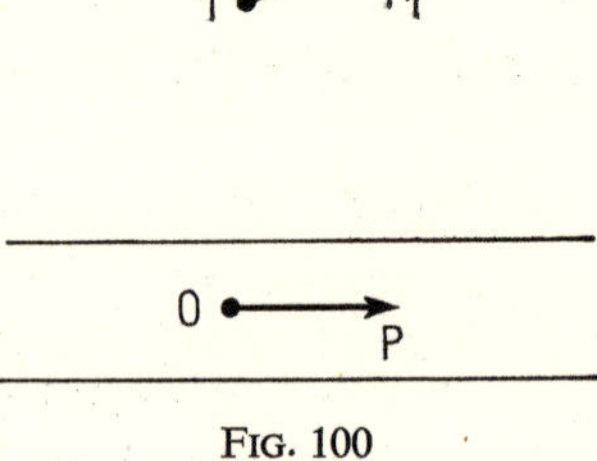

FIG. 100

Thus the slit has no effect on the radiation of the dipole, i.e. on the field in its wave zone.

In case (b) relationships (1) and (2) still hold. But now, in view of the continuity of the normal components of the induction vector, $\varepsilon'(\boldsymbol{E}_1(0) \cdot \boldsymbol{p}) = \varepsilon(\boldsymbol{E}_1^0(0) \cdot \boldsymbol{p})$, where ε' is the dielectric constant of the material filling the slit. Hence $\varepsilon'(\boldsymbol{p}_1 \cdot \boldsymbol{E}'(1)) = \varepsilon(\boldsymbol{p}_1 \cdot \boldsymbol{E}(1))$, whence $\boldsymbol{E}' = \varepsilon\boldsymbol{E}/\varepsilon'$. In particular, if $\varepsilon' = 1$, we have $\boldsymbol{E}' = \varepsilon\boldsymbol{E}$, i.e. the field-strength of the dipole $\boldsymbol{p}$ in its wave zone is increased ε times.

576. (a) $\boldsymbol{E}' = \boldsymbol{E}$. (b) $\boldsymbol{E}' = 2\varepsilon\boldsymbol{E}/(\varepsilon' + \varepsilon)$. In both cases the field $\boldsymbol{E}'$ is independent of the position of the dipole relative to the cavity axis. The solution reduces to the electrostatic problem of a dielectric cylinder in an external uniform field.

577. $\boldsymbol{E} = 3\varepsilon \boldsymbol{E}/(\varepsilon' + 2\varepsilon)$. The field $\boldsymbol{E}'$ is independent of the position of the dipole relative to the centre of the cavity.

578. If the metal can be regarded as ideally conducting (the situation is often very close to this in practice), the electric field in the vacuum is the field of the charge e and of its image $-e$, located in the metal at the same distance from the boundary as the charge e (in the vacuum). When the charge crosses the boundary, both the charge and its image so to speak vanish. The radiation will therefore be the same as when two charges e and $-e$ moving towards one another come to a stop (or combine). The situation for metals possessing high conductivity is qualitatively very close to that described.

579. *Solution.* The equations of motion of an elastically bound electron in a magnetic field (field H along the z axis) are

$$\ddot{x} + \omega_0^2 x = +\frac{e}{mc}\dot{y}H,$$

$$\ddot{y} + \omega_0^2 y = -\frac{e}{mc}\dot{x}H,$$

$$\ddot{z} + \omega_0^2 z = 0.$$

On introducing the variable $\eta = x + iy$, we can easily show that

$$\eta = e^{i\omega_L t}\{Ae^{i\omega_0 t} + Be^{-i\omega_0 t}\}$$

is the general solution of the first two equations (we have used the fact that $\omega_0 \gg \omega$, so that $\sqrt{\omega_0^2 + \omega^2} \approx \omega_0$). The presence of the factor $e^{i\omega_L t}$, where $\omega_L = eH/2mc$, shows that a rotation with frequency ω_L is superimposed on the oscillation in the magnetic field.

580. $\Delta K = \frac{1}{2}m(\omega_0 \pm \omega_L)^2 r^2 - \frac{1}{2}m\omega_0^2 r^2 \simeq m\omega_0\omega_L r^2$, $\omega_L = eH/2mc \ll \omega_0$.

The change in K is due to the work done by the electric field when the magnetic field is switched on.

581. $7°14{\cdot}7'$.

582. $R = 780$ minutes of arc/oersted cm.

583. $R = \alpha/lH = (n_- - n_+)(\pi/\lambda_0 H)$, where α is the angle of rotation of the plane of polarisation, λ_0 is the light wavelength *in vacuo*, and H is the magnetic field-strength.

Solution. Let the external magnetic field H be at right angles to the plane of the figure and directed towards the reader. The linearly polarised wave travels in the same direction. We resolve this wave into two components, with left- and right-hand circular polarisation. At the initial instant the electric vectors of these components are parallel and directed along OA (Fig. 101). On passing through a layer of material of thickness l the electric vector $\boldsymbol{E}_-$ of the first

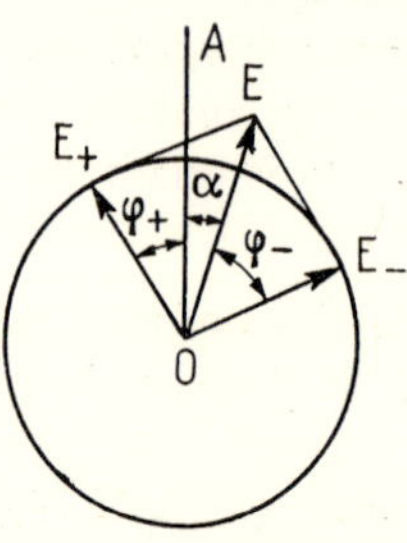

FIG. 101

component turns clockwise through the angle $\varphi_- = 2\pi l/\lambda_- = 2\pi l n_-/\lambda_0$. The electric vector $\boldsymbol{E}_+$ of the second component turns counter-clockwise through the angle $\varphi_+ = 2\pi l n_+/\lambda_0$. The resultant vector $\boldsymbol{E}$ of the two components bisects the angle between $\boldsymbol{E}_+$ and $\boldsymbol{E}_-$ and determines the new direction of the plane of vibration. This plane is turned through an angle α relative to the initial position. The rotation of the plane of vibration (and the plane of polarisation perpendicular to it) is regarded as positive when clockwise and viewed in the opposite direction to that of the light propagation. The angle of rotation of the plane of vibration is thus equal to

$$\alpha = \frac{\varphi_- - \varphi_+}{2} = \frac{\pi l}{\lambda_0}(n_- - n_+).$$

On comparing this expression with the relationship $\alpha = RlH$, we obtain the result given in the answer.

584. $R = \dfrac{e}{2mc^2}\lambda_0 \dfrac{\partial n}{\partial \lambda_0}$, where e is the charge of the electron (negative!), and λ_0 is the wavelength *in vacuo*. This formula refers to a substance whose molecules do not have a constant magnetic moment.

Solution. Suppose that, in the absence of a magnetic field, the medium has only one absorption line, which corresponds to the natural frequency ω_0. The refractive index of the medium is given by the dispersion formula and is a function of the argument $\omega^2 - \omega_0^2$, i.e. $n = n(\omega^2 - \omega_0^2)$. We decompose the harmonic vibration of the electron in the atom into three vibrations: one along the magnetic field and two circular vibrations in the plane perpendicular to the field, in opposite directions. If a magnetic field is imposed, the frequency of the counter-clockwise circular vibration (viewing in the direction opposite to that of the field) will be $\omega_0 + \omega_L$. The natural frequency is therefore changed. Thus the refractive index of the corresponding circularly polarised wave will be

$$n_+ = n\{\omega^2 - (\omega_0 + \omega_L)^2\} = n(\omega^2 - \omega_0^2 - 2\omega_0\omega_L - \omega_L^2).$$

Since the frequency ω_L of the precession of the orbit is small compared with ω_0 and ω, the term ω_L^2 can be neglected and we can write

$$n_+ = n(\omega^2 - \omega_0^2) - 2\omega_0\omega_L \frac{\partial n}{\partial \omega^2} = n(\omega^2 - \omega_0^2) - \frac{\omega_0\omega_L}{\omega}\frac{\partial n}{\partial \omega}.$$

Similarly,

$$n_- = n(\omega^2 - \omega_0^2) + \frac{\omega_0\omega_L}{\omega}\frac{\partial n}{\partial \omega}.$$

We can take $\omega_0 = \omega$ close to the absorption line. This gives

$$n_- - n_+ = 2\omega_L \frac{\partial n}{\partial \omega}.$$

Using the result of the solution of the previous problem, the formula given in the answer easily follows.

585. In the transparent region $dn/d\lambda$ is negative; hence the rotation is positive, i.e. clockwise, when viewed in the opposite direction to that of the light propagation. (The light travels in the direction of the magnetic field.)

586. $\dfrac{e}{m} = -5{\cdot}28 \times 10^{17}$ e.s.u.

587. The component with the higher frequency has left-hand circular polarisation, and the component with the lower frequency right-hand.

588. The polarisation will be circular: left- or right-handed. With right-handed polarisation (refractive index n_+) the electric vector rotates clockwise, and with left-handed (refractive index n_-) counter-clockwise, when viewed in the direction opposite to that of the wave propagation.

$$n_\pm^2 = 1 - \frac{4\pi e^2 N/m}{\omega(\omega \mp \omega_H)}$$

Here N is the electron concentration and ω_H the cyclotron frequency: $\omega_H = |eH/mc|$.

589. (See Problems 583 and 587).

$$\alpha = \tfrac{1}{2}(\omega/c)(n_- - n_+)L = 0{\cdot}93 \times 10^6 \frac{HNL}{\omega^2} \approx 1 \text{ rad.}$$

592. In order for the radiation to be almost completely depolarised, the rotation of the direction of vibration during the lifetime must be close to $\frac{1}{2}\pi$, which gives $eHT/2mc = \frac{1}{2}\pi$ and $H_k \approx 2$ oersted.

593. *Solution.* The forced solution of the given equation is $x = B\cos(\gamma t + \delta)$, where $B = f_0/\sqrt{(\omega_0^2 - \gamma^2)^2 + 4\lambda^2\gamma^2}$, $\tan\delta = 2\lambda\gamma/(\gamma^2 - \omega_0^2)$, whence sign $\delta = -$ sign λ.

The work done by the force in time $T = 2\pi/\gamma$ is

$$A = \int_0^T f\dot{x}\,dt = -B\gamma f_0 \int_0^{T=2\pi/\gamma} \cos\gamma t \sin(\gamma t + \delta)\,dt$$

$$= -\tfrac{1}{2}B\gamma f_0 T \sin\delta.$$

When $|\lambda| \ll \gamma$, $A = -B\gamma f_0\delta/2$. It is clear from this that, when $\delta < 0$ (the oscillator vibrations lag in phase behind the vibrations of the external field), $A > 0$, whereas when $\lambda < 0$, $\delta > 0$, $A < 0$, i.e. a transmission of energy from the oscillator to the external field occurs.

594. No. A constant electric field merely shifts the position of equilibrium; the frequency of the harmonic vibrations remains unchanged.

595. Through the angle $45° + 180° m$ (m is an integer).

596. The direction in which the light is passed is reversed.

597. No.

598. The light emitted by the body B (Fig. 45) and returning after reflection from the Nicol prism N_1 undergoes a 45° extra rotation of the plane of polarisation on passing through the rotating substance, and thus does not pass through the Nicol prism N_2. Having undergone total internal reflection in the prism N_2, this light returns (if we place a further mirror opposite S_2) to the body A. This solution of Wien's paradox is due to Rayleigh.

599. $\delta = 2\pi ClH^2 \approx 1{\cdot}88 \times 10^{-2}$ rad $\approx 65'$.

600. $n_0 - n_e = B\lambda_0 E^2 \approx 0{\cdot}13 \times 10^{-6}$.

601. $\delta = 2\pi BlE^2 \approx 3{\cdot}53°$.

602. $E \approx 16{,}000$ V cm^{-1}.

603. $I = \frac{1}{2}I_0$, where I_0 is the intensity of the light incident on the cell.

604. The optical sign of a doubly refracting medium consisting of a liquid or gas in an electric field is determined by the velocities of propagation of the ordinary and extraordinary waves. The latter depend on the refractive indices, which in turn are determined by the directional dependence of the optical polarisability of the medium. The orientation of the molecules in the field is determined by their resultant dipole moment, which is equal to the geometrical sum of the constant and induced moments of the molecules. In the case of polar molecules the induced moments are small compared with the constant moments—in this case the orientation is determined almost exclusively by the constant moment (see Problem 547). It is easily seen that, when the direction of the constant moment is the same as that of the major axis of the polarisability ellipsoid, an optically positive crystal is obtained. If the constant dipole moment is along the smallest axis of the ellipsoid, an optically negative crystal is obtained. The least favourable case for the appearance of the Kerr effect is when the constant dipole moment is directed roughly along the medium axis of the ellipsoid. In this case both an optically positive and an optically negative crystal can be obtained, depending on the ratios of the axes of the polarisability ellipsoid of the anisotropic molecule. Very often the substance remains almost optically isotropic in this case.

605. $$n_z - n_y = \frac{9}{2}\frac{n_0 - 1}{n_0}\left(\overline{\cos^2\vartheta} - \frac{1}{3}\right)$$

where $\overline{\cos^2 \vartheta}$ is the average over all the molecules of the square of the cosine of the angle ϑ between the direction of the field and the direction in which the molecule is polarised (the direction of polarisation).

Solution. The component of the polarisation vector in the direction of the field E producing the polarisation is

$$P = N\alpha E \overline{\cos^2 \vartheta},$$

where N is the number of molecules per unit volume, α is the polarisability of the completely anisotropic molecule (i.e. the dipole moment produced by a unit field directed along the "direction of polarisation" of the molecule). If the molecule axes are distributed at random, we have

$$\overline{\cos^2 \vartheta} = \tfrac{1}{3}$$

and

$$\varepsilon_0 = 1 + 4\pi N\alpha \overline{\cos^2 \vartheta} = 1 + \frac{4\pi N\alpha}{3};$$

since

$$n_0 = \sqrt{\varepsilon_0} \approx 1, \quad \text{then} \quad n_0 - 1 = \frac{2\pi N\alpha}{3}.$$

If the molecule distribution depends on the angle ϑ between the "direction of polarisation" and the z axis, we have for a light wave with electric vector $\boldsymbol{E}$ directed along the z axis:

$$\varepsilon_z = 1 + 4\pi N\alpha \overline{\cos^2 \vartheta}.$$

For the case when $\boldsymbol{E}$ is directed along the y axis:

$$\varepsilon_y = 1 + 4\pi N\alpha \overline{\sin^2 \vartheta \cos^2 \varphi} = 1 + 2\pi N\alpha \overline{\sin^2 \vartheta}.$$

Hence

$$\varepsilon_z - \varepsilon_y = n_z^2 - n_y^2 = 4\pi N\alpha \tfrac{3}{2}\left(\overline{\cos^2 \vartheta} - \tfrac{1}{3}\right),$$

and, since $n_z - n_y \ll n_0$, we obtain the answer given above.

606. $B = \dfrac{n_0 - 1}{5n_0\lambda_0}\left(\dfrac{\alpha}{k_B T}\right).$

Solution. The probability that the axis of a given molecule is at an angle between ϑ and $\vartheta + d\vartheta$ to the direction of the field is equal to $W(\vartheta)\,d\vartheta = Ce^{-U/k_B T}\sin\vartheta\,d\vartheta$, where C is a constant and U is the potential energy of the molecule. In our case, $U = p^2/2\alpha - pE_0\cos\vartheta$, where p is the induced dipole moment ($p = \alpha E_0 \cos\vartheta$). The first term in U is the energy expended in producing the dipole, the second term is the energy of the dipole in the external field. We have:

$$\overline{\cos^2\vartheta} = \frac{\displaystyle\int_0^\pi \cos^2\vartheta\, W(\vartheta)\,d\vartheta}{\displaystyle\int_0^\pi W(\vartheta)\,d\vartheta} \approx \frac{\displaystyle\int_0^\pi \cos^2\vartheta\left(1 + \frac{\alpha E_0^2\cos^2\vartheta}{2k_B T}\right)\sin\vartheta\,d\vartheta}{\displaystyle\int_0^\pi\left(1 + \frac{\alpha E_0^2\cos^2\vartheta}{2k_B T}\right)\sin\vartheta\,d\vartheta},$$

since $U/k_B T$ is assumed to be small. On integrating and substituting $\cos^2\vartheta$ in the formula obtained in the previous problem, we find $n_z - n_y$, and then B.

607. $B = \dfrac{n_0 - 1}{5n_0\lambda_0}\left(\dfrac{p_0}{k_B T}\right)^2.$

608. $\sigma = \dfrac{8\pi}{3}\left(\dfrac{e^2}{mc^2}\right)^2.$

Solution

$$m\ddot{x} = eE;\quad \ddot{\boldsymbol{p}} = e\ddot{\boldsymbol{x}};\quad I = \int I(\vartheta)\,d\Omega = \frac{e^4\overline{E^2}}{4\pi c^3 m^2}\,\frac{8\pi}{3}.$$

The time average of the incident energy flux is $I_0 = (c/4\pi)\overline{E^2}$. Hence

$$\sigma = \frac{I}{I_0} = \frac{8\pi}{3}\left(\frac{e^2}{mc^2}\right)^2 = 0{\cdot}6652 \times 10^{-24}\ \text{cm}^2.$$

609. $\sigma_{\text{prot}}/\sigma_{\text{el}} = (m_{\text{el}}/m_{\text{prot}})^2 = 29{\cdot}5 \times 10^{-8}.$

610. $d\Phi(\vartheta) = I_0\left(\dfrac{e^2}{mc^2}\right)^2\left(\dfrac{1 + \cos^2\vartheta}{2}\right)d\Omega.$

611. $\sigma = \frac{8\pi}{3}\left(\frac{e^2}{mc^2}\right)^2 \frac{\omega^4}{(\omega^2 - \omega_0^2)^2}$;

$$I(\vartheta) = I_0\left(\frac{e^2}{mc^2}\right)^2 \frac{\omega^4 \sin^2 \vartheta}{(\omega_0^2 - \omega^2)^2}.$$

612. $I(\vartheta) = I_0\left(\frac{e^2}{mc^2}\right)^2 \frac{\omega^4 \sin^2 \vartheta}{(\omega^2 - \omega_0^2)^2 + \omega^2\gamma^2}$;

$$\sigma = \frac{8\pi}{3}\left(\frac{e^2}{mc^2}\right)^2 \frac{\omega^4}{(\omega_0^2 - \omega^2)^2 + \omega^2\gamma^2};$$

$$\sigma_{\nu\approx\nu_0} = \frac{2\pi}{3}\left(\frac{e^2}{mc^2}\right)^2 \frac{\omega^2}{(\omega_0 - \omega)^2 + \frac{\gamma^2}{4}}.$$

613. $\Sigma = \frac{8\pi Npl}{3RT}\left(\frac{e^2}{mc^2}\right)^2 \frac{\omega^4}{(\omega_0^2 - \omega^2)^2} \approx 2 \times 10^{-5}$,

N is Avogadro's number.

614. $A = 0{\cdot}0246$; $B = 0{\cdot}106$.

616. $d\Sigma = \frac{V\pi^2(n^2 - 1)^2}{N\lambda^4} \sin^2 \vartheta \, d\Omega$ (Rayleigh's formula).

617. (1) $d\Phi = I_0 \frac{V\pi^2(n^2 - 1)^2}{N\lambda^4} d\Omega$;

(2) $d\Phi(\vartheta) = I_0 \frac{V\pi^2(n^2 - 1)^2}{N\lambda^4}\left(\frac{1 + \cos^2 \vartheta}{2}\right) d\Omega$,

where ϑ is the angle between the directions of the incident and scattered light.

618. $I_z = I_0 \frac{VN\alpha^2(2\pi)^4}{5\lambda^4} = \frac{9}{5} I_0 \frac{V\pi^2(n^2 - 1)^2}{N\lambda^4}$;

$$I_x = I_0 \frac{VN\alpha^2(2\pi)^4}{15\lambda^4} = \frac{9}{15} \frac{I_0 V\pi^2(n^2 - 1)^2}{N\lambda^4};$$

$$\Delta = \frac{I_x}{I_z} = \frac{1}{3}.$$

Note. For completely anisotropic molecules, the axes of which are distributed randomly, $n^2 - 1 = 4\pi N\alpha/3$. (See Problem 605.)

619. $I_z = \dfrac{6}{5} I_0 \dfrac{V\pi^2(n^2-1)^2}{N\lambda^4}$,

$$I_x = \frac{9}{15} I_0 \frac{V\pi^2(n^2-1)^2}{N\lambda^4},$$

$$\Delta = \frac{I_x}{I_z} = \frac{1}{2}.$$

620. $\Sigma = \dfrac{8\pi^3 l}{3N\lambda^4}(n^2-1)^2 \approx 0{\cdot}165 \times 10^{-4}\ \text{cm}^2$.

621. $\Sigma = 0{\cdot}0356\ \text{cm}^2$.

Note. The application of Rayleigh's formula to scattering in a liquid does not lead to accurate results.

622. (1) $S = S_0 e^{-\sigma h} = 1{\cdot}84$ cal, where $\sigma = 7{\cdot}94 \times 10^{-8}\ \text{cm}^{-1}$.

(2) $S = S_0 e^{-\sigma h} = 1{\cdot}34$ cal, where $\sigma = 4 \times 10^{-7}\ \text{cm}^{-1}$.

Thus in the first case about 92 per cent of the energy incident on the surface of the atmosphere, and in the second case 67 per cent, reaches the earth (compare with Problem 615).

623. (1) The light vector is twisted when it passes through the solution, with a different pitch for different λ. Scattering is absent in the direction of $\boldsymbol{E}$, so that coloured helices are seen. (2) The pitch of the helix is inversely proportional to the concentration. The dependence of the pitch on the wavelength is given by the expression in the solution of Problem 584.

624. The scattered light is elliptically polarised; the major axis of the vibration ellipse is perpendicular to the direction of propagation of the incident and scattered light; $\varrho = \cos\vartheta$.

625. The electric vector of the linearly polarised component of the scattered light will be perpendicular to the direction of propagation of the incident and scattered light.

$$I_{\text{pol}}/I_{\text{unpol}} = \tfrac{1}{2}\tan^2\vartheta.$$

626. The mercury line $\lambda = 2536$ Å is a resonance line.

By increasing the mercury vapour density, we can arrange for it to be extinguished in scattered light (Kirchhoff's law). If the wavelengths of the secondary lines of this line were the same, we should expect them to be also extinguished. Whereas if these wavelengths were different, the secondary lines would not be extinguished. Mandel'shtam and Landsberg in fact succeeded in extinguishing the resonance line, whilst the secondary lines were preserved.

627. $\nu \approx 1 \times 10^{13}$ sec^{-1}.

628. 4255·1 Å and 4466·7 Å.

629. 217 cm^{-1}; 315 cm^{-1}; 457 cm^{-1} and 774 cm^{-1}.

630. $\dfrac{\lambda}{\Delta\lambda} \approx 715.$

631. $I_v/I_{\text{red}} = e^{-h\nu/k_B T}$ and we obtain for the different normal vibrations: 0·35; 0·22; 0·11; 0·024.

632. $\omega_0 = \sqrt{k_B T/I_0} \approx 10^{13}$ sec^{-1}; here I_0 is the moment of inertia of the molecule.

633. $\Delta\nu = \dfrac{h}{8\pi^2 Ic} = 2{\cdot}2\,\text{cm}^{-1}.$

634. This vibration produces no change in the dipole moment of the CO_2 molecules.

635. The displacements change sign after half a period, whilst the polarisability tensor takes its initial value, since both directions of the principal axis of the tensor are physically equivalent.

636. After half a rotation the polarisability tensor returns to its initial value. This means that the period of oscillation of the tensor is half the period of rotation of the molecule.

637. *Solution.* The electromagnetic field $\boldsymbol{E}, \boldsymbol{H}$ is described in the medium by Maxwell's equations:

$$\text{curl}\,\boldsymbol{H} = \frac{\varepsilon}{c}\frac{\partial \boldsymbol{E}}{\partial t}, \quad \text{curl}\,\boldsymbol{E} = -\frac{1}{c}\frac{\partial \boldsymbol{H}}{\partial t},$$

$$\text{div}\,(\varepsilon \boldsymbol{E}) = \text{div}\,\boldsymbol{H} = 0. \tag{1}$$

We write these fields as the sum of the incident $\boldsymbol{E}_0$, $\boldsymbol{H}_0$ and the scattered $\boldsymbol{E}'$, $\boldsymbol{H}'$ waves:

$$\boldsymbol{E} = \boldsymbol{E}_0 + \boldsymbol{E}', \quad \boldsymbol{H} = \boldsymbol{H}_0 + \boldsymbol{H}'. \tag{2}$$

The incident wave satisfied the system of Maxwell's equations:

$$\text{curl } \boldsymbol{H}_0 = \frac{\varepsilon_0}{c} \frac{\partial \boldsymbol{E}_0}{\partial t}, \quad \text{curl } \boldsymbol{E}_0 = -\frac{1}{c} \frac{\partial \boldsymbol{H}_0}{\partial t},$$

$$\text{div } (\varepsilon_0 \boldsymbol{E}_0) = \text{div } \boldsymbol{H}_0 = 0. \tag{3}$$

In the case of a weak non-uniformity the intensity of the scattered field is small compared with that of the incident wave. On substituting (2) in (1) and neglecting products of the small quantities $\boldsymbol{E}'$, $\boldsymbol{H}'$, $\delta\varepsilon$, we obtain

$$\left.\begin{aligned} &\text{curl } \boldsymbol{H}' - \frac{\varepsilon_0}{c} \frac{\partial \boldsymbol{E}'}{\partial t} = \frac{4\pi}{c} \frac{\partial}{\partial t} \delta \boldsymbol{P}, \\ &\text{curl } \boldsymbol{E}' - \frac{\varepsilon_0}{c} \frac{\partial \boldsymbol{H}'}{\partial t} = 0, \\ &\text{div } (\varepsilon_0 \boldsymbol{E}') = -4\pi \text{ div } \delta \boldsymbol{P}, \quad \text{div } \boldsymbol{H}' = 0, \end{aligned}\right\} \tag{4}$$

where

$$\delta \boldsymbol{P} = \frac{\boldsymbol{E}_0}{4\pi} \delta\varepsilon. \tag{5}$$

These equations show that the medium can be regarded as uniform with dielectric constant ε_0. The effect of the non-uniformities present is equivalent to the existence in the medium of additional wave sources: each volume element dV of the medium yields additional radiation as a dipole with dipole moment $\delta \boldsymbol{P} dV$. This additional radiation is in fact the scattered light. The second assertion mentioned in the problem is an immediate consequence of the linearity and homogeneity of system (4) with respect both to the fields $\boldsymbol{E}'$, $\boldsymbol{H}'$ and to $\delta\varepsilon$.

638. *Solution.* We divide the medium by equidistant planes perpendicular to the vector $\boldsymbol{K}$ (Fig. 102). We choose the distance between two adjacent planes as $\Lambda = 2\pi/K$. Now, by (5) (see the solution of the previous problem), the phases of the secondary sources on these equidistant planes will be the same. If there were only non-uniformity in the layer *I*, and the medium were otherwise uniform, the incident wave would undergo reflection from this layer and would also be partially transmitted. If there were only non-uniformity in layer *II*, we should obtain another reflected wave with the same amplitude but different phase. If there were non-uniformity in layer *III* we should obtain a third reflected wave and so on. In the linear approximation (see the previous problem) the scattering field of the medium as a whole is obtained by simple superposition of these reflected waves. In order for them to intensify,

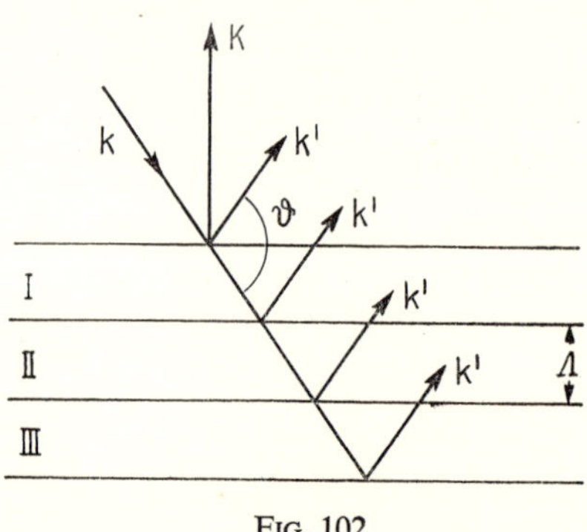

FIG. 102

instead of extinguish, one another, the Bragg condition, $2\Lambda \sin \frac{1}{2}\vartheta = m\lambda$, must be satisfied, where m is an integer and ϑ is the angle between the directions of the incident and scattered radiations. Let us show that $m = 1$. On addition, all the plane waves reflected by the different layers yield a wave of the form

$$\boldsymbol{E}' = A' \exp i[\omega t - (\boldsymbol{k}' \cdot \boldsymbol{r}')].$$

On the other hand, the extra polarisation of the medium is

$$\delta \boldsymbol{P} = \frac{\boldsymbol{E}_0}{4\pi} \delta\varepsilon = \frac{aA}{4\pi} e^{i[\omega t - (\boldsymbol{k} + \boldsymbol{K} \cdot \boldsymbol{r})]}.$$

On substituting these expressions in the next but last of equations (4) (see the solution of the previous problem) and equating exponents, we easily obtain $\boldsymbol{k}' - \boldsymbol{k} = \boldsymbol{K}$, whence

$$2\Lambda \sin \frac{\vartheta}{2} = \lambda. \tag{1}$$

Thus, in the linear approximation, a diffraction spectrum of only the first order is obtained for the diffraction of a wave at sinusoidal non-uniformities of the dielectric constant.

639. *Solution.* In the linear approximation $\Delta\varepsilon = (d\varepsilon/d\varrho)\,\Delta\varrho$. Every density non-uniformity appearing in the medium is a source of acoustic waves. We expand $\Delta\varrho$ into a Fourier integral or series. The only important acoustic waves for the scattering in the direction in question will be those whose wave vector $\boldsymbol{K}$ is along the bisector of the complementary angle to ϑ (see Fig. 102). The corresponding values of $\delta\varepsilon$ are written as sums of waves of the type

$$\delta\varepsilon_1 = a_1 \exp i[\Omega t - (\boldsymbol{K}\cdot\boldsymbol{r})] \quad \text{and} \quad \delta\varepsilon_2 = a_2 \exp\{-i[\Omega t + (\boldsymbol{K}\cdot\boldsymbol{r})]\}.$$

Corresponding to these we have the supplementary polarisation vectors:

$$\delta\boldsymbol{P}_1 = \frac{\boldsymbol{E}_0}{4\pi}\,\delta\varepsilon_1 = \frac{a_1\boldsymbol{A}}{4\pi}\,e^{i[(\omega+\Omega)t-(\boldsymbol{k}+\boldsymbol{K}\cdot\boldsymbol{r})]},$$

$$\delta\boldsymbol{P}_2 = \frac{a_2\boldsymbol{A}}{4\pi}\,e^{i[(\omega-\Omega)t-(\boldsymbol{k}+\boldsymbol{K}\cdot\boldsymbol{r})]}.$$

The sources of the scattered radiation, and hence also the scattered radiation itself, will thus have the frequencies $\omega + \Omega$ and $\omega - \Omega$ (modulation of the light wave by an acoustic wave). A doublet with the same frequencies will be observed in the scattered radiation spectrum. The phenomenon is called fine structure of the Rayleigh scattering lines. The frequency shift is $\Omega = Kv = 2\pi v/\Lambda$, where v is the velocity of sound, and Λ is the wavelength of the acoustic wave. On the basis of (1) of the solution of the previous problem,

$$\Omega = \frac{4\pi v}{\lambda}\sin\frac{\vartheta}{2} = 2\omega n\frac{v}{c}\sin\frac{\vartheta}{2}, \tag{1}$$

where c is the velocity of light *in vacuo*, and n is the refractive index of the medium. The fine structure of the Rayleigh scattering lines was predicted independently by L. I. Mandel'shtam and L. Brillouin. The phenomenon was discovered experimentally in liquids by E. Gross in Leningrad. It was found that in liquids, in addition to the two displaced components, an undisplaced component is also observed. The appearance of the undisplaced component was explained by Landau and Placzek. If we regard the specific volume V of the liquid as a function of the pressure and entropy, we can write

$$\delta V = \left(\frac{\partial V}{\partial p}\right)_S \delta p + \left(\frac{\partial V}{\partial S}\right)_P \delta S. \tag{2}$$

It is clear from this that there are two types of fluctuation of the specific volume: one type is called pressure fluctuation at constant entropy, the other entropy fluctuation at constant pressure. The fluctuations of the first type are propagated as acoustic waves and lead to the appearance of the displaced components. The fluctuations of the second type are dissipated by means of heat conduction, and consequently are propagated much more slowly; they lead to the appearance of the undisplaced component in the scattered light.

640. There are five components: one undisplaced component and two pairs of displaced components, one pair of which is obtained from scattering by longitudinal acoustic waves, the other by transverse.

641. 25 components: one undisplaced and 24 displaced. The fact is that one longitudinal and two transverse acoustic waves can be propagated in any direction in a crystal. Two light waves, polarised in mutually perpendicular planes, can be propagated in the same direction. Each of these light waves in turn splits up into two waves on reflection from the acoustic waves corresponding to the direction of propagation. This leads to the appearance in the scattered light of 24 undisplaced components. However, as a result of the weak anisotropy of all the crystals investigated, these 24 components are usually grouped into six groups with four lines in each and are not resolved by spectral devices. Six of the displaced components are observed experimentally.

642. Two pairs of displaced components. The fact is that the fluctuations of the second type mentioned in Problem 639 are dissipated in liquid helium II by means of the propagation of second sound. One pair of displaced components is obtained in the case of scattering at the waves of ordinary sound, and the other pair is due to second sound. No undisplaced component should be obtained. The phenomenon has not been investigated experimentally.

643. $v = \dfrac{c}{2n \sin \dfrac{\vartheta}{2}} \dfrac{\delta\lambda}{\lambda};$

$$v_{\text{long}} = 1{\cdot}8 \times 10^6 \text{ cm sec}^{-1} = 18{,}000 \text{ m sec}^{-1};$$

$$v_{\text{trans}} = 1{\cdot}1 \times 10^6 \text{ cm sec}^{-1} = 11{,}000 \text{ m sec}^{-1}.$$

Due to the high velocity of sound in diamond, it is possible to investigate the fine structure of the Rayleigh scattering lines by prism spectroscopes.

644. *Solution.* The frequency change on scattering at free electrons is determined by the Doppler effect. Since the thermal velocity $\boldsymbol{v}$ of the electrons is small compared with the velocity of light, the frequency ω of the scattered wave is connected with the frequency of the incident wave by

$$\omega - (\boldsymbol{k} \cdot \boldsymbol{v}) = \omega_0 - (\boldsymbol{k}_0 \cdot \boldsymbol{v})$$

or

$$\omega - \omega_0 = (\boldsymbol{v} \cdot \boldsymbol{k} - \boldsymbol{k}_0) = (\boldsymbol{v} \cdot \boldsymbol{q})$$

where $\boldsymbol{k}$ and $\boldsymbol{k}_0$ are the wave vectors of the scattered and incident waves, $|\boldsymbol{k}| = |\boldsymbol{k}_0| = \omega/c$ and $|\boldsymbol{k} - \boldsymbol{k}_0| = 2\,|\omega/c| \sin \tfrac{1}{2}\vartheta$ (ϑ is the scattering angle).

We split the electrons into groups, which have the same velocity components v_q in the direction of the vector $\boldsymbol{q}$. Each of these groups will produce a definite Doppler frequency shift. If $f(v_q)$ is the normalised distribution function, the number of electrons in a group will be

$$dN = Nf(v_q)\, dv_q.$$

The scattering cross section for this group of electrons is

$$\sigma_\omega \, d\omega = \sigma_e N f(v_q)\, dv_q = \sigma_e N f\left(\frac{\omega - \omega_0}{q}\right)\frac{d\omega}{q},$$

where σ_e is the scattering cross section of one electron and N is the total number of electrons. For a Maxwell velocity distribution,

$$\sigma_\omega = \frac{\sigma_e N}{q}\left(\frac{m}{2\pi k_B T}\right)^{\frac{1}{2}} e^{-\left(\frac{m}{2k_B T}\right)\frac{(\omega-\omega_0)^2}{q^2}}.$$

645. *Solution.* (1) Radiation must result when a charge moves uniformly in a medium with random non-uniformities. This is particularly clear for the long wave part of the radiation spectrum, when the wavelength is much greater than the size of the non-uniformities.

The field $\boldsymbol{E}(\boldsymbol{r}, t)$ of the moving charge can be represented as a set of components of the type $e^{i\omega t}$ with amplitudes $f(\omega, \boldsymbol{r})$. As a result, each non-uniformity acquires at the frequency ω a dipole moment $\boldsymbol{p} \sim \Delta\varepsilon(\boldsymbol{r})f(\omega, \boldsymbol{r})e^{i\omega t}$. At the same time, we know that the intensity of the dipole radiation is $W \sim (\ddot{\boldsymbol{p}})^2$. If we assume that all the non-uniformities radiate incoherently, the radiation energy of the uniformly moving charge in the medium will be expressible as the sum of the radiation energies of each non-uniformity separately.

(2) When the charge velocity approaches the velocity of light, the radiation must rise sharply, since the field of the charge, when its velocity $v \to c$, is strongly flattened in the direction perpendicular to the direction of motion, with the result that a large number of non-uniformities, including those remote from the path of the charge, can be polarised per unit path.

Made in Great Britain